FOOD SAFETY OFFICER EXAM

A COMPREHENSIVE APPROACH

SECOND EDITION

FOR ALL FSO EXAMS BY CENTRAL AND STATE GOVERNMENT

(CFSO & TO By FSSAI, FSO By RPSC, APPSC, TSPSC, TN MRB, KPSC, HPPSC, OPSC, HPSC, WBHRB)

JINISHA BLESSIE J P

SECOND EDITION - 2027

Price : 650 /-

ISBN : 978-81-19577-02-6

Navya Book House
Address-3386/1-A Ranjeet Nagar
New Delhi -110008
Near PUSA Gate
ph-8700393568
E-mail : navya.pub@gmail.com

Available in Delhi at :
Pusa Agricultural Books Service
29, Shishir Hostel, IARI, Delhi-12
Ph. 9868827628
8851222765
pusa.agri@gmail.com

Graphics and laser typesetting by :
for
Navya Graphic Designs

Printed at :
M B Prints , New Delhi-20

Preface

"We first make our habits and then our habits make us"

-John Dryden

'Food safety' is a shared responsibility between governments, producers and Consumers. Everybody has a role to play from farm to table to ensure the food we consume is safe and will not damage our health. Good hygiene practices in the food and Agricultural sectors help to reduce the emergence and spread of food borne diseases. Never give up on food safety; it's an investment you can't afford to not make.

Taking into consideration we have well prepared a book of "Food Safety Officer Exam – A Comprehensive approach". It's an right stuff to FSO aspirants who are aspiring for exams like Central Food Safety Officer & Technical Officer by FSSAI, Food Inspector, Food Safety Officer and Assistant Commissioner of FDA, etc. conducted by State and Central Government. As a complete guide we bringforth Syllabus, Syllabus wise Short notes, Tables for quick reference, Important points to ponder and Computer literacy & IT. Along with to "Evaluate yourself" we have framed Topic wise MCQs, Mock tests and Fill in the blanks. In addition to this, Solved Previous Year Question Papers is given for your reference. The most enthralling part of the book is "Tables for Quick Reference" which covers the key aspects of syllabus. Nowadays, computer literacy plays a vital role in most of the competitive exams. So make your preparation easier we have inculcated the "Computer literacy & Information Technology". These are the salient features of this book. *'I assure that, this book will enhance the knowledge and it can be used as ready reckoner to crack the exam'* **"Believe in yourself and you can achieve anything. Good Luck with your exams"**

Jinisha Blesssie J P

ACKNOWLEDGEMENT

I want to express my deep gratitude and sincere respect to Almighty God for granting me the strength and wisdom needed to complete this book. This journey has been shaped by many individuals who have played a crucial role in my personal and professional development. I dedicate this book to all those who have been instrumental in my success. First and foremost, I want to acknowledge my mentor, Dr. S.J. Aruna, who has significantly influenced and guided my path. Her support and guidance have been pivotal in shaping my journey, and I am deeply grateful for her impact on my life. I also want to extend my heartfelt thanks to my husband, whose unwavering support has been a constant source of motivation. My son has been a source of inspiration, reminding me of the importance of perseverance and hard work. I am equally grateful to my parents and Sister who have instilled in me the values and determination that have brought me this far. This book is a testament to the collective support and guidance I have received from these important individ uals, and I dedicate it to them with deep appreciation.

FOREWORD

The book titled "Food safety officer exam: A comprehensive approach" has been meticulousy written and will be highly useful for exams related to FSSAI like Food Safety Officer, Technical Officer and state level food safety officer. Preparations for these exams demand strategic and consistent approach with suitable study materials. In this context, I have found the contents of this book very much relevant for aspiring candidates who wish to have a single window delivery of entire exam syllabus.

It is my pleasure to write foreword for this book authored by my dearest Jinisha Blesie, a very hard working and passionate microbiologist. She had designed each and every word of this book over a period of three years. All the contents are rigourously planned and compiled for the benefit of student community. I am elated to inform that my friend is guiding so many candidates in their exam preparation process.

I wholeheartedly wish all the best for each and every one of you. This book will definitely support in your upcoming exams. Congratulations to the author and hoping to see more editions of the book in coming days.

Ana Raj J

Scientist

Indian Council of Agrl. Research (ICAR)

SYLLABUS

Central Food Safety Officer (Pay Level-07)/

Technical Officer (Pay Level-07)

Scheme of examination:

Exam Format

- Computer Based Test (Stage-1) will be of 180-minute duration with 120 MCQ questions.
- 4 marks would be given for each correct answer and 1 mark deducted for each wrong answer.

PART A

General Aptitude and Computer Literacy- indicative syllabus.

Subject and Syllabus	No. Of Ques
General Aptitude: **General Intelligence** : would include questions of both verbal and non-verbal type for e.g. Questions on analogies, similarities and difference, space visualization, problems solving, analysis, judgement, decision making visual memory, discriminating relationship concepts, arithmetical reasoning, verbal and figureclassification, arithmetical number series.	10
General Awareness: Questions to test the ability of the candidates General Awareness of the environment around him/her and its application to society. Also testing knowledge of currents events and matters of every day observation as may be expected of an educated person. The test will include questions relating to India and neighboring countries specially pertaining to History, Culture, Geography, Economic scene, General Polity including Indian Constitution, sports and scientific research etc. These questions will be such that they do not require a special study of any discipline.	10
English language Comprehension: Would test the candidates understanding of the English language its vocabulary, grammar etc. would include questions on comprehension, on word substitution, synonyms and antonyms, spelling error, spotting errors in sentences, grammar noun, pronoun, adjectives, verbs, prepositions, conjunctions, use of 'a 'an" and 'the', idioms And phrases etc, Parts of speech.	10
Computer Literacy: Candidate is expected to be able to handle all regular office work on computers. Knowledge of MS office (word, excel, power point) including basic commands, Google Doc, emails, digital signature, Commonly use social media handles (Whattsapp, FB, Twitter, etc). would be tested.	10

PART B : Functional Knowledge - Indicative syllabus.

Subject and Syllabus	No. Of Ques
Indian and International Food Laws (An Overview) • Food Safety and Standards Act of India, 2006 Provision, definitions and different sections of the Act and implementation. • FSS Rules and Regulations • Overview of other relevant national bodies (e.g. APEDA, BIS EIC, MPEDA, Spice Board etc.) • International Food Control Systems/Laws, Regulations and Standards/ Guidelines with regard to Food Safety– (i) Overview of CODEX Alimentarius. Commission (History, Members, Standard setting and Advisory mechanisms: JECFA, JEMRA, JMPR): WTO agreements (SPS/TBT). • Important national and international accreditation bodies	20
FSSAI-Role, Functions, Initiatives (A General Understanding) • Genesis and Evolution of FSSAI • Structure and Functions of Food Authority • Overview of systems and processes in Standards, Enforcement, Laboratoryecosystem, Imports, Third Party Audit etc. • Promoting safe and wholesome Food (Eat Right India, Food Fortification, snf, Clean Street Food Hub, RUCO and various other social and behavioural change initiatives) • Training and capacity building • Role of State Food Authorities	20
Principles of Food Preservation, Processing and Packaging • Food Processing Operations, Principles, Good Manufacturing Practices • Overview of food preservation methods and their under lying principles including novel and emerging methods/principles • Overview of food packaging methods and principles including novel packaging materials/techniques	40

Principles and Basics of Food Chemistry and their role in Human Nutrition • Structure and functions of macro-and micronutrients • Role of macro and micronutrients in human nutrition • Over view of food additives with respect to their technological functions • Over view of anti-nutritional factors and their removal from foods • Over view of enzymes as food processing aidsOver view of nutraceuticals and functions foods • Overview of food contaminants and adulterants and their effects on human health • Food allergens and allergen city • Importance of diet in alleviating health risks, especially non-communicable diseases	
Food Microbiology & General principles of Food Hygiene • General principles of food microbiology and over view of food borne pathogens • Over view of sources of microorganisms in food chain (raw materials, water, air, equipment etc.) and microbiological quality of foods • Microbial food spoilage and Food borne diseases • General principles and techniques in microbiological examination of foods • Overview of beneficial microorganisms and their role in food processing and human nutrition • General principles of food safety management systems including traceability and recall – sanitation, HACCP, Good production and processing practices (GMP,GAP,GHP, GLP, BAP, etc)	

General concepts of Food Analysis and Testing	
• Fundamentals of field level and laboratory sampling with reference to importance of statistical tools. • Over view of basic/classical methods of food analysis • Over view of modern analytical techniques including mass spectrometry and molecular techniques. • Principles of Quality assurance and Quality control with reference to food analysis and testing.	

Food Analyst (Pay Level-10)

Scheme of examination:

Exam Format

Written Test will be of 180-minute duration with 16 subjective type questions

A. **Food Laws and Standards of India and International Food Laws:**

(4 Questions x 2.5 Marks)

I. Food Safety and Standards Act of India, 2006, Provision, definitions and different sections of the Act and implementation.

II. FSS Rules and Regulations (2011) as amended from time to time –

a) Licensing and registration; Central license, State license, Registration, Responsibilities of the FBO, Role of Designated officer, Food Safety Officer and Food Analyst.

b) Standards of Quality and Safety of Food & Food Products laid down in the FSS Regulations, 2011. The different food categories in the Act. The relevance of the standards (Vertical and Horizontal) quality and safety parameters to particular foods including current food safety issues.

c) Regulations of food additive: What is an additive, various groups of additives and their technological functions, INS number: food colors, antioxidants, sweeteners, preservatives, processing aids. Food processing aids. The Indian Food Code and using the hierarchy to understand the category wise approval of food additives.

d) Packaging and labelling rules and regulations: List of ingredients, nutritional information, special label declarations, claims-Health, nutrition, nutrient led claims, use of words and phrases on label.

e) Regulations for Contaminants, Toxins and Residues and restriction of sales.

f) Food Safety and Standards (Food or Health Supplements, Nutraceuticals, Foods for Special Dietary Uses, Foods for Special Medical Purpose, Functional Foods and Novel Food) Regulations, 2016 Food Safety and Standards (Food Recall Procedure) Regulations, 2017 Food Safety and Standards (Import) Regulations, 2017.

g) Food Safety and Standards (Organic Food) Regulation, 2017.Food Safety and Standards (Fortification of Foods) Regulations, 2018 Food Safety and Standards (Alcoholic Beverages) Regulations, 2018.

h) Laboratory sampling and analysis: The role of Referral labs, FSSA notified laboratories and State Food Laboratories and function. Receiving legal samples, sample custody and sample custodian. Storage of sample. Required documentation and registration, storage of the sample Analyses as per FSS Rules and Regulations (2011).

III. Other National Laws and Standards:

a) Agricultural Produce Act, 1937 (Grading and Marketing)

b) Export (Quality Control & Inspection), Act, 1963 and Rules

c) Bureau of Indian Standards relevant to Food Safety (Water, Infant Formula etc.)

d) Legal Metrology Act

IV. International Food Control Systems/Laws, Regulations and Standards/Guidelines withregard to Food Safety:

a) CODEX Alimentarious Commission: History, Members, Standard setting and Advisory mechanisms: JECFA, JEMRA, JMPR

b) WTO agreements: SPS/TBT

c) Role of OIE, IPPC.

B. **Planning Organization and setting up of Food Analysis Laboratory including NABL /ISO / IEC-17025: 2017 and laboratory safety.** (4 Questions x 2.5 Marks)

I. Understand the requirements for setting up a laboratory for the legal defensibility of analytical data. The ideal structure design, environment, layout for chemical and microbiological testing, Air handling etc.

II. What is accreditation, Different accreditation bodies (NABL, APLAC, ILAC). Requirements for ISO/IEC 17025:2017, documentation, pre-requisites for accreditation, management requirements, technical requirements, measurement of traceability.

III. Laboratory safety: Personnel and laboratory hygiene, emergency planning, General hazards in a food laboratory, safety equipment, storage of chemicals, acids, flammables etc., handling compressed gases, centrifuge, chemical and biological spills and waste disposal.

C. **Physical, Chemical and Instrumental analysis** (4 Questions x 10 Marks)

I. *Sampling and sample preparation*: Definition, types of sample, sampling plan, subsampling, designing sampling plan, concept of sample size and representative. Sample preparations – particle size, homogeneity, dissolution technology and decomposition, storage of samples. Solid Phase Extraction - Introduction, sorbents, matrix solid phase dispersion and applications.

II. *Statistics and statistical terms*: Systematic and random errors. Mean distribution. Confidence interval. Confidence limits and confidence level, Outliers. Definition and calculation of: Average, Mean, Standard deviation, Relative standard deviation,

Coefficient of variation, Confidence limits of a measurement, Statistical Tests, Linear correlation and regression curve fitting, fitting of linear equations. Choosing and using statistical tests, Analysis of Variance (ANOVA).

III. *Basic principles of Classical Methods of food analysis:* Law of mass action, Le chateliers principle, stoichiometry, volumetric and gravimetric analysis. Preparation of standards, working standards and solutions of known concentration (percent, molar, molal, normal, ppm and ppb) and their dilution. Proximate analysis, physical methods for extraneous matter analysis.

IV. *Classical analytical techniques: Gravimetry, Titrimetry, Refractometry and Polarimetry:* Principle, Instrumentation and applications of each technique in food analysis.

V. *UV-Visible and Fluorescence Spectrometry:* Electromagnetic spectrum, Beer and Lambert's Law, Absorbance, Transmittance, Molar absorptivity (Molar Extinction coefficient), E 1%, λ Max. Components and functioning of an UV-vis spectrophotomer: Single beam and double beam. Components of a UV-VIS spectrum. Calibration curve and applications in food analysis.

VI. *Raman spectroscopy:* Principle Theory Instrumentation, techniques and Applicationsof Raman spectroscopy in food analysis.

VII. *Chromatographic techniques:* Fundamentals of chromatographic separations and their classification. The plate theory, Capacity factor and resolution factor, Chromatographic efficiency. Van Deemter's equation. Partition coefficient etc. Principles and applications of paper (Ascending, Descending, Radial, Two dimensional) Partition, Thin layer chromatography, HPTLC, size exclusion and ion exchange chromatography. Applications in food analysis.

VIII. *High Performance Liquid Chromatography (HPLC):* Basics of liquid chromatography, HPLC columns and Stationary phases (solid, liquid) – Bonded phase supports, mobile phases, isocratic and gradient elution, Detectors: UV absorption, Fluorescence detector, RI detectors, electrochemical detectors, Photo diode array, Evaporative light scattering detector, PHRED anatomy of a chromatograms. Modes of separation Normal and Reverse Phase. Sample Preparation Techniques, Applications in quantitative food analysis of aflatoxins, vitamins, sugars, sweeteners, preservatives etc.

IX. *Gas chromatography*: Basics of Gas chromatography, Mobile phase and criteria for itsselection- Sample introduction techniques – Stationary phases – Supports for liquid stationary phases, Selection of columns. Detectors FID, TCD, FPB, ECD, TID. Temperature programming in GC – Derivatization and sample preparation in GC – Fatty acid profile and quantitative analysis of fatty acids in fats and oils.

X. *Mass Spectrometry*: Basics of mass spectrometry, Components of a mass spectrometer, Ionization and ion sources: Electrospray, chemical, Fast Atom Bombardment, MALDI, Atmospheric Pressure Chemical ionization and other ionization methods. Mass analyzers: Quadrupole Analyzers, Ion Trap Analyzers, Electrostatic Trap or 'Orbitrap', Time-of- Flight Analyzers, Hybrid Instruments. Detectors: Photographic plate, Faraday cup Electron multipliers. Data acquisition, Data conversion, Data reduction and Library search. Tandem Mass Spectrometry and its applications.

XI. *Hyphenated Techniques*: Mass Spectrometry and Chromatography Coupling. GC- MS/MS, LC-MS/MS, Capillary electrophoresis-MS, Isotopic Ratio mass spectrometry. Analytical Information: Mass Spectrometry Spectral Collections, high resolution, quantitative data, fragmentation and spectrum interpretation.

XII. *Atomic absorption Spectroscopy, Atomic emission Spectroscopy, ICP-MS*: Principles- Atomization process, Atomic line widths and radiation sources for AAS, temperature gradients, cells detectors, interferences, Background correction methods and modifications in instrumentations, Atomic Emission Spectroscopy: Atomic spectra, Population distribution with temperature, Sources, spark laser microprobe for atomic emission, Spectrometers, Merits, demerits, and applications. Basic principles and instrumentation of ICP-MS; data acquisition and interpretation; application of ICP-MS for analysis of Metallic contaminants in food. Sample preparation, microwave digestion.

XIII. *Biological Techniques (DNA/protein based)*: Fundamental principles and instrumentation of the systems; measurement techniques and result interpretations of Polymerase Chain Reaction (PCR), Real-time Polymerase Chain Reaction (PCR) technique; Enzyme Linked Immunosorbent Assay (ELISA); Radioimmunoassay (RIA). Use of PCR for detection of genetically-modified organisms (GMO); meat and fish speciation and other applications in analysis of food adulteration.

XIV. *Measurements of Rheological Properties*: Instrumental measurement of Texture of Foods, Viscos Analysis, viscometer, texture analyser etc.

XV. *Quality assurance and Quality control*: Introduction to quality control in analytical chemistry. Terminology in analytical measurements: True value, Measured value, Accuracy, Precision, Uncertainty, Random errors. Sample traceability, Internal quality control, Certified reference materials. Spiked reference samples. Recovery studies. Method validation/verification (LOD, LOQ, specificity, selectivity, linearity, range, robustness, repeatability, reproducibility, External and internal standards; Control chart, Proficiency testing, Z scores.

D. **Case studies for interpretation and providing opinion based on an analysis report as perFSSR 2011** (4 Questions x 10 Marks)

Contents

Part – 1
Short Notes

CHAPTER-1

INDIAN AND INTERNATIONAL FOOD LAWS

(AN OVERVIEW)

"If you can't fly then run, if you can't run then walk, if you can't walk then crawl, but whatever you do you have to keep moving forward" - Martin Luther King

- Food Safety and Standards Authority of India (F.SSAI) – Inspiring trust, Assuring safe and nutritious food - comes under the Ministry of Health and Family Welfare, Government of India
- Food Safety and Standards Act (FSSA) 2006, passed by the Indian parliament and notified on 24th August 2006
- Present Chairperson of FSSAI is Ms. Punya Salila Srivastava, IAS (2026)
- Present CEO, Member Secretary of FSSAI is – Shri Rajit Punhani, IAS
- The theme for World Food Day 2026 (Observed on October 16) is "Nourish tomorrow."
- The headquarters of FSSAI is located in New Delhi
- Total Regional Office Zone – 5 (North Zone, South Zone, East Zone, West Zone, North East Zone)
- Total Regional Office – 8 (Delhi, Chennai, Kolkata, Mumbai, Chandigarh, Uttar Pradesh, Guwahati, and Kochi)
- FSSAI has published 4 books

1. Yellow book – Aimed at inculcating food habits at a young age, as habits formed in our early days
2. Orange book – Contains general practices recommended for safe and nutritious food in the workplace
3. Purple book – Contains food standards and practices followed by restaurants
4. Pink book – Contains tips and information about food safety and nutrition

- The vegetable oil products (control) order – 1947
- Prevention of Food Adulteration Act – 1954
- Fruit products order – 1955
- Essential Commodities Act – 1955
- The solvent extraction oil, De-oiled meal & edible flour order - 1967

- The meat food products order – 1973
- Milk & milk products order – 1992
- Edible oil packaging (regulation) order – 1998
- FSS Act 2006 has 12 chapters and 101 sections

Chapter 1: Preliminary (Sections 1 to 3)

Chapter 2: FSSAI (Sections 4 to 17)

Chapter 3: General Principles of Food Safety (Section 18)

Chapter 4: General provisions as to articles of food (Sections 19 to 24)

Chapter 5: Provisions relating to import (Section 25)

Chapter 6: Special responsibilities as to food safety (Sections 26 to 28)

Chapter 7: Enforcement of the Act (Sections 29 to 42)

Chapter 8: Analysis of food (Section 43 to 47)

Chapter 9: Offences and Penalties (Sections 48 to 67)

Chapter 10: Adjudication and food safety appellate tribunal (Section 68 to 80)

Chapter 11: Finance, Accounts, Audits, and Reports (Sections 81 to 84)

Chapter 12: Miscellaneous (Section 85 to 101)

- Adulterant – Any material could be employed for making food unsafe or containing extraneous matter
- Contaminant – Any substance, whether or not added to food, but which is present in such food as a result of production, manufacture, and processing
- Commissioner of Food Safety appointed under section 30
- Designated officer appointed under section 36
- Food analyst appointed under section 45
- Food safety officer appointed under section 37
- License granted under section 31
- Prohibition order issued under section 33
- Food safety appellate tribunal established under section 70
- According to FSSA Section 51, the penalty for any article of food for human consumption that is substandard may extend to 5 lakh rupees
- According to FSSA Section 52, the penalty for misbranded food may extend to 3 lakh rupees
- According to FSSA Section 53, the penalty for misleading advertisement may be extended to 10 lakh rupees
- According to FSSA Section 54, the penalty for food containing extraneous matter may extend to 1 lakh rupees

- According to FSSA, the penalty for unhygienic or unsanitary processing or manufacturing of food may extend to 1 lakh rupees
- According to FSSA, Punishment for interfering with seized items shall be imprisonment up to and a fine of up to 6 months and 2 lakh rupees
- Section 11 – Central Advisory Committee
- Section 12 – Functions of the Central Advisory Committee
- Section 13 – Scientific panels
- Section 14 – Scientific committee
- Section 22 – Genetically modified foods, Organic foods, Functional foods, Proprietary foods
- Section 23 – Packaging and Labelling of Foods
- Section 28 – Food recall procedures
- Section 32 - Improvement notices
- Section 81 – Budget of the food authority
- Section 83 – Accounts and audit of food authority
- Section 91 – Power of the central Government to make rules
- Section 96 – Recovery of penalty
- Section 101 – Power to remove difficulty
- According to FSSA, Risk, in relation to any article of food, means the probability of an adverse effect on the health of consumers of such food and the severity of that effect, consequential to a food hazard
- Risk analysis has 3 components: Risk assessment, Risk management, and Risk communication
- According to FSSA, Risk Assessment means a scientifically based process consisting of the following steps : (i) hazard identification, (ii) hazard characterization, (iii) exposure assessment, and (iv) risk characterization
- SOFTEL – Strengthening of Food Testing Laboratory Information Bank
- Adjudicating Officers have the powers of a civil court
- Code of Civil Procedure – 1908
- Appeal against the special court can be filed in high court within 45 days from the date on which the order was served, after payment of the fee
- Appeal against the tribunal can be filed in the High Court within 60 days of the decision/ order
- Food safety officer – Inspection of premises, sample drawn, and sending to food analyst
- Food analyst – Analysis of sample, preparation of report, and sending report

within 14 days to the designated officer and copy to commissioner of food safety

- Tamil Nadu comes under Zone I of first schedule
- Food Safety and Standards rules 2011, comprises of 3 chapters
- FoSCoRIS – Food Safety Compliance Through Regular Sampling and Inspection. Digital tool for recording observations during inspections
- License granted under these regulations shall be valid for a period of 1 to 5 years
- FSSAI issues license of food business for Registration: Turnover less than ₹12 Lakh
- FSSAI issues license of food business for State License: For Turnover between ₹12 Lakh to ₹20 Crore
- FSSAI issues license of food business for Central License: For Turnover above ₹20 Crore
- Receiving temperature of potentially high risk foods should be at or below 5^0C
- Receiving temperature of frozen food should be -18^0C or below
- Working surfaces of vending carts shall be placed at least 60 to 70 cm from above ground
- The temperature in fridge should be in the range of 4^0C to 6^0C
- Raw milk brought to a dairy plant by a producer within four hours of milking
- Stunning methods induce temporary loss of consciousness and rely on prompt and accurate sticking procedures to cause death
- Stunning of pigs by exposure of carbon dioxide may be preferred
- Cooked food served hot should be kept at a temperature of at least 60^0C to prevent microbial growth
- Reheated food must reach a minimum internal temperature of 74^0C
- Chopping instruments should be cleaned with hot water at a temperature of 82^0C
- Thawing in running water advisable to shellfish and sea foods
- Thawing in running water should not exceed 90 minutes
- After thawing product must be used within 12 hours
- Aflatoxin in all articles of food has a limit of 30μg/kg
- Aflatoxin M1 in milk has a limit of 0.5μg/kg
- Cream, coulommiers and cottage comes under soft unripened cheese
- Camembert and Brie are soft ripened cheese
- Samsoe, Emmentaler and cheddar are hard ripened cheese
- Dambo, Edam and Gowda are Semi hard ripened cheese
- Rigid packaging - Metal can, Corrugated fibreboard and Glass container

- Semi rigid packaging - Folding carton, Line carton and Aseptic carton
- Flexible packaging - Aluminium , Aluminium foil, Paper, Paper board and Plastic
- More than 180 grammage papers are called paperboard
- Thermoplastic – Melt under heat after curing
- Thermoset – Keep their form and remain solid under heat once cured
- Controlled Atmosphere Packaging – Controlling the known elements in the package environment such as O_2, CO_2, Water vapour and ethylene concentration reduce spoilage and contamination thus extending shelf life
- Modified Atmosphere Packaging – Modifies the internal package atmosphere of food and helps preserve packaged food
- Active packaging – Oxygen absorbers (Ferro compounds, Ascorbic acid, metal salts, Glucose oxidases, Alcohol oxidase
- Active packaging – Carbon dioxide absorbers – Calcium hydroxide, Sodium hydroxide or potassium hydroxide, calcium hydroxide and silica gel
- Active packaging – Ethylene absorbers – Aluminium oxide and Potassium permanganate (Sachet)
- Active packaging – Humidity absorbers – Polyacrylates (sheets), Propylene glycol (films), Silica gel (Sachet), Clays (Sachet)
- Intelligent packaging is a system which includes Time Temperature indicators, Oxygen indicators, Carbon dioxide indicator, Microbial growth indicators and pathogen indicators as present internal
- Codex Alimentarius commission was created in the year 1963
- Codex Alimentarius commission was created by joint efforts of WHO and FAO
- Consumer protection Act came into force on 24th December 1986
- Right to Information Act (RTI) was passed on Oct 2005
- AGMARK was promulgated in 1937
- AGMARK Act 1937 comes under Department of Agriculture and Cooperation
- Hallmark is certification maintained for standardization of Gold
- World Consumer Day is celebrated on 15th March every year
- Essential Commodities Act came into force in 1955
- Traceability of goods done with the help of Barcode systems and Batch code records
- Quality council of India set up in year 1997
- Technical Barriers to Trade emerged from the Tokyo round of WTO
- NCCP act as a link between the Codex Secretariat, National Codex Committee and Shadow Committee

- India is regional coordinator for FAO/WHO Coordinating committee for Asia (CCASIA)
- MPEDA stands for - Marine Products Export Development Authority
- Major functions of MPEDA - Registration of infrastructural facilities for seafood export trade, Promotion of Indian marine products in overseas markets, Market promotional activities and publicity of Marine products
- Major product exported by MPEDA - Frozen Shrimp
- Headquarters of MPEDA - Kochi
- BIS comes under - Department of Consumer affairs
- BIS was established on 23rd December, 1986
- WTO Head Quarters – Geneva, Switzerland
- WTO formed in 1 Jan 1995
- FAO was established on 16 Oct 1945
- FAO HQ – Rome, Italy
- WHO was established on 7 April, 1948
- WHO HQ – Geneva, Switzerland
- IAF – International Accreditation Forum
- ILAC – International Lab Accreditation Cooperation
- ILAC started as a conference in 1977
- APAC – Asia Pacific Accreditation Cooperation
- APAC was established in 1 Jan 2019
- FSSC 22000- Certification of Food Safety Managment System
- FSSC 22000 Head Quarters – Gorinchem, South Holland
- FSSC 22000 founded in 2009
- NETFISH – Network for Fish Quality Management and Sustainable Fishing
- AGMARK notified 227 Agricultural commodities
- PDP – Principal Display Panel
- Central Government has the power to make rules under FSSA
- FSSAI has power to make regulations under FSSA
- Food authority shall consist of a chairperson and the following 22 number of members
- Food safety commissioner is the highest position of state food safety and standards agency
- Designated officer has power to cancel the license
- During the course of lifting samples FSO serves the notice to the FBO in Form V A

- Central food laboratory is located at Kolkata
- Quality Council of India is the umbrella of five boards – NABL, NABH, NABET, NABCB and NBQP
- NABL grants accreditation as per ISO/IEC 17025 for Calibration Laboratories and Testing Laboratories
- NABL grants accreditation as per ISO/IEC 15189 for Medical Testing Laboratories
- NABL grants accreditation as per ISO/IEC 17043 for Proficiency Testing Providers
- NABL grants accreditation as per ISO 17034 for Reference Material Producers
- NABL grants accreditation as per ISO/IEC 17020 for Inspection Bodies
- The first hospital to be accredited by NABH is Malabar Institute of Medical Sciences (MIMS) Kerala accredited in 2007
- NABET is a member of IAF and PAC
- Accreditation - Independent, Third party evaluation of a conformity assessment body against recognized standards
- World Accreditation Day, a global initiative established by IAF and ILAC to promote the value of accreditation on 9 June
- Theme of Accreditation for 2022 is Accreditation: Sustainability in Economic Growth and the Environment
- The head office of the Tea board is in Kolkata, West Bengal
- Tea Board was established on 1st April 1954 by Tea Act (1953)
- Spices Board of India Headquarters at Kochi, Kerala
- Indian Cardamom Research Institute was established in 1978 as the research wing of spices board with its headquarters at Myladumpara, Idukki District to undertake research on small cardamom
- Coconut Development Board Headquarters at Kochi in Kerala
- Indian Institute of Packaging headquartered at Mumbai
- National Horticultural Board was set up by Government of India in April 1984
- Head office of National Horticultural Board is at Gurugram, Haryana
- Head office of coffee board is located at Bengaluru, Karnataka
- Coffee Board is under the control of Ministry of Commerce and Industry
- Rubber Board Headquarters at Kottayam in Kerala
- Tobacco Board constituted as a statutory body a on 1st Jan, 1976
- Tobacco Board Act – 1975
- National Bee Board head office at New Delhi
- Joint FAO/WHO Expert Committee on food additives (JECFA) active since 1956

- Joint FAO/WHO Expert Meetings on Pesticide Residues (JMPR) active since 1963
- Joint FAO/WHO Expert Meetings on Microbiological Risk Assessment (JEM-RA) active since 2000
- Joint FAO/WHO Expert Meetings on Pesticide Specification (JMPS) active since 2002
- JEMNU Stands for Joint FAO/WHO Expert Meeting on Nutrition
- TBT (Technical Barriers to Trade) Agreement covers - Technical regulations (mandatory), Standards (Voluntary) and Conformity assessment Procedures
- SPS (Sanitary and Phytosanitory measures) Agreement protects (Codex Alimentarius - Human health), (OIE – World Organization for Animal Health) and (IPPC – International Plant Protection Convention, FAO)
- American Type Culture Collection (ATCC) is located in Rockville, Maryland

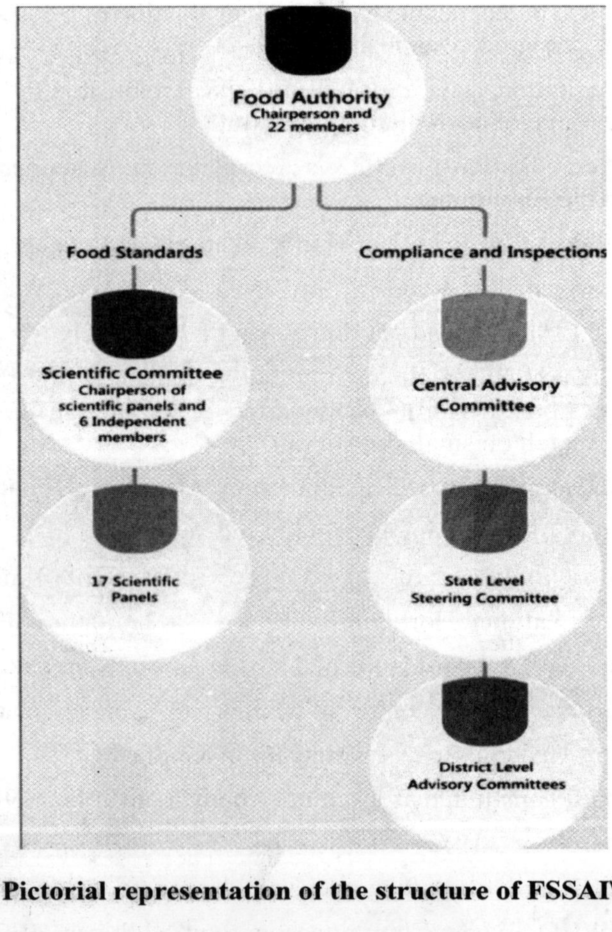

Pictorial representation of the structure of FSSAI

CHAPTER-2

FSSAI – Role, Functions, Initiatives (A General Understanding)

- Food Standards and Safety Bill – 2005
- Objective of FSS act, 2006 is to make available safe and wholesome food to the public, in keeping with changing needs and requirements
- Food safety is the primary responsibility of the Food business Operator
- Ministry of Health and Family Welfare, Government of India is the Administrative ministry for the implementation of FSSAI
- Chairperson is in the rank of Secretary to Government of India
- Food Safety and Standards rules, 2011 comprises of 3 chapters. Chapter 1- General descriptions about rules and definitions. Chapter 2- Detailed structure about enforcement structures and procedures. Chapter 3 – Adjudication proceedings
- Functional head of food authority is the Chairperson appointed for a period of 3 years
- CEO is the legal representative of the authority
- Scientific panels are constituted under Section 13 of Food Safety and Standard Act, 2006
- As per section 14 of FSS act FSSAI has constituted a scientific committee
- FSSAI comprises of 22 members
- FSSAI comprises of 22 members of which at least one third are women
- Horizontal standards cut across various food categories relate to food safety covering limits for various contaminants, toxins in foods and also requirement for packaging, labeling and claims
- Vertical standards mainly include identity and compositional standards of specific food products and are covered under FSS regulations
- Currently food authority has commissioned 21 scientific panels that comprise of 11 vertical and 10 horizontal panels
- In codex horizontal committees are also called General subject committees
- GSFA – General Standard for Food Additives
- No person below the rank of Commissioner and secretary to state Government shall be eligible to be appointed as the commissioner of food safety
- Designated Officer shall be a whole time officer not below the rank of sub

divisional officer

- Powers and duties of the commissioner of food safety shall be as provided in the section 30(2) of food safety and Standards Act 2006
- Powers and duties of the designated officer shall be mentioned in section 36 (3) of FSS act, 2006
- Prevention of Food Adulteration Act, 1954
- Notified Laboratory means any of the laboratories notified by the food authority under subsections (1) and (2) of section 43 of act
- Referral laboratories means any of the laboratories established or recognized by the food authority by notification under subsection (2) of section 43 of act
- Presently there are 20 referral food laboratories, 11 NRLs, 2 ANRLs and 225 Primary food laboratories
- Import means bringing into India any article of food by land, sea or air
- Licensing and Registration of Food Business Regulations, 2011
- No article of food shall be cleared from the custom unless it has a valid shelf life of not less than 60 percent at the time of import
- Third party audits will reduce the burden on regulatory inspection conducted by central or state licensing authorities
- IS/ISO 19011: 2011 – Guidelines for auditing management Systems
- Forward the audit report to the food authority within 15 days of the conduct of food safety audit
- Food Business Operator shall maintain all records of audit findings and rectification for a period of 5 years
- Tagline of Eat Right India is "Sahi Bhojan Behtar Jeevan"
- Eat Right India is based on 3 key themes – Eat safe, Eat healthy and Eat Sustainable
- National Health Policy – 2017
- Health care flagship programmes – Ayushman Bharat, POSHAN Abhiyaan, Anemia Mukt Bharat and Swacch Bharat Mission
- Food Safety Training and Certification (FoSTac) – a unique program to ensure a trained and certified food safety supervisor on each food business premise
- Demand side initiatives of FSSAI aim at large scale social and behaviour changes by engaging consumers and educating them on eating right
- FSSAI has launched mass awareness campaigns to reduce salt, fat and sugar in the diet "Aaj Se Thoda Kam" and Trans fat free India @ 75 to eliminate trans fats by 2022
- Sustainability initiatives is to encourage and support responsible production and consumption of food to protect the environment
- "Jaivik Bharat" to promote authentic organic food

- Food fortification – Addition of key vitamins and minerals such as Iron, Iodine, Zinc, Vitamin A, Vitamin D to staple foods such as rice, wheat, oil, milk and salt to improve their nutritional content
- Deficiency of micronutrient malnutrition also known as hidden hunger
- Copenhagen Consensus estimates that every 1 rupee spent on fortification results in 9 rupees in benefits to the economy
- FFRC – Food Fortification Resource Centre
- SNF (Safe and Nutritious Food) – SNF@home, SNF@school, SNF@Workplace and SNF@Eat out
- During frying, several properties of oil are altered, Total Polar Compounds (TPC) are formed on repeated frying
- As per the FSSAI notification under Food Safety and Standards (Prohibition and Restriction Sales) Regulation, the total polar compounds in unused or fresh vegetable fat or oil shall not be more than 15%
- For those used vegetable fat or oil, total polar compounds of more than 25% shall not be used
- FSSAI is implementing an EEE strategy (Education, Enforcement, Ecosystem) to divert used Cooking oil from the food value chain and curb current illegal practices
- FSSAI has initiated "Diet 4 life" to help people understand about metabolic disorders (Inborn Errors of Metabolism)
- All food businesses having central licenses or state licenses should have at least one trained and certified food safety supervisor for every 25 food handlers
- Under FoSTaC 16 courses in three levels: Basic, Advanced and Special
- Basic - 5 courses of short duration – 4 hours
- Advanced - 4 courses of 8 hours each
- Special – 9 courses of 4-8 hours each
- Food Safety on wheels (FSW) performs 3 key functions – Testing, Training and Awareness generation
- DART – Detect Adulterants with Rapid Testing
- Food Safety Magic Box is a self contained portable food testing kit useful as a pedagogical tool for school children in primary health centre, for frontline health workers. A total of 102 very simple tests can be performed with the magic box
- Consumer can lodge the complaints through Facebook, twitter, whatsapp, SMS, FSSAI App, written letters, email or toll free number. All the complaints are received through various channels are fed in "Food Safety Connect Portal".
- As per Food safety and standards Act, 2006, the state food safety machinery is headed by the commissioner of food safety of state for efficient implementation of food safety and standards

- Commissioner of food safety may delegate such of his powers and functions under this act (except the power to appoint Designated Officer, Food Safety Officer and Food Analyst) to any officer subordinate to him
- Commissioner conduct or organizes training programmes for the personnel of the office and carry out survey of the industrial unit
- Main role of the food authority is Monitoring the food, Regulating the food, Monitoring manufacturing and processing of food, and Monitoring sale of food
- The annual return for business other than milk and milk product is in Form D - 1
- Fees for registration with FSSAI is Rs 100
- On 19 July 2021, conditional licensing framework for proprietary food products has been proposed by The Food Safety and Standards Authority of India (FSSAI)
- Paramparagat Krishi Vikas Yojana Scheme was launched in 2014 to promote natural farming
- India today ranks fifth in terms of area under natural farming and first in terms of total number of producers
- Under the new regulations, in the food products which comprises of the edible oils and fats as an ingredient the total amount of industrial trans fats should not exceed 2% of the total oils or fats present in the product. This regulation will be applicable from January 1, 2022
- The National Food Security Act (NFSA) was introduced by the Government of India in 2013. It is responsible for the provision of subsidized food grains to the population
- In 2006, the Finance Minister announced the introduction of the National Food Security Act under which BPL families in rural and urban areas will be entitled by law to 25 kg of wheat or rice per month at Rs. 3 per kg
- Schemes such as the Mid-Day Meal Scheme (MDM), the Public Distribution System (PDS), and the Integrated Child Development Services (ICDS) are included under the National Food Security Act
- The Induction Training will be given to the FSOs who are newly recruited/ appointed or are new to the service. Induction Training will for a period of 40 (working) days
- Classroom training for FSOs will be for 14 days and will be conducted at the institutes empanelled by FSSAI across all the States/UTs or at any other venue mutually agreed by FSSAI and State/UT Government
- On the job training will be for 26 days. It has been divided in six parts and in each part the training, FSOs will be attached with various offices viz DOs, FBOs, Laboratories etc and will get first hand experience and will be able to correlate the classroom learning's with the on the job working

CHAPTER-3

FOOD SAFETY ECOSYSTEM IN INDIA

- IS : 10146 (Specification for Polyethylene in contact with foodstuffs)
- Tin and plastic containers once used, shall not be re-used for packaging of edible oils and fats
- All milk and milk products derived solely from milk are class titled as Milk solids
- Cocoa bean, Coconib, Cocomass, Cocoa press cakes, Cocoa powder (Fine/ Dust) are class titled as Cocoa solids
- "Health claims" means a relationship exists between a food or a constituent of that food and health and include nutrition claims which describe the physiological role of the nutrient in growth, development and normal functions of the body, other functional claims concerning specific beneficial effect of the consumption of food or its constituents
- "Nutrition claim" means that a food has particular nutritional properties which are not limited to the energy value but include protein, fat carbohydrates, vitamins and minerals
- A batch number or code number or lot number which is a mark of identification by which the food can be traced in the manufacture and identified in the distribution, shall be given on the label
- On packages of Aspartame, instead of Best Before date, Use by date/ recommended last consumption date/expiry date shall be given, which shall not be more than three years from the date of packing
- In case of infant milk substitute and infant foods instead of Best Before date, Use by date/ recommended last consumption date/expiry date shall be given
- The protein efficiency ratio (PER) which shall be minimum 2.5 if the product other than infant milk substitute is claimed to have higher quality protein
- Lactose free Infant Milk Substitute should only be used in case of diarrhea due to lactose intolerance
- The package, label or the advertisement of edible oils and fats shall not use the expressions "super refined", "Extra-Refined", "Micro-Refined", "Double-Refined", Ultra-Refined", "Anti-Cholesterol", "Cholesterol Fighter", "Soothing

to Heart", "Cholesterol Friendly", "Saturated Fat Free" or such other expressions which are an exaggeration of the quality of the Product

- "Food with added prebiotic ingredients" means food that contains added prebiotic ingredients which are nonviable food components that confer health benefits to the consumer by modulation of gut microbiota
- "Food with added probiotic ingredients" means food with live micro-organisms beneficial to human health, which when ingested in adequate numbers as a single strain or as a combination of cultures, confer one or more specified or demonstrated health benefits in human beings
- "Functional food" shall have the meaning assigned to it in section 22 of the act
- "Health supplements" shall have the meaning assigned to it in section 22 of the act
- "Non-food" means an ingredient or a substance which is not a 'food' as referred to in clause (j) of section 3 of the act
- "Novel food" shall have the meaning assigned to it in section 22 of the act
- "Nutraceuticals" shall have the meaning assigned to it in section 22 of the Act
- Nutritional ingredients" means the ingredients specified in Schedules other than the food additives specified in Schedule VA to Schedule VF
- "Nutrient ingredients" means vitamins, minerals, and amino acids as specified in Schedule I and Schedule II
- The health supplements shall contain any of the ingredients specified in Schedule I or Schedule II or Schedule IV or Schedule VII or Schedule VIII or enzymes only of Schedule VI.
- Every package of health supplement shall carry the following information on the label, namely.- the words "HEALTH SUPPLEMENT, an advisory warning 'NOT FOR MEDICINAL USE' prominently written
- No food business operator shall use additives for health supplement formulation except those specified in Schedule VA or Schedule VE or Schedule VF
- Nutraceuticals shall provide a physiological benefit and help maintain good health
- Nutraceuticals shall contain any of the ingredients specified in Schedule I or Schedule II or Schedule IV or Schedule VI or Schedule VII or Schedule VIII.
- A food business operator may prepare and sell the nutraceuticals in the food-format of granules, powder, tablet, capsule, liquid, jelly or gel, semi-solids and other formats and may be packed in sachet, ampoule, bottle, and in any other format as measured unit quantities except those formats that are meant for parenteral administration

- No ingredient other than those specified in Schedule VI shall be used as nutraceutical with standardization to marker compounds specified and at daily usage levels specified therein
- No food business operator shall use the extract of ingredient as nutraceutical other than that specified in Schedule IV
- Provided that the ingredient of plant or botanical origin specified in Schedule IV and Schedule VI may be used either in the given form, or their extract, subject to the extractive ratios in relation to the daily usage value
- Every package of food containing nutraceutical shall carry the following information on the label, namely:- the word "NUTRACEUTICAL", an advisory warning for 'recommended usage', an advisory warning 'NOT FOR MEDICINAL USE' prominently written, an advisory warning in cases where a danger may exist with excess consumption
- No food business operator shall use additives for nutraceutical formulation except those specified in Schedule VA or Schedule VE or Schedule VF
- Food for special medical purpose shall include food specially prepared for weight reduction and intended as total replacement of normal diet
- Food for special medical purpose shall contain any of the ingredients specified in Schedule I or Schedule II or Schedule III or Schedule IV or Schedule VII or Schedule VIII or enzymes only of Schedule VI
- No food business operator shall use probiotic ingredients in food except the probiotic culture of the microorganisms specified in Schedule VII or those probiotic microorganisms approved by the Food Authority from time to time.
- The viable number of organisms in food with added probiotic ingredients shall be $\geq$108 CFU/g
- Every package of probiotic food shall carry the following information on the label, namely:- the words "PROBIOTIC FOOD", an advisory warning 'NOT FOR MEDICINAL USE' prominently written, viable numbers at the end of the shelf-life of probiotic strain corresponding to the level at which the efficacy is claimed
- No food business operator shall use prebiotics in manufacturing food containing prebiotics except those specified in Schedule VIII or those prebiotics approved by the Food Authority from time to time.
- Specialty food containing plant or botanical ingredients with safe history of usage.- (1) (i) A food business operator shall use only plant or botanical ingredients specified in Schedule IV for the preparation of specialty food containing plant or botanical ingredients
- "Organic food" means food products that have been produced in accordance with specified standards for organic food production

- "Participatory Guarantee System for India" means a quality assurance initiative by the Department of Agriculture Co-operation and Farmer's Welfare, Ministry of Agriculture and Farmer's Welfare, Government of India for organic production which emphasizes the participation of producers, consumers and other stakeholders and operate outside the framework of third party certification
- Labelling on the package of organic food shall convey full and accurate information on the organic status of the product
- The organic food offered or promoted for sale shall also comply with all the applicable provisions of one of the following systems, namely: (i) National Programme for Organic Production (NPOP); (ii) Participatory Guarantee System for India (PGS-India). (iii) Any other system or standards as may be notified by the Food Authority from time to time
- "Non-specified food" means any food other than proprietary food or food ingredients, including additives, processing aids and enzymes for which standards have not been specified in any regulation made under the Act.,
- "Custom House Agent" shall have the meaning assigned to it in clause (c) of section 2 of the Custom House Agent Regulations, 2004
- "Food Importer" means a Food Business Operator importing or desirous of importing article of food into Indian territory, who is duly licensed as Importer under the Food Safety and Standards (Licensing and Registration of Food Businesses) Regulations, 2011 made under the Act
- "Non-conformance report" means a report issued to the customs authorities and the food importer by the Authorized Officer, or any other officer specifically authorized for this purpose, by the food authority, for non-compliance of the provisions of the Act and the rules and regulations made there under, of the consignment of the Food Importer
- "Transit Country List" means the list of countries through which the imported articles of food transits before it reaches the Indian territory
- The Authorized Officer shall issue a 'no objection certificate' in FORM – 3, after assessing the safety of food being imported under these regulations under his seal and signature for allowing import of food, and shall communicate such order in a specified manner to the customs and the Food Importer
- Importer is required to scan the documents and upload them in pdf format with the annual fee of Rs 7500 payable for import license
- Importer can apply for license for a period of one year and upto a maximum of five years
- Importer must apply within 30 days before the expiry of license for renewal
- FICS – Food Import Clearance System

- CHA – Custom House Agent
- Supply side initiatives – FoSTaC, Clean Street food hub, Clean and fresh fruits and vegetables market, Eat Right Station, BHOG (Blissful Hygienic Offering To God), Hygiene rating and catering Establishments, Sweet and meat shops
- Demand side initiatives – Eat Right Campus, Eat Right School, Eat Right Toolkit, DART, Mobile food testing van called Food Safety On Wheels, Food fortification, Awareness campaign – (To reduce salt, fat and sugar in the diet - Aaj Se Thoda Kam) and (Trans Fat Free India@75 to eliminate trans fats by 2022)
- Sustainability side initiatives – Jaivik Bharat, Save Food, Share food, Safe and Sustainable Packaging in food, Repurpose Used Cooking Oil (RUCO)
- FSSAI launched Eat Right India Movement on 10th July, 2018
- Rating of the campus – Evaluated based on total score out of 100

85/100 – and above it receives 5 stars and Excellent rating

75/100– and above it receives 4 stars and Very Good rating

65/100– and above it receives 3 stars and Good rating

55/100– and above it receives 2 stars and Needs Improvement Rating

Below 55/100– and above it receives Urgent Improvement Rating

- (ERCC) - Eat Right Creativity Challenge
- Eat Right India Campaign Vision for 2050 is about creating a culture of safe, healthy and sustainable food for all, Making Indian food Trans fat free by 2022, Aims to cut down salt/sugar and oil consumption by 30% in 3 years
- PHVO – Partially Hydrogenated Vegetable Oil
- From 1st Jan 2022 regulation was issued stating that all edible oils and fats shall limit the trans fat content not more than 2% by weight
- Heart Attack Rewind was launched by FSSAI on 30th November 2018 in the form of a Public Service Announcement (PSA) aimed to create awareness about harmful effects of trans fat
- Eat Right Station Initiative is designed to ensure that safe and wholesome food is served to passengers, visitors to railway stations and railway officials
- First Railway Station to be certified was Mumbai Central Railway Station
- Enrichment – Addition of micronutrients to a food which are lost during processing
- Food fortification does not alter the characteristics of the food like the taste, aroma or their texture of food
- Fortification – Addition of Key vitamins and minerals such as Iron, Iodine, Zinc, Vitamins A and D to staple foods such as Rice, wheat, Oil, Milk, Salt to improve

their nutritional content. These nutrients may or may not have been originally present in the food before processing or may have been lost during processing

- Fortification of Foods Regulation 2016 for fortifying staples namely Wheat flour and Rice (with Iron, Vitamin B12 and folic acid), Milk and Edible oil (With Vitamins A and D) and double fortified salt (with Iodine and Iron) to reduce the high burden of micronutrient malnutrition in India
- As of now standards have been issued for Fortification in Rice, wheat, Edible oil, Milk, double fortified salt
- End of milling process the micronutrient premix is added for fortifying flour
- Blue coloured ring shows the presence Vitamin A in fortified oil
- DART booklet is a compilation of common quick tests for detection of food adulterants at household by the citizens themselves so as to induce awareness among the consumers about food safety
- FSSAI declared Kankaria Lake area in Ahmedabad as a country's first clean street food hub in 2018
- FSSAI launched BHOG (Blissful Hygienic Offering To God) in 2018
- To prevent food waste and fight hunger the "Save Food, Share Food, Share Joy" initiative has been launched
- More recently a new campaign "Small Gesture : Big Difference" to prevent food waste in small gatherings has been launched
- APEDA implemented National Programme For Organic Production
- Sikkim has been declared as the India's first fully organic state. Total area under organic certification is 5.71million hectares
- India ranks first in terms of number of organic producers
- India ranks 9th in area under organic certification
- India exports around 1.35 million mts of certified organic foods
- CAPA – Corrective and Preventive Action
- World Food Safety Day is celebrated globally on June 7 every year as per the World Health Organization (WHO)

CHAPTER-4

Principles and Basics of Food Chemistry and their role in Food Chemistry

- Electrostatic forces provide a major contribution to the energy of the hydrogen bond, and lead to an essentially correct geometric picture of HOH molecules
- A carbohydrate is a chemical compound made up of carbon, hydrogen, and oxygen
- The basic unit of a carbohydrate is a monosaccharide. It contains a series of carbon atoms linked together in a chain, attached with oxygen and hydrogen atoms. Its formula is $C_6H_{12}O_6$
- Monosaccharides - They are 3, 4, 5, and 6 carbon unit sugars called trioses, tetroses, pentoses, and hexoses. Glucose, fructose, galactose, arabinose, and ribose are examples of this class
- Glucose is the sugar that is necessary for all the body systems. It is abundantly found in nature
- Fructose is the fruit sugar found in honey and fruits
- When two molecules of monosaccharides combine with the removal of one molecule of water, disaccharides are formed. Maltose, Lactose, and sucrose are examples of this class
- Sucrose is found in almost all plants, such as sugarcane and beet, being rich sources.
- Lactose is found predominantly in milk. It helps to absorb the calcium present in large amounts in milk
- The concentration of lactose in milk varies with the mammalian source from 2.0 to 8.5%. Cow and goat milk contain 4.5–4.8%, human milk about 7%
- Lactose stimulates intestinal adsorption and retention of calcium
- Lactose is not digested until it reaches the small intestine, where the hydrolytic enzyme lactase is present
- Lactase (a β-galactosidase) is a membrane-bound enzyme located in the brush border epithelial cells of the small intestine. It catalyzes the hydrolysis of lactose into its constituent monosaccharides, d-glucose and d-galactose
- Maltose or malt sugar is found in all sprouted and malted products. It is produced when starch is digested by amylases. Sprouted cereals and beer contain large amounts of maltose

- Monosaccharides are carbohydrate molecules that cannot be broken down to simpler carbohydrate molecules by hydrolysis, so they are sometimes referred to as simple sugars
- Naturally occurring glucose is designated as the D form
- Polysaccharides are complex compounds with high molecular weights. They are formed by a combination of more than two molecules of a monosaccharide. Their structural formula is $(C_6H_{10}O_5)n$. Starch, Dextrin, and glycogen are examples of this class
- Starch is the storage form of carbohydrates in plants and comprises the primary source of energy in the diet
- Resistant starch includes all the starch that escapes digestion in the small intestines
- All digestible forms of complex carbohydrates, mainly starches, are broken down by the action of the enzyme ptyalin in the mouth and further by pancreatic and intestinal enzymes amylase and maltase to the simple sugar glucose (monosaccharide) by the process of enzyme hydrolysis
- Fats are a more concentrated form of storage of energy than carbohydrates. They are found in the adipose (fatty) tissue of animals
- The simple lipids are the neutral fats. These are chemically made up of triglycerides. Triglycerides contain a glycerol base with three fatty acids
- Compound Lipids - chemically made up of simple lipids containing phosphorus, carbohydrate, or protein. Such compound lipids are known as phospholipids, glycolipids, and lipoproteins
- Derived Lipids - They are fat-like substances produced from fats and fatty compounds. The important members of this group are glycerol and fatty acids
- Unsaponifiable Lipids - steroids, terpenoids
- Vanaspati, a common cooking medium, is a hydrogenated fat
- Fatty acids consist of a hydrophobic hydrocarbon chain with a terminal carboxylic acid hence it is also termed aliphatic carboxylic acids.
- Stearic acid, palmitic acid, capric acid, lauric acid, and myristic acids are examples of saturated fatty acids
- Saturated fatty acids are the simplest form of fats that are unbranched linear chains of CH_2 groups linked together by carbon-carbon single bonds with a terminal carboxylic acid.
- Saturated fatty acids are mostly found in animal fats like butter, meat, and whole milk
- Saturated fatty acids increase LDL cholesterol levels in the body.
- Linoleic acid, linolenic acid, oleic acid, and crotonic acid are examples of unsaturated fatty acids
- Unsaturated fatty acids decrease LDL cholesterol levels in the body

- Unsaturated fatty acids are more complex fatty acids with bent hydrocarbon chains linked together by carbon-carbon double bonds with a terminal carboxylic acid group.
- Unsaturated fatty acids are mostly found in plant sources like vegetable oil, sunflower oil, mustard oil, and avocado oil
- Essential fatty acids are the type of fatty acids that cannot be synthesized by the body. That means we need to include essential fatty acids in our diet.
- The two essential fatty acids in the human body are linoleic acid (LA) and α-linoleic acid (ALA)
- Nonessential fatty acids are arachidic acid, stearic acid, palmitic acid
- Normal adults synthesize about 1 g of cholesterol daily
- Total cholesterol level of less than 200 mg/dl is normal
- Important dietary omega-3 fatty acids are (a) Alpha Linolenic Acid (ALA), (b) Eicosapentaenoic Acid (EPA), and (c) Docosahexaenoic Acid (DHA)
- Linoleic Acid (LA) and Arachidonic Acid (AA) are common omega - 6 fatty acids
- Omega-3 fatty acids reduce the LDL cholesterol, which may thus reduce the risk of coronary heart disease
- Hydrogenation is a process that hardens a liquid fat by converting unsaturated fatty acid components to their saturated form
- Unsaturated vegetable oils such as cottonseed, corn, soyabean, etc. They are treated with hydrogen to produce a plastic fat for cooking purposes or to resemble and substitute a table fat like butter and ghee.
- Vanaspati and margarine sold in the market are examples of hydrogenated fats
- Partially hydrogenated vegetable oils are the major contributors of TFA in foods
- Partially hydrogenated vegetable oil have a long shelf life, they are stable during frying and their semi-solidity can be customised to enhance the palatability of baked goods and sweets
- Elaidic acid (C18:19t) is the major trans isomer (80–90%)
- TFA in the diet comes from deep fried fast foods, bakery products, and packaged snack foods
- Each amino acid contains a carboxyl (COOH) or acidic group and an amino (NH_2) or basic group
- Proteins are complex organic compounds containing carbon, hydrogen and oxygen
- Hormones such as adrenocorticotrophic hormone (ACTH) and insulin, are protein in nature
- Protein malnutrition - kwashiorkor meaning red boy
- Dry skimmed milk is one of the most effective foods for treatment and prevention of such protein malnutrition in children

- Good sources of plant proteins are legumes, pulses, nuts and oilseeds
- Biological value = Nitrogen retained/ Nitrogen absorbed 100
- Eggs have a biological value of 94
- The biological value (BV) measures how efficiently the body converts absorbed protein into body tissue – a score of 94 is exceptionally high
- Protein Efficiency Ratio = Weight gain in grams/Dietary protein in grams
- (PDCAAS) - Protein Digestibility Corrected Amino Acid Score. It represents the amino acid score after correcting for digestibility
- PDCAAS of Milk, Egg, whey protein, cottage cheese and yoghurt is 1.0
- Amino Acid Score - It is a chemical score based on chemical analysis of the protein and not on a biological test
- Wheat, the limiting amino acid is lysine
- Ovolactovegetarians: This diet consists of plant foods, along with eggs, milk, and milk products.
- Lactovegetarians: This diet is of plant origin, supplemented with milk and milk products
- Pure vegetarians or vegans: Eat all foods of plant origin
- Plant sources of iron are absorbed less than animal sources of iron
- Our body contains about 65 percent water.
- An infant's body contains more water than that of an adult
- A thin person has a higher percentage of water than a fat person
- Fruits and vegetables contain 80–90 percent water.
- Milk contains 80–88 percent.
- Flour, crackers and bread contain 5–35 percent.
- Meats contain 40–75 percent water
- IDF (Insoluble Dietary Fibre): which are non-viscous slowly fermentable, e.g., Cellulose, lignin and some portions of hemicellulose
- SDF (Soluble Dietary Fibre): which are viscous and fermentable, e.g., Pectins, gums, Beta-glucans, mucilages and major portions of hemi cellulose
- The word vitamin was coined by Casimir Funk who discovered a water-soluble substance in rice polishings that prevented beri-beri
- Fat-soluble vitamins are A, D, E and K
- Water-soluble vitamins are B group vitamins and vitamin C
- A provitamin is a substance which the human body can convert into a vitamin, e.g. Beta carotene, a precursor of vitamin A, is called a provitamin
- Dehydrocholesterol and Ergosterol are precursors (provitamins) of vitamin D.
- Deficiency of Vitamin D in adults causes Osteomalacia

- Vitamin E deficiency causes Increased haemolysis of RBC and Creatinuria
- Rough, scaly skin, dry mucous membranes are the deficiency of Vitamin A
- Keratomalacia - softening and destruction of eyeball leading to blindness which is incurable
- Xerophthalmia occurs when deficiency of Vitamin A is severe and prolonged
- Vitamin E was named tocopherol from a Greek word meaning childbirth or to bring forth
- Tocopherols themselves act as anti-oxidants. Delta tocopherol shows the highest anti-oxidant power
- Vitamin C is required to build bone matrix, cartilage, dentine (tooth), collagen, capillaries and connective and general body tissue
- Thiamine functions mainly as thiamine pyrophosphate (TPP), also known as cocarboxylase
- Deficiency of Thiamine causes Polyneuritis (malfunctioning of the nervous system)
- Deficiency of Riboflavin is Ariboflavinosis
- Niacin or nicotinic acid is the P-P vitamin or pellagra-preventing vitamin
- Pellagra is characterized by dermatitis, diarrhoea, dementia and death
- The active form of Vitamin B6 is pyridoxal phosphate
- Pantothenic is a word derived from the Greek word pantothen which means in every corner or from all sides
- Deficiency of Cyanocobalamin (B_{12}) causes pernicious anaemia (large nucleated red blood cells)
- Major minerals or macrominerals required in large amounts at least 100 mg/day, e.g. Calcium, phosphorus, sodium, chlorine, potassium
- Minor minerals required in small quantities. E.g. Iron, sulphur, magnesium
- Goitre is an enlargement of the thyroid gland since the size (hypertrophy) and the number of (hyperplasia) epithelial cells in the gland increase.
- People of the hilly regions and those who are far from the sea suffer simple or endemic goiter
- The term myxoedema refers to the thickened, non-pitting, oedematous changes to the soft tissues of patients in a markedly hypothyroid state
- Substances known to interfere with the activity of thyroxine to produce goitre in spite of a normal intake of iodine are known as goitrogens
- Iron is present principally as haemoglobin of the Red Blood Cell (RBC)
- After the life span of the RBC is complete (120 days), the iron from it is removed and sent to the bone marrow where it is used for synthesis of new red blood cells (haemopoiesis)
- Myoglobin is the iron-protein complex found in muscles, which stores some

oxygen for immediate use by the cell

- Transferrin or siderophilin is the circulating form of iron
- Ferritin or haemosiderin is the storage form of iron
- Hyperkalemia or excess of potassium may occur in conditions of severe dehydration, renal failure, after very rapid administration of potassium and in adrenalin sufficiency
- A hormonal deficiency of ACTH in Addison's disease leads to large loss of sodium
- Sulphur is a constituent of thiamine and biotin, two water-soluble vitamins. Skin, hair, nails and connective tissue are rich in sulphur
- Anti-nutritional Factor- interfere with the assimilation of nutrients like protein, iron, zinc, calcium and iodine
- Trypsin Inhibitors - soya, lima and kidney beans as well as duck egg white
- Phytates bind with iron, zinc, calcium and magnesium
- Tannins bind with iron, forming compounds which are not absorbed in the gut
- Millets like bajra, ragi and sorghum also contain a fair amount of tannin
- Tannins are also known to bind proteins and reduce their availability
- Oxalic acid, a dicarboxylic acid or its salts (oxalates) are widely distributed in plant foods generally as calcium salts
- The highest oxalate content is found in horsegram and kesari dal
- Oxalates interfere with calcium salts by forming insoluble calcium salts
- Toxic amino acid (BOAA) from khesari dal can be removed by using a process similar to that of parboiling paddy
- Cyanogenic glycosides of cassava can be leached out with water
- Phytochemicals are non-nutritive plant chemicals that have protective or disease preventive properties
- Isoflavones found in soy imitate human estrogen and help to reduce menopausal symptoms and osteoporosis
- Phytochemicals with Antioxidant activity - Allyl sulphides - Onion, Garlic, Leeks, Polyphenols - Tea, grapes, Carotenoids - Fruits, Carrots, Flavonoids - Fruits, Vegetables
- Saponins found in beans interfere with the replication of cell DNA, thereby, preventing the multiplication of cancer cells. Capsaicin, found in hot peppers, protects DNA from carcinogens
- Indoles, which are found in cabbages, stimulate enzymes that make the estrogen less effective and could reduce the risk for breast cancer
- Proanthocyanidins are responsible for the anti-adhesion properties of cranberry. Consumption of cranberries will reduce the risk of urinary tract infections and will improve dental health

- In 1989, Dr Stephen defelice coined the term "Nutraceutical" to refer to any substance that may be considered as food or part of a food and provides medical or health benefits including prevention and treatment of diseases
- The addition of appropriate phosphates increases the water-holding capacity of raw and cooked meats
- Polyphosphates and EDTA are used in canned sea foods to prevent the formation of glassy crystals of struvite or magnesium ammonium phosphate
- The addition of chelating agents to vegetables prior to blanching can inhibit metal induced discolorations, and can remove calcium from pectic substances in cell walls and thereby promote tenderness
- Citric and phosphoric acids are employed as acidulants in soft drink beverages
- Butylated hydroxyanisole (BHA), butylated hydroxytoluene (BHT), propyl gallate, and di-tbutylhydroquinone (TBHQ), which are synthetic phenolic antioxidants currently approved for use in foods
- Tocopherols are naturally occurring substances possess antioxidant capabilities
- Sulfur dioxide (SO_2) and its derivatives have long been used in foods as general food preservatives. They are added to food to inhibit nonenzymic browning, to inhibit enzyme catalyzed reactions, to inhibit and control microorganisms, and to act as an antioxidant and a reducing agent
- Most frequently used sulfiting agents are the sodium and potassium metabisulfites because they exhibit good stability toward autoxidation in the solid phase
- Potassium and sodium salts of nitrite and nitrate are commonly used in curing mixtures for meats to develop and fix the color, to inhibit microorganisms, and to develop characteristic flavors
- Nitrites in meat form nitric oxide, which reacts with heme compounds to form nitrosomyoglobin, the pigment responsible for the pink color of cured meats
- Nitrites (150–200 ppm) inhibit *clostridia* in canned-comminuted and cured meats
- Nitrite is more effective at pH 5.0–5.5 than it is at higher ph values.
- Vinegar (4% acetic acid) and acetic acid, also used in food are sodium acetate (CH_3COONa), potassium acetate (CH_3COOK), calcium acetate [(CH_3—COO)2Ca], and sodium diacetate Vinegar and acetic acid are used in pickled meats and fish products.
- Propionic acid (CH_3—CH_2—COOH) occurs naturally in Swiss cheese (up to 1% by weight), where it is produced by *Propionibacterium shermanii*
- Sorbic acid (C—C==C—C==C—COOH) and its sodium and potassium salts are widely used to inhibit mold and yeasts in a wide variety of foods including cheese, baked products, fruit juices, wine, and pickles. Levels of use generally range up to 0.3% by weight.
- Sorbic acid is effective up to pH 6.5

- Natamycin or pimaricin is a polyene macrolide antimycotic (III) that has been approved in the United States for use against molds on cured cheeses.
- Benzoic acid (C_6H_5COOH) has been widely employed as an antimicrobial agent in foods and it occurs naturally in cranberries, prunes, cinnamon, and cloves
- Benzoic acid of undissociated acid is the form with antimicrobial activity, exhibits optimum activity in the pH range of 2.5–4.0, making it well suited for use in acid foods such as fruit juices, carbonated beverages, pickles, and sauerkraut
- Sodium benzoate was the first chemical preservative permitted in foods (preferably less than pH 3.6)
- Nisin, a small amphiphilic peptide produced by some strains of *Lactococcus lactis*. It affects gram-positive bacteria by binding to lipid II during peptidoglycan synthesis and forming pores in the plasma membrane
- Nisin is effective in low-acid foods, where it improves inactivation of *Clostridium botulinum* during the canning process and inhibits germination of any surviving spores
- Diethyl pyrocarbonate has been used as an antimicrobial food additive for beverages such as fruit juices, wine, and beer
- Cyclamates are about 30 times sweeter than sucrose
- Saccharin is about 300 times as sweet as sucrose
- Acesulfame K is about 200 times as sweet as sucrose at a 3% concentration in solution,
- Aspartame (XIII), Neotame (XIV), and Alitame (XV) comprise the group of peptide sweeteners
- Aspartame (l-aspartyl-l-phenylalanine methyl ester; XIII) with a sweetening power of 180–200 times that of sucrose
- Neotame was high sweetening power (7,000–13,000 times that of sucrose)
- Alitame is an amino acid-based sweetener that possesses a sweetening power of about 2,000 times that of sucrose
- Glycyrrhizin (glycyrrhizic acid) is a triterpene saponin that is found in licorice root, and is 50– 100 times sweeter than sucrose
- Pure stevioside is about 300 times as sweet as sucrose.
- Neohesperidin dihydrochalcone is a non-nutritive sweetener that is 1,500–2,000 times as sweet as sucrose, and it is derived from the bitter flavonones of citrus fruit
- Sweet proteins Thaumatin I and II obtained from the tropical African fruit katemfe (*Thaumatococcus daniellii*)
- Monellin is a sweet protein obtained from the serendipity berry
- Brazzein is a sweet plant protein (54 amino acid residues) that was initially discovered in the fruits of the African vine, *Pentadiplandra brazzeana*

- Basic protein, miraculin, has been isolated from miracle fruit (*Richadella dulcifica*), and this protein is tasteless
- Polyols are generally quite water-soluble, hygroscopic materials that exhibit moderate viscosities at high concentrations in water, and the polyhydroxy structures of these compounds provide water-binding properties that have been exploited in foods.
- IMF (Intermediate Moisture Foods) contain substantial moisture (15–30%), yet are stable to microbiological deterioration without refrigeration
- Most IMF possess water activities of 0.70–0.85, and those containing humectants contain moisture contents of about 20 g of water per 100 g of solids (82% H_2O by weight).
- Many stabilizers and thickeners are polysaccharides, such as gum arabic, guar gum, carboxymethylcellulose, carrageenan, agar, starch, and pectin
- Masticatory substances are employed to provide the long-lasting, pliable properties of chewing gum
- Masticatory base employed in chewing gum is derived directly from plant gums
- The most commonly used firming texturizers salts include calcium chloride, calcium citrate, calcium sulfate, calcium lactate, and monocalcium phosphate
- Flour bleaching agents of benzoyl peroxide are usually added to flour (0.025–0.075%) at the mill
- Flour bleaching involves primarily the oxidation of carotenoid pigments
- Chlorine gas, often containing a small amount of nitrosyl chloride, is used extensively as a bleach and improver for soft wheat cake flour
- Calcium stearyoyl-2 lactylate are used at low levels (up to 0.5%) to improve mixing qualities of dough and to promote increased loaf volume
- Carrageenan, carboxymethylcellulose, locust bean gum, and methylcellulose are among the more useful hydrocolloids in baking applications
- Methylcellulose and carboxymethylcellulose have been found to retard retrogradation and staling in bread, and they also retard migration of moisture to the product surface during subsequent storage
- Carrageenan (0.1%) softens the crumb texture of sweet dough products
- Carboxymethylcellulose at 0.25% may be incorporated into doughnut mixes to significantly decrease the amount of fat absorbed during frying
- Anticaking agents are used to maintain free-flowing characteristics of granular and powdered forms of foods that are hygroscopic in nature
- Calcium silicate is used to prevent caking in baking powder (up to 5%), table salts, (up to 2%), and in other foods and food ingredients
- Other anticaking agents employed in the food industry include sodium silicoaluminate, tricalcium phosphate, magnesium silicate, and magnesium carbonate

- SO_2 is used to inhibit enzymic browning in dried fruits
- Ethylene oxide is used as a sterilant for spices
- Air is used to oxidize ripe olives for color development
- Addition of carbon dioxide (carbonation) to liquid products, such as carbonated soft drinks, beer, some wines, and certain fruit juices causes them to become effervescent, tangy, slightly tart, and somewhat tactual
- Formation of carbonic acid (H_2CO_3) and bicarbonate ions also aid in stabilizing the carbon dioxide system
- Anaphylaxis is a severe and systemic allergic reaction
- Big eight allergens are Eggs, Fish, Milk, Nuts from trees including Hazelnuts, Walnuts, Cashews and Pistachios, Peanuts or Groundnuts, Shellfish, Soybeans and Wheat
- Diagnosing food allergies tests are Skin prick test, Blood test. Food Diary and Physician Supervised blinded oral food challenge
- If a person has a food allergy, their immune system overreacts to the food by producing antibodies called Immunoglobulin E
- Medications helpful in allergic reactions are Antihistamines and Epinephrine (Adrenaline)
- Most common food allergies in children includes Eggs, Milk and Peanuts
- Allergic responses organized into 4 categories
- Type I Allergies occur within a few minutes to several hours after consumption of food
- Type II and III onset from 4 – 6 hours after exposure
- Type IV allergies delayed over hours rather than minutes. Called cellular hypersensitivity
- Major allergen in milk is Casein and Beta Lactoglobulin
- Egg white has more allergens than egg yolk
- Oral allergy syndrome also known as pollen associated food allergy syndrome is most common among children and adults with pollen allergy
- Celiac disease is caused by immunological reaction to gluten, a family of proteins found in wheat, Barley, Rye and Oats
- Isomerases enzymes catalyze geometric or structural changes within a molecule
- Ligases are also called Synthetases catalyze the cleavage of two molecules
- Decarboxylase, Aldolase and Dehydratase are examples of Lyases
- Protease, Nuclease and Phosphatase are examples of Hydrolases
- Oxidoreductases enzymes catalyze Oxidation and reduction reactions
- Strecker degradation can be seen during Maillard reaction
- BMI is equal to Weight / $(\text{height in meter})^2$

- Vitamin C favours the absorption of Iron
- Vitamin D helps the absorption of Phosphorus, Calcium
- Celiac disease is the manifestation of Gluten intolerance
- Monosodium glutamate is a Flavour enhancer
- Colorant used in butter is Annato
- In disaccharides two monosaccharides are joined together by Glycosidic bond
- Polishing of rice removes Vitamin B1
- Keshan's disease is due to the deficiency of Selenium
- Measurement of energy value of food is called Calorimetry
- Sucrose is a combination of (1 glucose , 1 fructose)
- Lactose is a combination of (1 galactose , 1 glucose)
- Maltose is a combination of (2 glucose) molecules
- A skin condition known as "Phrynoderma" (toad skin) is observed in due to the deficiency of Essential fatty acids
- Major TFA present in ruminant fat is Vaccinic acid
- Food allergen Labelling and Consumer Protection Act of 2004
- Synthetic colors- Iron oxide (Redness), Titanium dioxide (Whiteness)
- Synthetic colors (Red) – Ponceau 4 R, Carmoisine, Erythrosine
- Synthetic colors (Yellow) – Tartrazine, Sunset yellow FCF
- Synthetic colors Blue – Indigo carmine, Brilliant Blue FCF
- Synthetic colors Green – Fast Green FCF
- Caramelization – (Sugar – Sugar interaction). Also known as pyrolysis of sugar
- Maillard reaction discovered by – Louis Camille Maillard. Reaction between amino acids and reducing sugars
- Enzymatic browning – Polyphenol oxidase. Ascorbic acid - Can inhibit browning reaction
- 1 Kilo calorie – 4.184 Kilojoule
- Carbohydrates – 4 k/cal/gram
- Fat – 9 k/cal/gram
- Proteins - 4 k/cal/gram
- Organic acid - 3 k/cal/gram
- Polyols – 2.4 k/cal/gram
- Fibre – 2 k/cal/gram
- Respiratory Quotient also known as the respiratory ratio is defined as the volume of carbon dioxide released over the volume of oxygen absorbed during respiration

- Respiratory Quotient of Glucose – 1.00
- Respiratory Quotient of Fatty acid – 0.7
- Respiratory Quotient of Protein – 0.9
- Iodine value – Measure the degree of unsaturation of fat
- Saturated fatty acids – Fatty acids has all hydrogen atoms
- Unsaturated fatty acids – Some of the hydrogen atoms are missing, replaced by double bond between carbon atoms
- Enzymatic browning examples – Apple slice, Banana
- Non enzymatic browning examples – Ready to eat cereals, baked foods, milk
- National Health Mission – 2013
- National Health Policy – 2017
- Newtonian fluids have a constant viscosity, whereas non- Newtonian fluids have a variable viscosity
- Newtonian foods – Water, Fruit juice, Oil, Milk, Honey
- Non Newtonian foods – Tomato paste, Mayonnaise, Margarine, Apple sauce, corn starch suspensions
- Imino acid – Proline
- Amino acids, the building blocks of proteins, play a crucial role in various biological processes.
- Amino acid tastes sweet – Glycine, Alanine, Valine
- **Essential amino acids** cannot be synthesized by the human body and must be obtained through diet.
- Essential Amino acids – Isoleucine, Leucine, Valine, Lysine, Methionine, Phenylalanine, Threonine, Tryptophan and Histidine
- **Nonessential amino acids** are those that the body can produce on its own, even if we do not consume them in our diet
- Non Essential Amino acids – Alanine, Arginine, Aspargine, Asparitic acid, Cysteine, Glutamic acid, Glutamine, Glycine, Proline, Serine and Tyrosine

CHAPTER-5

Food Microbiology and General Principles of Food Hygiene

- Moldy bread of green growth most likely is a *Penicillium sp*; the black growth is characteristic of *Rhizopus stolonifer*
- Contamination of grains by the ascomycete, *Claviceps purpurea* causes ergotism, a toxic condition. Hallucinogenic alkaloids produced by this fungus can lead to altered behavior, abortion, and death if infected grains are eaten
- Anaerobic breakdown of proteins is called putrefaction
- Coumarins found in fruits and vegetables have antimicrobial activity
- Eggs are rich in the enzyme lysozyme, which lyses the cell walls of contaminating Gram positive bacteria
- Storing meat in a high $C0_2$ atmosphere inhibits Gram-negative bacteria
- Microorganisms can be removed from water, wine, beer, juices, soft drinks, and other liquids by filtration
- *Listeria monocytogenes*, which can grow at temperatures used for refrigeration
- Refrigeration slows the metabolic activity of most microbes, but it does not lead to significant decreases in existing microbial populations
- Heating processes, first used by Nicholas Appert in 1809, provide a safe means of preserving foods, particularly when carried out in commercial canning operations
- Canned food is heated in special containers called retorts at about 115°C for intervals ranging from 25 to over 100 minutes
- Pasteurization involves heating food to a temperature that kills disease-causing microorganisms and substantially reduces the levels of spoilage organisms
- Low-temperature holding (LTH) pasteurization, the liquid is maintained at 62.8°C for 30 minutes
- Products can be held at 72°C for 15 seconds, a high-temperature, short-time (HTST) process
- Milk can be treated at 138°C for 2 seconds for ultra-high-temperature (UHT) processing
- Dehydration, such as lyophilization to produce freeze-dried foods, is a common means of preventing microbial growth
- GRAS - "Generally Recognized As Safe". Includes simple organic acids, sulfite, ethylene oxide as a gas sterilant, sodium nitrite, and ethyl formate

- Sodium nitrite is an important chemical used to help preserve ham, sausage, bacon, and other cured meats by inhibiting the growth of *Clostridium botulinum* and the germination of its spores
- Organic acids (1-3%) can be used to treat meat carcasses, and poultry can be cleansed with 10% lactic acid/sodium lactate buffer (pH 3) prior to packaging
- Breads, with their low pH values, often contain sodium propionate as a preservative
- Water availability is measured in terms of water activity (aw)
- Most spoilage bacteria that thrive at an aw of about 0.9, these microbes grow best at an aw of 0.6 to 0.7
- Osmophilic (Greek osmus, impulse, and philein, to love) microbes grow best in or on media with a high osmotic concentration (e.g., jams and jellies)
- Xerophilic (Greek xerosis, dry, and philein, to love) microorganisms thrive in low aw environments (e.g., dried fruits, cereals) and may not grow under high aw conditions
- HHP (High Hydrostatic Pressure) is the application of pressures from 100 to 800 millipascals (mpa) without significant changes in temperature. Pressures typically range from 350 to 600 MPa for 5 to 15 minutes at temperatures from 5 to 35°C
- Gram-positive bacteria are harder to kill than gram-negative
- Gamma irradiation of food most often uses a cobalt-60 source; however, cesium-137 is employed in some facilities
- Gamma radiation has excellent penetrating power but must be used with moist foods because radiation is effective only if it generates peroxides from water in the microbial cells, resulting in oxidation of sensitive cellular constituents
- To sterilize meat products, 4.5 to 5.6 megarads are commonly used
- Bacteriocins are bactericidal proteins that kill closely related microbes by binding to specific sites on the target cell
- The only bacteriocin currently approved for food preservation is nisin
- CO_2 content of 60% or greater in the atmosphere surrounding a food, spoilage fungi will not grow
- Food borne infection eg) *Salmonella*
- Food borne intoxication eg) Botulinum toxin, Staphylococcal enterotoxin, *Bacillus cereus* toxin
- Food toxicoinfection- food intoxication + infection. e.g., Clostridium *perfringens*
- *Aspergillus flavus* was found in the contaminated peanut meal, together with toxins termed aflatoxins
- Aflatoxin B1 is the most common and the most potent carcinogen

- Fumonisins are fungal contaminants of corn that were first isolated in 1988. These are produced by *Fusarium moniliforme* and cause leukoencephalomalacia in horses (also called "blind staggers" it is fatal within 2 to 3 days), pulmonary edema in pigs, and esophageal cancer in humans
- Fumonisins inhibit ceramide synthase, a key enzyme for the proper use of fatty substances in the cell
- The CDC oversees a program called Pulsenet for the early detection of food-borne pathogens, particularly during an outbreak. The basis for this program is the use of pulsed-field gel electrophoresis
- Majority of fermented milk products rely on lactic acid bacteria (LAB), which include species belonging to the genera *lactobacillus, lactococcus, leuconostoc,* and *streptococcus*
- *Lactococcus lactis subspecies diacetylactis* converts milk citrate to diacetyl, which gives a richer, buttery flavor to the finished product
- Thermophilic fermentations are carried out at temperatures around 45°C. An important example is yogurt production
- Yeast-lactic fermentations include kefir, a product with an ethanol concentration of up to 2%. These are coagulated lumps of casein (milk protein) that contain yeasts, lactic acid bacteria, and acetic acid bacteria, which are recovered at the end of the fermentation
- Kefir - prepared by inoculating cow, goat, or sheep's milk with kefir grains
- Kumis is a fermented dairy product traditionally made from mare's milk. 0.7 and 2.5% alcohol
- Mold-lactic fermentation results in a unique fermented milk called viili. Milk is inoculated with a mixture of the fungus *Geotrichum candidum* and lactic acid bacteria. Lactic acid reaches a concentration of 0.9%
- Cheeses are classified based on texture or hardness as soft cheeses (cottage, cream, brie), semisoft cheeses (muenster, limburger, blue), hard cheeses (cheddar, colby, swiss), or very hard cheeses (parmesan)
- Rennin, an enzyme from calf stomachs but now produced by genetically engineered microorganisms, can also be used to promote curd formation
- *Lactococcus lactis* is used as a starter culture for a number of cheeses. Starter culture density is often over 10^9 colony-forming units (CFU) per gram of cheese curd before ripening
- Camembert cheese is inoculated with spores of *Penicillium camemberti*
- Soft cheeses are ripened for only about 1 to 5 months, whereas hard cheeses need 3 to 12 months, and very hard cheeses such as Parmesan require 12 to 16 months of ripening
- Swiss cheese; gas production by propionibacteria contributes to final flavor development and hole or eye formation in this cheese

- *Pediococcus acidilactici* and *Lactobacillus plantarum* are most often involved in sausage fermentations
- Izushi is based on the fermentation of fresh fish, rice, and vegetables by *Lactobacillus spp*
- Katsuobushi results from the fermentation of tuna by *Aspergillus glaucus*
- Wine production - enology
- Collection of grapes continues with their crushing and the separation of the liquid, called must
- To avoid unpredictable fermentation, fresh must is treated with a sulfur dioxide fumigant and a desired strain of the yeast *Saccharomyces cerevisia*e or *S. ellipsoideus* is added. The final product may contain 10 to 14% alcohol
- Microbial growth during the fermentation process produces sediments, which are removed during racking
- Beer and ale production uses cereal grains such as barley, wheat, and rice
- Hops (dried flowers of the female vine *Humulus lupulus*), which were originally added to the mash to inhibit spoilage microorganisms. Hops also provide flavor and assist in clarification of the liquid portion called the wort
- Most beers are fermented with bottom yeasts, related to *Saccharomyces pastorianus*, which settle at the bottom of the fermentation vat
- Bottom yeasts require 7 to 12 days of fermentation to produce beer with a ph of 4.1 to 4.2. With a top yeast, such as *Saccharomyces cerevisiae*, the pH is lowered to 3.8 to produce ale
- Freshly fermented (green) beers are aged, and when they are bottled, $C0_2$ is usually added
- Beer can be pasteurized at 40°C or higher or sterilized by passage through membrane filters to minimize flavor changes
- Rye and bourbon are examples of whiskeys
- Rye whiskey must contain at least 51% rye grain, and bourbon must contain at least 51% corn
- Scotch whiskey is made primarily of barley. Vodka and grain alcohols are also produced by distillation
- Gin - to which resinous flavoring agents, often juniper berries, have been added to provide a unique aroma and flavor
- Baker's strain of the yeast *Saccharomyces cerevisiae*
- Tempeh, a soybean mash fermented by *Rhizopus spp*
- Sauerkraut or sour cabbage is produced from shredded cabbage
- Concentration of 2.2 to 2.8% sodium chloride restricts the growth of Gram-negative bacteria while favoring the development of lactic acid bacteria in Sauerkraut

- Primary microorganisms contributing to Sauerkraut are *Leuconostoc mesenteroides* and *Lactobacillus plantarum*
- The final acidity of Sauerkraut is generally about pH 1.7, with lactic acid comprising 1.0 to 1.3% of the total acid in a satisfactory product
- Pickles are produced by placing cucumbers and components such as dill seeds in casks filled with a brine. The sodium chloride concentration begins at 5% and rises to about 16% in 6 to 9 weeks
- Salt not only inhibits the growth of undesirable bacteria but also extracts water and water-soluble constituents from the cucumber
- Grass, chopped corn, and other fresh animal feeds, if stored under moist anoxic conditions, will undergo a mixed acid fermentation that produces pleasant-smelling silage
- Yogurt, which commonly contain bacteria in the genera *Lactobacillus* and *Bifidobacterium*
- Feeding chickens a strain of *Bacillus subtilis* leads to increased body weight and feed conversion
- *Salmonella enterica* can be controlled by spraying a patented blend of 29 bacteria, isolated from the chicken cecum, on day-old chickens
- Flavor-enhancing compounds - monosodium glutamate (MSG)
- Dextrans are used as blood expanders and absorbents
- *Erwinia* polysaccharides are used in paints
- Polyesters, derived from *Pseudomonas oleovorans*, which are used for specialty plastics
- Cellulose microfibrils, produced by an *Acetobacter* strain, that serve as a food thickener
- Polysaccharides such as scleroglucan used by the oil industry as drilling mud additives
- Xanthan polymers have a variety of applications as food additives as well to enhance oil by thickening drilling mud. Xanthan gum, produced by *Xanthomonas campestris*
- Biosurfactants are amphiphilic molecules; they possess both hydrophobic and hydrophilic regions
- Microbial energy conversion includes the microbial transformation of organic materials into biofuels, such as ethanol and hydrogen
- Primary metabolites consist of compounds related to the synthesis of microbial cells during exponential growth. They include amino acids, nucleotides, and fermentation end products such as ethanol and organic acids
- Secondary metabolites usually accumulate when nutrients become limited, or waste products accumulate following the active growth phase

- The process of exploring nature for new and potentially useful organisms and their products is called bioprospecting
- The presumptive step is carried out by means of tubes inoculated with three different sample volumes to give an estimate of the most probable number (MPN) of coliforms in the water
- The membrane filter technique is a common and preferred method of evaluating the microbiological characteristics of water
- To test for both coliforms and E. Coli, the related Colilert defined substrate test can be used
- Wastewater treatment involves three spatially segregated steps: primary, secondary, and tertiary treatment
- Primary treatment prepares the wastewater for treatment by physically removing much of the solid material
- Secondary treatment of the effluent promotes the biological transformation of dissolved organic matter (DOM) into microbial biomass and carbon dioxide
- Aerobic secondary treatment is often carried out with a trickling filter
- Carbon removal during wastewater treatment is measured several ways, including (1) as total organic carbon (TOC), (2) as chemically oxidizable carbon by the chemical oxygen demand (COD) test, or (3) as biologically usable carbon by the biochemical oxygen demand (BOD) test
- Bioleaching is the use of microorganisms that produce acids from reduced sulfur compounds to create acidic environments that solubilize desired metals for recovery
- Bioleaching carried out by natural populations of Leptospirillum-like species and *Thiobacilli*, for example, allow recovery of up to 70% of the copper in low-grade ores
- The acceleration of microbiological processes by the addition of known active microorganisms to soils, waters, or other complex systems is called bioaugmentation
- Flat sour spoilage - *B. coagulans and B. stearothermophilus*
- Thermophilic anaerobic spoilage – *Clostridium thermosaccharolyticum*
- Sulfide spoilage - *Clostridium nigricans*
- Putrefactive anaerobic spoilage - *Clostridium sporogenes*
- D Value: Time required to destroy 90% of the organisms
- Z Value: Temp required to reduce the population by one log cycle
- F Value - Time in minutes at 250 degree F with respect to its capacity to destroy spores or vegetative cells
- Those parameters of plant and animal tissues that are an inherent part of the tissues are referred to as Intrinsic parameters. They are

  1) pH
  2) Moisture content

3) Oxidation reduction potential
4) Nutrient content
5) Antimicrobial constituents
6) Biological structures

- Parameters of foods those properties of the storage environment that affect both the foods and their microorganisms called Extrinsic parameters. They are
  1) Temperature of storage
  2) Relative humidity of the environment
  3) Presence and concentration of gases in the environment
- Good hygienic principles – 8
- Good Hygienic Principles – Water Quality, Air Quality, Drainage and waste disposal, Temperature control, Personal hygiene, Lighting and Storage
- As per GHP water used in food processing units should meet the Portability test
- Good Agricultural Practices Pillars– Economic Viability, Environmental sustainability, Social acceptability, Food safety and Quality
- Good Agricultural Practices – 4 pillars, 9 Key elements
- Good Manufacturing Practices – 5 Ps – People, Products, Process, Procedures, Premises
- GMP is also sometimes referred to as cGMP (c - refers to current)
- BAP – Best Aquaculture Practices
- FSSC 22000- Food Safety System Certification
- Baird Parker Agar – Enumeration of *Staphylococcus aureus*
- EMB – For Gram Negative Bacteria
- NAMAS – National Measurement Accreditation Service
- Keeping away from microbes (asepsis)
- Removal of microbes (filtration, centrifugation, washing, trimming, blanching)
- Hindering the growth of microbes (refrigeration, drying, adding chemicals)
- Killing microbes (irradiation, heat processing
- The activities of food borne microorganisms can be slowed down or stopped at temperatures above freezing and generally stopped at subfreezing temperatures
- Chilling temperature are those between the usual refrigerator temperatures and room temperature, usually about 10-15°C
- Freezer temperatures are those at or below –18°C
- Quick or fast freezing is the process by which the temperature of foods is lowered to about –20°C within 30 min
- The small ice crystals are formed due to fast freezing
- Slow freezing refers to the process whereby the desired temperature is achieved within 3-72 hours

- Some foods that are improperly wrapped during freezer storage undergo freezer burn
- UV light is a powerful bactericidal agent with the most effective wave length being about 2600A
- UV light has germicidal effect at wave length between 250 – 280 nm
- 1 Gy = 1 Joule/kilogram = 100 rad (Gray can be used for any type of radiation)
- Irradiation dose range (in KGy) for inhibition of sprouting - 0.05-0.15
- Q fever is a disease caused by infection with *Coxiella_burnetii*
- Commercial and household refrigerators are operated at temperatures - 4.5- 7° C
- Stable or non-perishable foods - Sugar, flour, dry beans etc
- Semi perishable foods- Potatoes, certain varieties of apples etc
- Perishable food - Meat, fish, poultry, most fruits, vegetables, milk etc are coming under this group.
- Rotting is the most common form of bacterial spoilage found in eggs

1. Green rot – *Pseudomonas sp, P. fluorescens*
2. Colourless rot - *Pseudomonas* and *Acinetobacter*
3. Black rot - *Proteus, Pseudomonas,* and *Aeromonas*
4. Pink rot – *Pseudomonas*
5. Red rot - *Serratia*
6. Custard rot - *Proteus vulgaris*
7. *Proteus sp* and *Pseudomans graveolens* also cause a condition in eggs known as mustiness

- *Lyngbya majuscule* causes Ciguatera poisoning
- Scombroid fish poisoning has been associated with *Proteus morganii*, *Klebsiella pneumonia*
- Traveler's diarrhea is caused due to the toxins produced by *Escherichia*
- *Alcaligenes viscolactis* causes ropiness in Milk
- *Alcaligenes metalcaligenes* gives limy growth on Cottage cheese
- *Bacillus linens* produces orange red pigmentation and helps ripening in Brick or Limburger Cheese
- Soil is the primary source of *Clostridium spp*
- *Photobacterium phosphoreum has been known to cause phosphorescence of meats and fish*
- *Staphylococcus are beta- hemolytic, coagulase positive strains produce enterotoxin*
- Molds examples for rhizoids or holdfasts mycelial structures are *Rhizopus* and *Absidia*

- Molds examples for foot cell mycelial structures is *Aspergillus*
- Molds examples for rhizoids or holdfasts mycelial structures
- Molds examples for dichotomous or Y shaped, branching mycelial structures is *Geotrichum*
- Eight spores found per ascus
- Basidium produces four sexual spores
- *Trichothecium roseum* is a Pink mold
- *Geotrichum candidum* is a Dairy mold
- *Neurospora sitophila* is a Red bread mold
- White spot in meat is caused by *Sporotrichum carnis*
- Methods of pure culture isolation are the Streak plate method, Pour plate method and Spread plate method
- Floppy baby syndrome is caused by Infant botulism
- Diptheria toxin are produced by *Corynebacterium diptheriae*
- Streptolysin O and Streptolysin S is produced by *Streptococcus pyogenes*
- Endotoxins are soluble proteins found in cell extracts or in the growth medium found in gram negative bacteria
- Exotoxins are soluble proteins secreted outside the bacteria through their cell wall and these substances are heat labile, being inactivated by boiling
- *Vibrio alginolyticus is found in sea water causes soft tissue and ear infections in humans*
- *Clostridium perfringens* causes Gas gangrene
- Widal test is used to detect the *Salmonella*
- Kauffman white serotyping scheme was proved the most useful technique for differentiating with the genus *Salmonella*
- Eggs should be cooked at >145°F (67°C) for 15 seconds
- Raw eggs should be stored at < 45°F (7.2°C)
- *Yersinia pestis* causes Plague
- Beer is spoiled by the yeast *Hansenula*
- Cheese is spoiled by the yeast *Debaromyces*
- Black rot of cabbage and cauliflower is caused by *Xanthomonas campestris*
- Norwalk virus infection is an intestinal illness that often occurs in outbreaks
- 12D concept is used mainly in Low acid canned foods (pH >4.6)
- According to the World Health Organization (WHO) Hygiene refers to conditions and practices that help to maintain health and prevent the spread of diseases
- F diagram depicts how germs spread and how that can be prevented

- On 2nd October 2014, the Prime Minister, Shri Narendra Modi, launched the Swachh Bharat Mission (SBM)
- Waste water generated in the kitchen, bathroom and laundry is called Grey water
- Central Rural Sanitation Programme (CRSP) in 1986
- Total Sanitation Campaign (TSC) in 1999
- Nirmal Bharat Abhiyan in 2012
- Radappertization – Equivalent to radiation sterilization. 30-40 kGy
- Radicidation – Equivalent to pasteurization of milk. 2.5 - 10 kGy
- Radurization – Equivalent to Pasteurization. 0.75 – 2.5 kGy
- HACCP is a tool to assess hazards and establish control systems that focus on prevention rather than relying mainly on end-product testing

Principles of HACCP

1) Conduct hazard analysis
2) Determine critical control point
3) Establish critical limit
4) Establishing monitoring procedure
5) Establish corrective action
6) Establish verification procedure
7) Establish record keeping and documentation procedure

HACCP Steps

1) Assemble HACCP team
2) Describe the product
3) Identify intended use
4) Construct flow diagram
5) On-site confirmation of flow diagram
6) Conduct hazard analysis
7) Determine critical control point
8) Establish critical limit
9) Establishing monitoring procedure
10) Establish corrective action
11) Establish verification procedure
12) Establish record keeping and documentation procedure

CHAPTER-6

Food Science and Nutrition

- Adulteration is the process of adding unwanted substances to the food, with similar appearance/colour for making profits
- Most commonly adulterated food product is milk
- Adulterants used in milk are Water, Chalk, Urea, caustic soda and skimmed milk
- Khoya is adulterated with Paper, refined oil and skimmed milk powder
- Adulteration in milk causes highest chances of stomach disorders
- Tea leaves are usually adulterated with same colored leaves
- Liver infection has been reported due to consumption of adulterated tea
- Coffee seeds adulterated with Tamarind seeds, mustard seeds, Chicory
- Adulterants with coffee causes diarrhea
- Wheat is adulterated with Ergot
- Vegetables are mostly adulterated with malachite green, known to have carcinogenic
- Common adulterants in fruits and vegetables are oxytocin, Sachharin, Wax, Calcium carbide and copper sulphate
- Sweets are adulterated with Khoya, Chenna and Starch
- Honey is commonly adulterated with molasses sugar to increase the bottle quantity
- Arhar dal is adulterated with metanil yellow
- Metanil yellow is non permitted food colour used extensively in India
- Long term consumption of metanil yellow causes neurotoxicity
- Metanil yellow in dal can be tested by adding a few drops of HCl to a test sample, if the solution turns pink in colour, it indicates the presence of metanil yellow
- Turmeric is adulterated with metanil yellow and red oxide of lead are highly carcinogenic

- Soap stone or other earthy material and foreign resin are the common adulterant used in Asafoetida
- Papaya seeds, Black berries are common adulterant used in black pepper
- Red chilli powder is adulterated with brick powder, salt powder or talc powder and artificial colours like Sudan dye
- Saffron is adulterated by coloured dried tendrils of maize cob
- Butter can be adulterated with water or partially replaced with cheaper plant oils such as palm oil, Sunflower oil and soybean oil
- Common adulterants in ice cream are pepperoni, Ethylacetate, Butraldehyde, Emil acetate, Nitrate, Washing powder
- Pepper oil is used as a pesticide and ethyl acetate causes terrible diseases affecting lungs, Kidneys and heart
- Ice cream is manufactured in extremely cold chamber where fat is hardened and several harmful substances are added
- In ice cream a kind of gum is added which is sticky and slow melting. This gum is obtained by boiling animal (Beaver) parts like tail, the nose, the udder , etc
- Protein Energy Malnutrition (PEM) is a macronutrient deficiency or a deficiency of calorie and protein
- PEM occurs in three clinically distinguishable forms, viz. Kwashiorkor, marasmus and marasmic-kwashiorkor
- Different types of PEM of Sub-Clinical Forms are Underweight, Wasting and Stunting
- Kwashiorkor is an African word, meaning a "disease of the displaced child", who is deprived of adequate nutrition
- Kwashiorkor occurring mostly in children between the ages of 1 and 3 years
- The three essential manifestations or signs of kwashiorkor are: Oedema (swelling of feet), Under weight (<80% of normal weight for age, Apathy and irritability, Moon face, Hair and skin changes and micronutrient changes
- Oedema refers to accumulation of fluid in the tissues and usually begins with a slight swelling in feet gradually spreading up the legs
- Marasmus is common in children below the age of 2 years
- The characteristic manifestations of Marasmus are Severe growth retardation, Extreme emaciation, Old man's or monkey's face, and Loose and hanging skin folds over arms and buttocks

- 'Marasmic kwashiorkor' children will have extreme wasting of different degrees (representing marasmus) and also oedema (a sign of kwashiorkor)
- Signs and Symptoms of Marasmic Kwashiorkor are Extreme muscle wasting - "skin and bones", Loose and hanging skin folds, Old man's or monkey's face, Absolute weakness and Oedema
- For population - based assessment, the Z-Score (or standard deviation classification) system is widely used. The Z-score system expresses the anthropometric value as a number of standard deviation or Z-Score below or above the reference mean or medium value
- Severe Acute Malnutrition (SAM) is the severest form of undernutrition and may result from inadequate recent food intake or illness and mainly manifests as 'wasting.'
- Stunting children have a low height with respect to their age
- Wasting occurs when a child has a low weight with respect to his height
- Underweight is defined as low weight for age. A child who is underweight may be stunted, wasted or both
- Essential Components to Prevent PEM are Supplementary feeding Immunization, Control of minor infections, Promotion of food and nutrition security, Behaviour change communication, Empowerment of women and Poverty alleviation
- Common Micronutrient Deficiencies are Vitamin A deficiency, Iron deficiency anaemia, Iodine deficiency disorders and Zinc deficiency
- Vitamin A deficiency (VAD) is a major public health problem, and the most vulnerable are preschool children and pregnant women in low income countries
- Night blindness is the earliest symptom of Vitamin 'A' deficiency
- Corneal Xerosis is a sign of severe vitamin 'A' deficiency, in which the cornea loses its normal smooth and glistening appearance and becomes dry and rough
- Keratomalacia are rapid destruction and liquefaction of full thickness of cornea, leading to prolapse of the iris, resulting in permanent blindness
- All forms of vitamin A deficiency are treated with a massive oral dose of vitamin A in oil (200,000 IU), immediately after diagnosis.
- Iron Deficiency Anaemia (IDA) is the most common micronutrient deficiency in the world, particularly in the developing countries like India
- Mostly anaemia is due to iron deficiency. The other causes of anaemia may include folate and vitamin B12 deficiency or anaemia of chronic diseases.

- Manifestations of Iron Deficiency Anaemia are Paleness of conjunctiva, Paleness of tongue, Paleness of mucosa of soft palate, Low haemoglobin, Swelling of feet in severe anaemia and Koilonychia
- Anaemia is a condition in which the blood cannot carry enough oxygen
- Iron is the main component of haemoglobin. Lack of dietary iron is the world's leading nutritional deficiency and the most common cause of anaemia
- Phytates and tannins present in the Indian diet interfere with iron absorption to a significant extent
- In moderate to severe anaemia, 2 tablets of ferous sulphate (each equivalent to 100 mg of elemental iron and 500 mcg of folic acid) are given
- In very severe anaemia with very low levels of haemoglobin (< 5-7 g/100 ml), packed cell transfusion is recommended
- The Government of India launched the 'National Nutritional Anaemia Control Programme' in 1970 to prevent and control nutritional anaemia
- Iodine deficiency is a naturally occurring ecological phenomenon that is present in many parts of the world
- The term iodine deficiency disorders (IDD) includes a spectrum of disabling conditions affecting the health of human beings starting from foetal life through adulthood resulting from inadequate dietary intake of iodine
- When iodine intake falls below the recommended levels, the thyroid gland is no longer able to synthesize sufficient amounts of thyroxine hormone
- One of the well-recognized features of iodine deficiency disorders is goiter
- Thyroid gland in its efforts to produce the required thyroxine, in the presence of iodine deficiency, swells up leading to enlargement of the thyroid gland This condition is known as goitre
- The major effect of foetal iodine deficiency is endemic cretinism. It is characterized by growth failure, mental deficiency, deaf mutism and spastic paralysis of leg
- Inadequate production of thyroid hormone leads to hypothyroidism.
- Hypothyroidism is the principal factor responsible for the damage done to the developing brain and the other harmful effects known collectively as iodine deficiency disorders (IDD)
- Manifestations of IDD are Goitre, Abortions, Congenital abnormalities, Increased perinatal mortality and Cretinism
- Certain chemical substances like thiocyanates, phenols, disuphides, flavanoids etc, found in the environment, can interfere with iodine metabolism. These substances are known as goitrogens, which could cause goiter. Common foods such as cabbage, sorghum, finger millets and mustard contain goitrogens

- The oldest and the commonest control measure of Prevention of IDD is fortification of common salt with potassium iodate
- The Government of India launched National Goitre Control Programme, in 1962, to supply iodized salt in endemic areas
- Since, iron deficiency anaemia and iodine deficiency disorders often co-exist, the most effective approach to control these public health problems would be simultaneous fortification of salt with iron and iodine. The technology for double fortification of salt has been successfully developed at NIN
- Intramuscular injection of iodized oil has been used for tackling goitre and cretinism in hyper-endemic areas in many countries of the world. The advantage of the injection procedure is that a single dose of 1 ml will provide protection for 3-5 years
- Zinc deficiency can occur in several pathological conditions like chronic alcoholic liver disease, sickle cell anaemia and chronic malabsorption like celiac disease
- Communicable diseases are capable of being transmitted from person to person or from the environment to person
- Communicable diseases can be classified on the basis of the causative organisms. They are as follows:
    1. Bacterial: typhoid, cholera, tuberculosis
    2. Viral: common cold, influenza, HIV infection, dengue
    3. Protozoal: malaria, kala azar
    4. Fungal: fungal infections of nails, groin, skin, hair
    5. Parasitic: infestations of intestinal worms, like roundworm, or lice
- The non–communicable diseases may occur due to genetic and lifestyle factors. When these are caused by an unhealthy lifestyle, these diseases are also called lifestyle diseases
- Lifestyle diseases, such as diabetes, hypertension, heart diseases, stroke and cancer
- Diabetes mellitus is one of the endocrine diseases. It is caused due to inadequate secretion of the hormone insulin from the pancreas
- Type I diabetes developed in childhood or at young stage
- Type II diabetes causes difficulty in the body's use of Insulin
- HIV stands for 'Human Immunodeficiency Virus'. It is a virus that is found only in human beings and affects the immune system in humans

- HIV is transmitted through: (a) having unsafe sexual contact with an HIV infected person. This is the most common route of transmission (b) HIV infected mother to her newborn child (c) transfusion of HIV infected blood and (d) sharing of needles and syringes with a person infected with HIV
- Coronary artery disease also known as Coronary heart disease is the most common type of heart disease
- When plaque builds up in the arteries it is called atherosclerosis
- Arrhythmia refers to an irregular heartbeat. Various types of arrhythmias, including
    1. Tachycardia – Rapid heartbeat
    2. Bradycardia – Slow heartbeat
    3. Premature contractions – Refers to an early heartbeat
    4. Atrial fibrillation – A type of irregular heartbeat
- Myocardial infarction also known as a heart attack
- Stroke occurs due to a decrease or blockage in the brain's blood supply
- Stroke is a cerebrovascular diseases
- Cancer begins when genetic changes interfere with this orderly process. Cells start to grow uncontrollably
- Cancerous tumors are malignant, meaning it can grow and spread to other parts of the body
- Benign tumor means the tumor can grow but will not spread
- Four main types of cancer are
    1. Carcinomas – Form solid tumors. Eg) Prostate cancer, Breast cancer, Lung cancer and colorectal cancer
    2. Sarcomas – Develop in fat, Muscles, nerves, tendons, Joints, blood vessels, Lymph vessels, cartilage or bone
    3. Leukemias – Cancer of the blood
    4. Lymphomas – Begin in the lymphatic system
- Biopsy is the removal of a small amount of tissue for further study
- Chronic Obstructive Pulmonary Disease (COPD) is a chronic inflammatory lung disease that causes obstructed airflow from the lungs
- Emphysema and chronic bronchitis are the most common conditions that contribute to COPD
- Official color of COPD awareness is Orange colour

- Biofortification is a method of breeding crops to increase their nutritional value
- 17 biofortified crop varieties dedicated to nation by honorable Prime Minister on World Food Day
- Small scale purification - Water intake, Coagulation, Sedimentation, Filteration, Disinfection (Chlorination) and Distribution
- Small scale purification - Filteration, Disinfection and Boiling
- To remove very fine suspended particles from water, the method adopted is Filteration
- Maximum efficiency of filteration for microorganism removal is 95%
- Residual chlorine 0.2 ppm is to safeguard against pollution during distribution of water to final consumers
- Food and Nutrition Council (FNC) constituted in the year 1997
- Consumers protection enacted in 1986
- An ionised molecule with positive and negative charges called Zwitter ion
- Reversal of freezing process is Thawing
- Plasma protein involved in coagulation of blood is Fibrinogen
- Crystalline structure of starch is lost during baking is called Staling
- Rasagulla is prepared us in Channa (Indian cottage cheese)
- Rapid enumeration and detection of food borne micro-organisms both spoilage and pathogens can be accomplished by biochemical, immunological, genetic method, Flow Cytometry, and Impedance method
- Immunological Methods are Latex Agglutination Assay, Immuno-diffusion Format, Enzyme Linked Immunosorbent Assay (ELISA) and Immuno-magnetic Separation (IMS)
- Genetic Methods are Nucleic Acid Probes, Polymerase Chain Reaction, DNA Chips and Micro-Arrays
- Unique feature of flow cytometry is that it measures fluorescence per cell or particle
- The most common type of detector used in flow cytometry is the photomultiplier tube
- The data from the light detector and the colour detectors is sent to a computer and plotted on a graph called a histogram
- Enzyme linked immunosorbent assay (ELISA) is the most popular rapid method for the detection of food borne pathogens. Based on the specificity of antigen-antibody reaction

[illegible]

Enzyme-linked immunosorbent assay [illegible] method for the detection of food [illegible] antigen-antibody reaction.

CHAPTER-7

Food Quality

- Food Safety and Standards (Food Safety and Auditing) Regulations Act 2018
- Audit report – Written record of observation, findings, and conclusions of audit
- Valid Accreditation ISO/IEC 17020, ISO/IEC 17021
- Fees for recognition of an auditing agency is Form A (Rs. 5000). Certificate validity for 3 years. Renewal of certificate Rs. 5000
- IS/ ISO 19011:2011 – Guidelines for Auditing Management System
- Auditing agency declaration of Audit should be given to Form C to FBO
- FBO maintains audit record for past 5 years
- Food Safety Officer takes sample of food for analysis
- Authorized officer take sample of imported article of food for analysis
- After the analysis report will be signed by the director of referral laboratory or report signed by food analyst will be provided to the sender. Certificate = Rs 1000/sample
- Four major category of analysis – Chemical analysis, Microbial analysis, Physical analysis and Sensory analysis
- Statistical design for sampling – No of packages <100 – Minimum 10 packages to be sampled. No of packages >100 – Root of total numbers to be sampled eg) $\sqrt{153} = 13$
- Isopropyl alcohol, Ethyl alcohol used for disinfecting sampling tools
- Plastic bags should not be used for pesticide sample
- Method of sampling – Random/Probability and Non random/Non Probability
- Random/Probability sampling. Is used when a representative sample is desired, and uses principles of statistical sampling and probability i.e. elimination of human bias. The population gets an equal opportunity to be selected as a representative sample
- Random/Probability – Simple random, Systemic Random, Stratified, Cluster, Composite sampling

- Simple random sampling requires that the number of units in the population be known and each unit is assigned a number
- Systematic sampling is used when a complete list of sample units is not available, but when samples are distributed evenly over time or space, such as on a production line. The first sample is selected at random and then every nth unit after that
- Stratified sampling involves dividing the population into overlapping subgroups so that each subgroup is as homogenous as possible
- Cluster sampling entails dividing the population into clusters or subgroups so that cluster's characteristics are as identical as possible, that is, the means are very similar to each other
- Composite sampling is used to obtain samples from bagged products such as flour, seeds, and larger items in bulk. Two or more samples are combined to obtain one sample for analysis, which reduces differences between samples
- Non Random Non /Probability sampling is a method of sampling wherein it is not known which individual from the population will be selected as a sample
- Non-probability sampling is used when it is not possible to collect a representative sample, or a representative sample is not desired
- Random/Non Probability – Judgemental, Convenience, Restricted and Quota Sampling
- Judgement sampling is solely at the discretion of the sampler and therefore is highly dependent on the person taking the sample
- Convenience sampling is performed when ease of sampling is the key factor. The first pallet in a lot or the sample that is most accessible is selected
- Restricted sampling may be unavoidable when the entire population is not accessible. For example, if sample is to be taken from a loaded truck, but the sample is not a representative of the entire population
- Quota sampling is the division of a lot into groups representing various categories, and samples are then taken from each group
- "Food recall" means the action to remove food from the market at any stage of the food chain, including that possessed by consumers
- "Recall alert" means any alert issued to the public by the chief executive officer, food safety and standards authority of India or the commissioner of food safety of the state or union territory or the food business operator under intimation to chief executive officer, food safety and standards authority of India and the concerned commissioner(s) of food safety of the state(s) about the food under recall
- "Traceability" means the ability to follow the movement of a food article through specified stage(s) of its production, processing and distribution

- "Unsafe food" means food as defined under clause (zz) of sub- section (1) of section 3 of the Act
- The food business operator shall initiate a recall process to fulfill his responsibility in accordance with section 28 of the Act
- The food business operator shall submit information as specified under Schedule I to the concerned authority immediately but not exceeding twenty-four hours from the time it comes to his notice that such food requires recall in accordance with the provisions of these regulations and initiate the recall exercise, such information alert(s) may be sent by the quickest means of communication including fax, e-mail, and speed post.
- The food business operator shall store the recovered food in an area which is separated from any other food and is identified by a label plate including prominently that "recalled product not fit for human consumption"
- The food business operator may request termination of recall by submitting a written request to the chief executive officer, food safety and standards authority of India along with recall status report or post-recall report certifying that the recall was effective. The request may be made in the form specified in Schedule- III
- Food safety means assurance that food is acceptable for human consumption according to its intended use
- Toxicity is the capacity of a substance to produce harm or injury of any kind under any conditions
- Hazard is the relative probability that harm or injury will result when substance is not used in a prescribed manner and quantity
- Hazards can be physical, chemical and biological causing harmful / adverse effects on the health of consumers
- Physical hazard is any physical material not normally found in food, which causes illness or injury and includes wood, stones, parts of pests, hair, etc
- Chemical hazards are chemicals or deleterious substances which may be intentionally or unintentionally added to foods. This category of hazards includes pesticides, chemical residues, toxic metals, polychlorinated biphenyls, preservatives, food colours and other additives
- Biological hazards are living organisms and include microbiological organisms
- Contamination: It is the presence of harmful, or objectionable foreign substances in food such as chemicals, micro-organisms, dilutants before/ during or after processing or storage
- Adulteration: Food adulteration is the process in which the quality of food is lowered either by the addition of inferior quality material or by extraction of valuable ingredient

- Adulterants: are those substances which are used for making the food products unsafe for human consumption
- Food Quality: The term food quality refers to attributes that influence a product's value to consumers. This includes both negative attributes such as spoilage, contamination, adulteration, food safety hazards as well as positive attributes such as colour, flavour, texture
- Safety is a preliminary attribute and precursor of quality
- Effective food standards and control systems are required to integrate quality into every aspect of food production and service, to ensure the supply of hygienic, wholesome food as well as to facilitate trade within and between nations. There are four levels of standards, which are well coordinated
    1. Company Standards: These are prepared by a Company for its own use. Normally, they are copies of National Standards.
    2. National Standards: These are issued by the national standards body, Food Safety and Standards Authority of India (FSSAI).
    3. Regional Standards: Regional groups with similar geographical, climate, etc. have legislation standardization bodies
    4. International Standards: The International Organization for Standardization (ISO) and Codex Alimentarius Commission (CAC) publish international standards
- Voluntary product certification: There are voluntary grading and marking schemes such as ISI mark of BIS and AGMARK
- The Bureau of Indian Standards (BIS) deals with standardization of various consumer goods including food products and runs a voluntary certification scheme known as 'ISI' mark for processed foods
- BIS launched Food Safety Management Systems (FSMS) Certification IS/ISO 22000:2005 scheme which envisages grant of FSMS Certification license to organizations according to IS/ISO 22000
- AGMARK is a voluntary scheme of certification of agricultural products (raw and processed) for safeguarding the health of consumers
- The word AGMARK is derived from Agricultural Marketing
- The AGMARK standard was set up by the Directorate of Marketing & Inspection (DMI), Ministry of Agriculture, Government of India by introducing an agricultural produce Act in 1937
- The word AGMARK ensures about quality and purity of the food products. The quality of the product is determined with reference to the size, variety, weight, colour, moisture, and fat content

- Indian Government has passed Food Safety and Standards Act (FSSA), 2006, to bring the different pieces of legislation pertaining to food safety under one umbrella
- Food Safety and Standards Authority of India (FSSAI) has been established under the Food Safety and Standards, 2006, which consolidates various acts and orders that have hitherto handled food related issues in various Ministries and Departments
- Food Safety and Standards Authority of India was established for laying down science-based standards for food and to regulate their manufacture, storage, distribution, sale and import, to ensure availability of safe and wholesome food for human consumption
- Food Safety and Standards (Prohibition and Restriction on Sale) Regulation, 2011, has prescribed mandatory certification for Blended Edible Vegetable Oils and Fat Spreads
- However, in case of Til Oil, Carbia Callosa, Honey dew, Tea and Ghee, FSSAI has prescribed few conditional restrictions
- The major organizations which are playing a key role a role in enhancing food safety, quality and security, facilitating research and trade are Codex Alimentarius Commission (CAC) 2. International Organization for Standardization 3. World Trade Organization
- CAC is an intergovernmental body formed with the objective of establishing international standards to protect the health of the consumers and facilitate food and agricultural trade
- Codex Alimentarius Commission is an international body constituted by Food and Agriculture Organization (FAO) and World Health Organization (WHO) of the United Nations with an objective to protect health of consumers and to ensure fair practices in the food trade
- In 2017, the membership of Codex was 187 member countries and one Member Organization (European Community)
- India is a member through the Ministry of Health and Family Welfare.
- CAC has become the single most important international reference point for developments associated with food standards
- The document published by the CAC is Codex Alimentarius, which means 'Food Code' and is a collection of internationally adopted Food Standards
- Codex standard - Maximum residue limits (MRLs) for residues of pesticides or veterinary drugs in foods are examples of standards dealing with only one characteristic
- The Prevention of Food Adulteration Act 1954 (PFA, 1954) was enacted by the Government of India to prevent adulteration of food

- The International Organization for Standardization (ISO) is a worldwide, non-governmental federation of national standards bodies (ISO member bodies)
- ISO 9000 is an international reference for quality requirements. It is concerned with "Quality Management" of an organization
- WTO was established in 1995. The main objective of WTO is to help trade flow smoothly, freely, fairly and predictably, by administering trade agreements, settling trade disputes, assisting countries in trade policy issues
- The last round, the 1986-94 Uruguay Round, led to the WTO's creation
- The WTO Agreement covers goods, services and intellectual property
- An effective food control system must consist of (i) Food Inspection and (ii) Analytical capability
- Conformity of products to standards is verified through inspection
- A food hazard can enter/come into the food at any stage of the food chain, therefore, adequate control throughout the food chain is essential. Food safety and quality can be ensured through: Good Manufacturing Practices (GMP), Good Handling Practices (GHP), Hazard Analysis Critical Control Points (HACCP)
- Good Manufacturing Practices (GMP) are a part of quality assurance to ensure that manufacturers/processors take proactive steps to ensure that their products are safe
- GMP is a good business tool that helps to refine compliance and performance by the manufacturers/producers
- Good Handling Practices indicate a comprehensive approach from the farm to the store or consumer, in order to identify potential sources of risk and indicates what steps and procedures are taken to minimize the risk of contamination
- HACCP is a means of providing assurance about safety of food. It involves identification of hazards, assessment of chances of occurrence of hazards during each step /stage in the food chain — raw material procurement, manufacturing, distribution, usage of food products and defining measures for hazard(s) control
- FSSA, 2006 places primary responsibility for safe food with producers and suppliers through HACCP, GMP, GHP
- (HACCP) system developed by Codex Alimentarius Commission and combines the HACCP plan with Prerequisite Programmes (PRPs) and is fully compatible with Quality Management Systems (QMS) as per ISO 9001: 2000
- In order to protect the consumers from exploitation and to save them from adulterated and substandard goods and deficient services, the Consumer Protection Act came into force on 15th April, 1986 and it applies to the whole of India except the State of Jammu and Kashmir

- A Statutory Consumer Protection Council has been set-up under the Consumer Protection Act, 1986, implemented by the Ministry of Consumer Affairs Food and Public Distribution. The main aim of the council is to redress the grievances of the consumers about quality of purchased goods, including food articles
- A primary sample is the 'portion of product' collected from a lot during the first stage of the sampling process, and will normally be in the form of an item (if collected from a lot of pre packed products) or of an increment (if collected from a bulk lot)
- For Perishable products - Ice packs can be used during transportation and temperature is to be maintained between 4-6 degree C
- For Non Perishable products, transportation should be done at temperatures not more than 40 degree Celsius
- For microbiological samples, analysis should initiate within 24 hours of sample being drawn
- For chemical tests analysis to be initiated within 48 to 72 hours
- A lot is a definite quantity of some commodity manufactured or produced under conditions, which are presumed uniform for the purpose of these Guidelines
- A consignment is a quantity of some commodity delivered at one time
- Sample - A number of food units that resembles the characteristics of the lot
- Sampling - Procedure used to draw or constitute a sample
- Sampling plan - Planned procedure which enables one to choose, or draw separate samples from a lot, in order to get the information needed, such as a decision on compliance status of the lot
- A characteristic is a property, which helps to identify, or differentiate between, items within a given lot
- A defect (nonconformity) occurs within an item when one or more, quality characteristic does not meet its established quality specification
- Moisture content is an important consideration during sampling procedures, in part because it affects the extent of sample heterogeneity
- Bulk sampling involves the selection of a sample from a lot of material that does not consist of discrete, identifiable or constant units. Sampling may be performed in static or dynamic situations.
- Acceptance sampling differs from the previous types and involves the application of a predetermined plan to decide whether a lot of goods meet defined criteria for acceptance
- There are two broad categories of acceptance sampling: sampling by attributes and sampling by variables

1. In sampling by attributes, the unit of product is classified as defective or nondefective, or the number of defects in a unit of product is counted with respect to a given requirement
2. In variable sampling, sampling is performed to estimate quantitatively the amount of a substance (e.g., salt) or a characteristic (e.g., color) on a continuous scale

- The inspection of a lot using either an variables sampling plan will allow a decision to be made on the quality of the lot. The Acceptable Quality Level (AQL) for a given sampling plan is the rate of nonconforming items at which a lot will be rejected with a low probability, usually 5 %
- Operating Characteristic (OC) curves are used extensively in acceptance sampling. The OC curve shows the relationship between the quality and the per cent of lots expected to be acceptable for the quality characteristic inspected
- If the lot quality is 0.093 fraction defective, then the probability of acceptance, Pa, is 0.05
- If the lot quality is 0.018 fraction defective, then the probability of acceptance, Pa, is 0.95
- To protect against changes in moisture content, samples should be stored in an airtight container
- Light sensitive samples should be stored in containers made of opaque glass, or the container wrapped in aluminum foil
- Oxygen sensitive samples should be stored under nitrogen or an inert gas. Refrigeration or freezing may be necessary to protect chemically unstable samples
- However, freezing should be avoided when storing unstable emulsions
- Preservatives (e.g., mercuric chloride, potassium dichromate, and chloroform) can be used to stabilize certain food substances during storage
- Limiting Quality (LQ) - For a given sampling plan is the rate of nonconforming items at which a lot will be accepted with a low probability, usually 10%
- Sampling devices used for different food products depend on the physical form of the food (eg liquid, powder, granules, seeds, grains etc.)
- Sampling liquids: vacuum pumps, dipping vessels, pipette-type samplers, sampling scoops, piston-tube samplers etc.
- Sampling solids in powder or granulated form: spear samplers, tube-type samplers, zone samplers, sampling trowels, spiral samplers
- Sampling frozen goods: hand-drill samplers, etc

- Stirrer (Plunger): It is a device used for manual mixing in vessels. It is an equipment commonly used to mix the milk or cream to make it uniform in composition throughout the container or can
- Agitator: It is an apparatus used for mechanical agitation of the liquid or semi-solid products. Paddles agitators consist of usually flat blades attached to a vertical shaft and normally operated at low speed (100-rpm)
- Dipper : This device consists of a small cup fixed to one end of a long handle and is mainly used to collect the sample from the container. The tapered form of the cup permits nesting of the dippers. The capacity of the dipper is usually 50 ml
- Tube Samplers : The tube samplers are advantageous in that a representative sample can be obtained regardless of how long the milk has stood before sampling. A column of milk which represents the milk from top to bottom of the container is collected as sample
- Piston-tube sampler : Syringe-like sampler consisting of a body and a piston. Made from PTFE or polypropylene (PP) with a stainless-steel connecting rod. It can be used for liquids, oils, emulsions, pastes
- Borers : The borers are used for sampling of powdered products. For example, milk powder, flour etc. The protruding borer edge and point should be sufficiently sharp to serve as a scraper and to facilitate sampling
- Sampling Trowel (Sampling scoop/hand scoop): Trowel are made from plastics (PP) or metal (stainless steel), of variable volumes and different handle lengths. Sampling of solids such as grain, free flowing powders and granules
- Spiral screw sampler : The spiral sampler is pressed into the sampled material by pushing and twisting, which ensures the sample is loaded into the spiral. The sampler is then withdrawn and the sample is scraped off by a spatula or scraper into the wide mouth container. Used for paste-like foodstuffs such as peanut butter vegetable or animal fat, jam or honey
- Sampler for frozen foods (ice borer) : The sampler operates on the principle of a screw: the sampler screws into the sample material and simultaneously extracts and conveys the sample into the sampling cylinder. Sampling from frozen and deep-frozen materials and semi-solid substances e.g Deep-frozen goods such as meat or fruit juice concentrates
- Hand drill sampler : (Conical sampler, tubular sampler): Conical or tubular hand drill with sharp cutting edges and a solid handle, drilling depth 13 cm. Taking samples from soft and semi-solid materials. Useful for cheese, butter, cottage cheese paneer, solidified oils etc.
- Spear-type sampler : this is a metal or plastic sampler. Usually equipped with a telescopic rod. Used for taking direct samples of bulk goods from sacks,

bags or plastic drums, if these goods are in powder or granulated form. The sampler is introduced into the product by piercing the packaging. The hole in the packaging must be closed using tape or a sticker (or a control seal). Also suitable for vertical zone sampling of free flowing materials such as grain, sugar, flour, semolina, milk powder

- Zone sampler : The zone sampler is a metal spear-type sampler with a body having several openings (closed chambers) along its length. Useful for taking of samples from bulk goods in transport containers, big bags, silos and tanks or goods packed in bags, sacks, barrels or drums. It is suitable for both very fine powders, granules and coarse grains, semolina and nuts. Sampling is possible up to a depth of 2.5 metres. Used for cross-sectional sampling
- Spoons, scalpels, spatula, scoops, knives made up of stainless steel etc are used for solid and semi solid products. Other versatile tools may be useful for sampling, for example knives, stainless steel axes, scissors, swabs forceps, tongs, cleaning brushes and flashlights etc
- Sampling by hand : This method is appropriate for all species of grains, legumes, oilseeds etc. Moreover, it is potentially the most suitable method for seed that could get damaged using triers, seeds with wings, and seeds with low moisture content
- The Legal Metrology Act, 2009 repeals and replaces the Standard of Weights and Measures Act, 1976 and the Standards of weights and Measures (Enforcement) Act, 1985. The Act has come into force from 1st April, 2011
- The Legal Metrology (Packaged Commodities) Rules, 2017 were prescribed in order to regulate pre-packaged commodities
- The Export Inspection Council (EIC) was set up by the Government of India under Section 3 of the Export (Quality Control and Inspection) Act, 1963 (22 of 1963), in order to ensure sound development of export trade of India through Quality Control and Inspection and for matters connected therewith
- Units have been set-up by the Ministry of Commerce for ensuring promotion and quality control of export of food item, under the Export (Quality Control and Inspection) Act, 1963: a) Agricultural and Processed Food Export Development Authority (APEDA) b) Spices Board c) Coffee Board d) Tea Board, and e) Marine Products Export Development Authority (MPEDA)
- Surface tension can be measured by Capillary rise method, Drop weight method and Torsion balance method
- Direct method of Moisture analysis of food - Oven drying, Vacuum drying, Freeze drying, Distillation method, Karl Fisher method, Thermo gravimetric analysis and Gas chromatography
- The most widely used water determinations for foods, grains, and oilseeds are oven drying methods

- The Karl Fischer titration method is a chemical analysis method. It is quite rapid and sensitive and it can be used for determination of water in many low-moisture food products
- Indirect method of Moisture analysis – Refractometer, Infrared absorption, NMR spectroscopy, and Mass spectrometry
- Protein analysis of food by direct method – Formal titration method, Spectrophotometric method
- Indirect method of protein analysis – Kjeldahl method, Dumas Combustion method
- Determination of organic nitrogen in grains was developed by the Danish investigator, Kjeldahl, in 1883
- In the Kjeldahl method, the digestion temperature has been found to affect the conversion speed and generally digestion temperatures of 37^0C–41^0C are considered to be the best
- Most proteins exhibit a distinct ultraviolet absorption maximum at UV 280 nm, primarily due to tryptophan and tyrosine residues in the protein
- Fat in the presence of food can be analyzed by Direct solvent extraction method, the solubilization extraction method, and the volumetric method
- Surveillance – Section 29 (3) FSS Act 2006. Collection, analysis, interpretation, and dissemination of data related to food/nutrient uptake
- Active surveillance – Staffs in the active surveillance will be contacting health care provider/manufacturing unit to seek the infection about quality of food items procured
- Passive Surveillance – Collect, collected data of food consumption, biological risk contaminants
- The additives like plasticizers, antioxidants, UV Stabilizers, colors, printing inks can migrate into the packaged food
- Printing inks and chemical used in the pulp and paper production can migrate through paper boards into the foods. Chlorophenols formed during the bleaching of wood pulp for paper manufacture can be responsible for taints
- Global migration – It refers to the total transfer that is the quantity of all substances migrating from the package into the packaged food (Unit: mg/dm2
- Specific migration – Related to transfer of one or more identifiable substances that is a constituent of the packaging material (Unit: mg/kg)
- Non destructive testing makes it possible to examine the condition or quality of food without damaging it
- Three most popular, practical and widely used nondestructive methods are Spectroscopy, Ultrasound and Nuclear Magnetic Resonance (NMR)

- **Spectroscopy** is a technique where the interaction between matter and electromagnetic radiation
- The nature of the interactions in spectroscopy techniques between radiation and matter may includes- absorption, emission or scattering
- Qualitative spectroscopy: This technique studied the radiation absorbed or emitted by an atom or molecule which will give information about its identity
- Quantitative spectroscopy: This technique will give information about the number of absorbing or emitting atoms or molecules by measuring the total amount of radiation
- **Frequency (v)** of the electromagnetic radiation is the number of oscillations made by wave in 1 second
- Frequency is measured in hertz (Hz), where 1Hz = 1 cycle per sec.
- Wavelength (λ): It is the length of on complete wave cycle.
- Wavelength is generally measured in centimeters (cm).
- Wavelength is inversely proportional to the frequency
- The relation between wavelength and frequency is defined by
  $V = c/\lambda$, where, c= speed of light.
  $E = hv = hc/\lambda$ where, Planck's constant (h) = 6.6×10^{-34} joules per second.
- Wave number: It defines the number of completed wave cycles per distance. It is measured in 1 cm^{-1} wave number is reciprocal to the wavelength
- Absorption spectroscopy is based on law known as **Beer-Lambert law**
- Lambert's law: It states that when monochromatic light passes through a transparent medium, the intensity of transmitted light decreases exponentially as the thickness of absorbing material increases.
- Beer's law: It states that the intensity of transmitted monochromatic light decreases exponentially as the concentration of the absorbing substances increases.

$$A = \log I_0 / I\ e.c.l$$

- A = absorbance,
- I_0 = intensity of incident light,
- I = intensity of light through the sample,
- e = extinction coefficient or absorption coefficient
- c = concentration,
- l = path length (cm)

- Spectroscopic techniques can detect the composition of foods, microbes, pest pathogens, and adulteration that occur within the food
- Spectroscopic techniques such as UV–visible, fluorescence, infrared, mid-infrared, near-infrared, Raman, and nuclear magnetic resonance spectroscopy are used to determine food quality
- The PV value can be measured easily using a UV–visible spectrometer at an absorbance maximum of 240 nm
- Foods contain fluorophores, many industries use the fluorescence technique to determine food quality. The fluorophores present in foods include rhodamine B, quinine, Acridine Orange, fluorescein, and pyridine. This technique is often used in combination with other techniques such as high-performance liquid chromatography (HPLC).
- The amount of phenolic compounds, TBARS, anisidine and iodine values of oligomers and monomers, toxins of bacteria, can be determined by fluorescence spectroscopy
- Mid-infrared (MIR) spectroscopy can detect functional groups and carbon, nitrogen, and lignin
- MIR spectroscopy is employed to detect fungal disease and mycotoxins in cereals during processing and storage
- Near-infrared (NIR) spectroscopy is a primary technique for the rapid detection of moisture, carbohydrates, proteins, and fat within a food
- When photons interact with molecules in matter the Raman effect or Raman scattering is produced
- Nuclear magnetic resonance (NMR) is a spectroscopic method used to determine the molecular structure and physical properties of substances
- NMR is a rapid and noninvasive analytical method that was initially used to study moisture in food. The structural composition of food can be determined by analyzing the components of oil, protein and carbohydrates
- Atomic emission spectroscopy (AES) is used to determine the chemicals and also elements present within foods
- Spectroscopic techniques can measure the AV value, PV value and colour. In addition lipid, carbohydrate, fat, and water content of foods to determine the quality of the food
- Ultrasound is composed of mechanical sound waves that originate from molecular movements that oscillate in a propagation medium
- Sounds and ultrasounds differ in frequency: sound waves propagate at frequencies audible to the human ear (from 16 Hz to 16–20 kHz), while US waves propagate at frequencies greater than 20 kHz (upper limit of audibility

for the human ear) up to frequencies of 10 MHz, which then proceeds to the so-called hypersonic region

- Most common applications in the food industry include cell destruction and extraction of intracellular material
- Ultrasound is used for the activation or deactivation of enzymes, mixing and homogenization, emulsification, dispersion, preservation, stabilization, dissolution and crystallization, hydrogenation, tenderization of meat, ripening, ageing and oxidation
- Ultrasound has been used to evaluate the quality of many foods, such as meat, fish, vegetables, and dairy products, in a non-destructive manner
- Ultrasound technology can replace traditional sanitization methods, and US does not alter the organoleptic properties of foods
- Process of compression and rarefaction of the particles in the medium and their subsequent collapse is known as the phenomenon of cavitation, the most important effect of high-energy US waves
- Cavitation is a physical phenomenon that leads to the formation and activity of bubbles (or cavities) inside a liquid when it is subjected to the action of high-speed pressure and depression waves generated by ultrasound waves in an intense ultrasonic field
- Two types of cavitation have been distinguished: first type, known as stable cavitation, the bubble remains stable around an equilibrium size for many compression-decompression cycles and the second type, known as transitory or unstable cavitation, the bubble grows in a single cycle, doubles its size, and then collapses
- In the medical field, controlled cavitation is used to remove kidney stones (lithotripsy), which are precisely crushed through the formation of micro bubbles that implode the solid formations inside the kidneys, as well as for diagnosis and antalgic thermal effects
- Cavitation is also used in aesthetic medicine to eliminate or reduce adiposity, a technique known as non-surgical non-bloody liposuction (Ultrasound Lipoclasia)

CHAPTER-8

General Concepts of Food Analysis and Testing

- The common methods for relating concentration and instrumental response are calibration, standard addition, and the use of internal standards
- An internal standard is a substance that is similar (but not identical) to the analyte and is added to the sample
- Selectivity of a method is its ability to measure the analyte in the sample matrix in the presence of other sample components
- Reliability of a method is based on its accuracy and precision
- Accuracy, the difference between a measured value and the true value, is expressed in terms of error
- Precision is the amount of scatter in replicate measurements of the same quantity, and is expressed in terms of deviation
- Measurement, sampling, and calibration errors all contribute to decreased precision and increased uncertainty
- The detection limit, or minimum detectable value, is the lowest concentration of analyte that produces a signal that can be detected above instrumental noise. Usually, a signal-to-noise ratio (S/N) of at least 3 is required for a reportable result
- Quantification limit, also called the quantitation limit or minimum quantifiable value, is the lowest analyte level that can be measured with accuracy and precision
- Range of a method is the extent of concentrations within which accuracy and precision are retained, and the relationship between concentration and response is constant
- Supercritical fluid extraction, especially using CO_2, is today a popular technology for rapid, contamination-free extraction in the food and pharmaceutical industries
- First commercial applications of SCF technology were the decaffeination of coffee

- Supercritical fluids can have solvating powers similar to organic solvents, but with higher diffusivities, lower viscosity, and lower surface tension
- SFE is an excellent technique for examining volatile components because the extractions can be conducted at relatively low temperatures and in a non-oxidative environment
- Supercritical fluid extraction with CO_2 delivers the most natural-smelling and -tasting extracts because there are no volatiles removed in a residual solvent-removal post-processing step
- The use of CO_2 as a supercritical fluid extractor limits the polluting
- Ion chromatography uses ion-exchange resins to separate charged species (i.e., atomic or molecular ions) based on their coulombic interaction with the resin
- Coulombic interaction is the physical process of the attraction of opposite charges and repulsion of like charges over
- MS is an instrumental technique based on the separation of ions in a vacuum, in the gas phase, according to their mass-to-charge ratios (m=z)
- Chlorophylls absorb in the violet (420 nm) and red (650 nm) regions, transmitting the green light, while heme absorbs in the green region, transmitting the red light
- In algae, the cu- phthalocyanine complexes (26 double bonds) absorbing in the red region (>550 nm) transmit the blue-green light
- Many synthetic colorants (malachite green, crystal violet, phenolphthalein) containing triphenylmethane conjugated chromophores linked to auxochromes (donor–acceptor groups) have different colors dependent of different factors (pH and ionic environment) and therefore they can be used as analytical indicators
- Many natural pigments found in food are chromophores, e.g., carotenoids, chlorophylls, flavonoids (quercetin- yellow), anthocyanins (cyaniding - red, purple, or blue in acidic, neutral, or alkali environments, respectively), and betalains
- Hue is the quality that normally identifies a color such as red, green, and blue
- Chroma or saturation is the clarity of a color, expressed as the intensity of hue compared with its own brightness. A saturated color looks clear and bright, but an unsaturated color appears pale, muddy, or dull.
- The light value is represented by its lightness or brightness
- Lightness considers color as a source of reflected light by an illuminated surface and is related to the connotations light and dark

- Brightness represents the total light from an illuminated object or reflected from a surface
- Rod-shaped receptors in the eye are responsible for night vision
- Cone-shaped receptors are responsible for daylight and color vision
- Color measurement detecting instruments generally fall into one of the four categories: colorimeters, densitometers, spectral cameras, and spectrophotometers
- Colorimeters measure color using three or four filters that match human color receptors
- Densitometers measure the density of layers using one or more filters. Densitometers do not give color information, but are useful for the control of juice concentrations
- Spectral cameras provide measurements with full spectral and spatial information
- Spectrophotometers operate on the principle of absorption/transmittance or reflected light. They give reproducible complete spectral and intensity informations under standardized conditions
- Oil determination by standard reference methods - Solvent extraction methods (Soxhlet method)
- Total sugar determination - High performance liquid chromatography, Polarimetry
- Polarimetry measures the rotary power exerted by a compound in solution on the polarization plane of incident light
- The refraction index (RI) is defined as the ratio of the sine of the incidence angle to the sine of the refraction angle of light
- RI depends on concentration, temperature, and wavelength of the light. The standard RI value is measured at 20^{0}C using monochromatic sodium light (at ~589 nm)
- RI is performed with a refractometer that has been calibrated, for example, with sucrose; the results obtained are expressed as percent sugar wt=wt
- The atomic absorption spectroscopy method has become very popular for the elemental analysis of solutions
- ICP (Inductively Coupled Plasma) – OES (optical emission spectroscopy) has emerged as a major analytical technique for trace metal determinations
- Chromatography is a general term applied to a wide variety of separation techniques based on the partitioning or distribution of a sample (solute) between a moving or mobile phase and a fixed or stationary phase.

- Sharp peaks are indicative of the efficiency of the chromatographic process. Efficiency is also called plate number
- Gas chromatography is a column chromatography technique, in which the mobile phase is gas and the stationary phase is either an immobilized liquid or a solid packed in a closed tube.
- GC is used to separate thermally stable volatile components of a mixture
- Gas Chromatography (GC) - Mobile phase is a gas. Nitrogen, helium, and hydrogen are used. The gas only acts as a carrier
- Gas Chromatography Detectors The most common detectors are the FID, thermal conductivity (TCD), electron capture (ECD), flame photometric (FPD), pulsed flame photometric (PFPD), and photoionization (PID) detectors
- Thermal Conductivity Detectors - Universal detector, but suffers from a lack of sensitivity as compared to the other detectors
- Flame Ionization Detector (FID) - Detects C and H. This includes, for example, flavor studies, fatty acid analysis, carbohydrate analysis, sterols, contaminants in foods, and antioxidants
- Electron-Capture Detector (ECD) - widely used to detect chlorinated compounds
- Flame Photometric Detector - This detector is well adapted for sulfur and phosphorus determination
- Paper chromatography, thin layer chromatography (TLC) (both of these techniques may be referred to as planar chromatography), and column liquid chromatography, all of which involve a liquid mobile phase and either a solid or a liquid stationary phase
- In paper chromatography, the stationary phase and the mobile phase are both liquid (partition chromatography)
- In paper and thin-layer chromatography, components of a mixture are characterized by their relative mobility (Rf) value, where: Rf = Distance moved by component/ Distance moved by solvent
- Affinity chromatography is unique in that separation is based on the specific, reversible interaction between a solute molecule and a ligand immobilized on the chromatographic stationary phase
- Immobilization generally consists of two steps: activation and coupling
- Ligands for affinity chromatography may be either specific or general (i.e., group specific)
- Specific ligands, such as antibodies, bind only one particular solute

- General ligands, such as nucleotide analogs and lectins, bind to certain classes of solutes
- A chromatographic peak is defined by several parameters including retention time of peak width, and peak height
- Chromatographic resolution is a function of column efficiency, selectivity, and the capacity factor
- HPLC was the acronym for high-pressure liquid chromatography, reflecting the high operating pressures generated by early columns
- A detector translates sample concentration changes in the HPLC column effluent into electrical signals
- The most widely used HPLC detectors are based on ultraviolet-visible (UV-Vis) and fluorescence spectrophotometry, refractive index determination, electrochemical analysis, Radioactive detectors and chemiluminescent nitrogen detector (CLND)
- UV-Vis absorption detector, which can measure the absorption of radiation by chromophore-containing compounds
- RI detectors are widely used for analytes that do not contain UV-absorbing chromophores, such as carbohydrates and lipids, when the analytes are present at relatively high concentration
- Amperometric detectors measure the change in current as the analyte is oxidized or reduced by the application of voltage across the electrodes of the flow cell. This method is highly selective (nonreactive compounds give no response) and very sensitive
- A major application of electrochemical detection has been for the routine determination of catecholamines, which are phenolic compounds of clinical importance that are present in blood and tissues at very low levels
- Radioactive detectors are widely used for pharmacokinetic and metabolism studies with radiolabeled drugs
- A chemiluminescent nitrogen detector (CLND) allows nitrogen-containing compounds, such as amino acids, to be detected without using chemical derivatization
- Electrophoresis is the migration of electrically charged particles or ions in solution due to an applied electric field
- Calibration is a "set of operations that establish, under specified conditions, the relationship between values of quantities indicated by a measuring instrument or measuring system, or values represented by a material measure or a reference material and corresponding values realized by standards"

- Dynamic range: that range of concentrations of the test substance over which a change in concentration produces a change in detector signal.
- The lower limit of the dynamic range is defined as the concentration producing a detector output signal equal to a specified multiple of the detector short-term noise level
- The upper limit of the dynamic range is the concentration at the point where the slope of the curve obtained by plotting detector response as a function of concentration becomes zero
- Linear range: that range of concentrations over which the sensitivity (S) is constant to within a defined tolerance
- Limit of detection: this is defined as the concentration below which the analytical method cannot reliably detect a response
- Limit of quantification: the smallest quantity of compound to be determined in given experimental conditions with defined reliability and accuracy. A signal-to-noise ratio of 10 is adequate
- Detector noise: short-term noise in the maximum amplitude of response for all random variations of the detector signal of a frequency greater than 1 cycle per minute
- Repeatability (ISO 3534) - Qualitative: the closeness of agreement between the results obtained by the same method on identical test material under the same conditions (same operator), same laboratory, same apparatus, and short interval of time (same day). Quantitative: the value below which the absolute difference between two single test results obtained under the above conditions may be accepted to lie with a specified probability (usually 95%)
- Reproducibility (ISO 3531) - Qualitative: the closeness of agreement between individual results obtained with the same method on identical test material but under different conditions (different operators, different apparatus, different times, interday, etc.). Quantitative: the value below which the absolute difference between two single test results on individual material obtained by operators in different laboratories using the standardized test method may be expected to lie with specific probability (usually 95%)
- Selectivity - This is a measure of the extent to which the method is able to determine a particular compound in the matrices without interference from matrix components
- Accuracy: this measures the difference between the true value and the mean value obtained from repeated analyses.
- Analysis of variance (ANOVA) estimates the within-run precision and the between-run precision

- Reliability: this means the probability that the results lie in the interval defined by two selected limits. It gives a rigorous method for evaluating the correctness of a method of analysis in relation to two limits for error
- Ruggedness: the capacity of an analytical method to produce accurate data despite small changes in experimental conditions (for example, small flow-rate variation in HPLC)
- The percentage recovery of the extraction is determined by comparing the detector response of an extracted sample with that of a directly injected standard
- Internal Standard is mostly used in chromatography and capillary electrophoresis. It monitors the behavior of sample solutes to be analyzed and quantitatively determined
- Biosensors' basic principle is to convert a biologically induced recognition event into a usable signal
- Rheometers are devices used to determine the viscosity and other rheological properties of materials
- Differential scanning calorimetry (DSC) is the most frequently used thermal analysis technique and probably accounts for 70% of all thermal analysis measurements. DSC is the universal detector for measuring structure
- Color, flavor, and texture are the three principal quality attributes that determine food acceptance, and color has a far greater influence on our judgment than most of us appreciate
- Form VA- Notice given to Food Business Operator by Food Safety Officer
- Form 6 – Sent to food analyst by Food Safety Officer
- Form VII A –report of Analysis given by food analyst to Designated officer (2 copy), Food Safety Officer (1 copy), Food Business Operator (1 copy)
- Form V B – Purchaser food article to be analysed
- Molisch's test – General test for carbohydrates
- Anthone's test - General test for carbohydrates
- Iodine test for Glycans (Starch, Glycogen)
- Barfoed's test – To distinguish between monosaccharides from reducing disaccharides
- Seliwanoff's test for Ketose
- Fehling's test, Benedict's test and Picric test for reducing sugars
- Bial's test for pentoses

- Acid value – Number of milligrams of KOH required to neutralize the free fatty acids present in 1 gram of fat
- Saponification number - Number of milligrams of KOH required to saponify 1 gram of fat. Saponification number indicates Molecular weight
- Iodine value (Koettstorfer number) - Number of grams of iodine absorbed by 100 grams of fat
- Polanske no – Number of millilitres of 0.1 N KOH required to neutralize the insoluble fatty acids obtained from 5 grams of fat. Indicates volatile insoluble fatty acids
- Reichert Meissl number - Number of millilitres of 0.1 N KOH required to neutralize the soluble, volatile fatty acids derived from 5 gram of fat
- Acetyl number - Number of milligrams of KOH required to neutralize the acetic acid obtained by saponification of 1 gram of fat after it has been acetylated

CHAPTER-9

Food Processing, Preservation and Packaging

- Viscosity is a liquid's internal resistance to flow
- The force that moves the liquid is known as the shearing force or shear stress and the velocity gradient is known as the shear rate
- If shear stress is plotted against shear rate, most simple liquids and gases show a linear relationship and these are termed Newtonian fluids. Examples include water, most oils, gases, and simple solutions of sugars and salts. The relationship is non-linear, the fluids are termed 'non Newtonian.'
- Many liquid foods are non-Newtonian, including emulsions and suspensions, and concentrated solutions that contain starches, pectin, gums and proteins. Non-Newtonian fluids can be classified broadly into the following types
    1. Pseudoplastic fluid – viscosity decreases as the shear rate increases (e.g., emulsions, and suspensions such as concentrated fruit juices and purees)
    2. Dilatant fluid – viscosity increases as the shear rate increases. (This behaviour is less common but is found with liquid chocolate and corn flour suspension.)
    3. Bingham or Casson plastic fluids – there is no flow until a critical shear stress is reached and then shear rate is either linear (Bingham type) or non-linear (Casson type) (e.g., tomato ketchup)
    4. Thixotropic fluid – the structure breaks down and viscosity decreases with continued shear stress (most creams)
    5. Rheopectic fluid – the structure builds up and viscosity increases with continued shear stress (e.g., whipping cream)
- Chemicals that reduce the surface tension in the surface of a liquid are termed surface active and are known as 'surfactants', 'emulsifying agents' or 'detergents.'
- Surface active agents contain molecules which are polar (or 'hydrophilic') at one end and non-polar (or 'lipophilic') at the other end
- Water content is a very important factor controlling the rate of deterioration
- The dry-weight basis is more commonly used for processing calculations, whereas the wet-weight basis is frequently quoted in food composition tables

- Almost all microbial activity is inhibited below aw 0.6, most fungi are inhibited below aw 0.7, most yeasts are inhibited below aw 0.8, and most bacteria below aw 0.9
- The interaction of aw with temperature, pH, oxygen and carbon dioxide, or chemical preservatives has an important effect on the inhibition of microbial growth.
- 'Quality Assurance' was developed during the 1980s, based on the principles of Good Manufacturing Practice (GMP)
- Hazard analysis is 'the identification of potentially hazardous ingredients, storage conditions, packaging, critical process points, and relevant human factors which may affect product safety or quality
- HACCP is used throughout each stage of a process, and includes raw materials, processing, storage and distribution
- The concept of combining several factors to preserve foods has been developed by Leistner (1995)
- Hurdle Technology, where an understanding of the complex interactions of temperature, water activity, pH, chemical preservatives, etc. Is used to design a series of hurdles that ensure microbiological safety of processed foods
- Canning steps - Cleaning, Blanching, Filling, Exhausting, Sealing, Sterilizing, Cooling and Labelling
- Cleaning is the unit operation in which contaminating materials are removed from the food and separated to leave the surface of the food in a suitable condition for further processing
- Wet cleaning is more effective than dry methods for removing soil from root crops or dust and pesticide residues from soft fruits or vegetables
- Sorting is the separation of foods into categories on the basis of a measurable physical property
- Size sorting (termed sieving or screening) is the separation of solids into two or more fractions on the basis of differences in size
- Sorting is 'the assessment of the overall quality of a food using a number of attributes'
- Eggs are visually inspected over tungsten lights (termed 'candling') to assess up to twenty factors and remove those that are for example, fertilized or malformed and those that contain blood spots or rot
- Apples are graded with the assistance of coloured cards that show the required characteristics of different grades in terms of color distribution across the fruit, surface blemishes and size and shape of the fruit
- Peeling is used in the processing of many fruits and vegetables to remove unwanted or inedible material, and to improve the appearance of the final product

- Foods (for example root crops) are fed in batches into a pressure vessel which is rotated at 4–6 rpm. High-pressure steam (1500×10^3 Pa) is introduced in Flash steam peeling
- Knife peeling is particularly suitable for citrus fruits where the skin is easily removed and there is little damage or loss of fruit
- In Caustic peeling, dilute solution of sodium hydroxide (named lye) is heated to 100–120°c. A development of lye peeling is named dry caustic peeling
- Flame peeling was developed for onions. The outer 'paper shell' and root hairs are burned off, and the charred skin is removed by high-pressure water sprays. Average product losses are 9%.
- Size reduction or 'comminution' is the unit operation in which the average size of solid pieces of food is reduced by the application of grinding, compression or impact forces
- Ball mills are used to produce fine powders, such as food colourants
- Disc mills employs shearing forces for fine grinding or shearing and impact forces for coarser grinding
- Hammer mills are widely used for crystalline and fibrous materials including spices and sugar
- Roller mills are widely used to mill wheat
- Emulsification is the formation of a stable emulsion by the intimate mixing of two or more immiscible liquids, so that one (the dispersed phase) is formed into very small droplets within the second (the continuous phase)
- Homogenization is the reduction in size (to 0.5–30 μm), and hence the increase in number, of solid or liquid particles in the dispersed phase by the application of intense shearing forces
- The two types of liquid–liquid emulsions are: 1. Oil in water (o/w) (for example, milk) 2. Water in oil (w/o) (for example margarine)
- Naturally occurring proteins and phospholipids act as emulsifying agents, but in food processing synthetic agents (including esters of glycerol or sorbitan esters of fatty acids) are more effective and these are normally used
- Synthetic emulsifying agents are classified into polar and non-polar types. Those that contain mostly polar groups bind to water and therefore produce o/w emulsions. Non-polar agents are adsorbed to oils to produce w/o emulsions. They are characterized by their hydrophile - lipophile balance (HLB) value
- Agents with low HLB values (below 9) are lipophilic and used for w/o emulsions; those with HLB values between 8 and 11 are intermediate and used as wetting agents; and those with high values (11 to 20) are hydrophilic and are used for o/w emulsions, detergents and solubilizers
- Cream is an o/w emulsion that is mechanically agitated (churned) to cause a partial breakdown of the emulsion when it is made into butter

- Margarine and low-fat spreads are w/o emulsions. They are produced from a blend of oils, which is heated with a solution of skim milk, salt, added vitamins and emulsifying agents
- Cake batters are similarly o/w emulsions, in which the continuous phase is colloidal starch, a solution of sugar and flavours, and a foam produced during mixing
- Commercial ice creams usually have a softer texture than home-made products due to faster freezing, which produces smaller (40– 50μ) ice crystals , the overrun, and emulsifiers (e.g. Esters of mono- and diglycerides) and stabilisers (e.g., alginates, carrageenan, gums or gelatin)
- Mixing (or blending) is a unit operation in which a uniform mixture is obtained from two or more components, by dispersing one within the other(s)
- Filtration is the removal of insoluble solids from a suspension (or 'feed slurry') by passing it through a porous material (or 'filter medium')
- Expression are in the extraction of components plant materials either for direct consumption (for example, fruit juices) or for use in subsequent processing (for example sugar, grape juice for wine, and vegetable oils)
- Reverse osmosis (RO) (or 'hyperfiltration') and ultrafiltration (UF) are both unit operations in which water and some solutes in a solution are selectively removed through a semi-permeable membrane
- Reverse osmosis is used to separate water from low-molecular-weight solutes (for example salts, monosaccharides and aroma compounds), which have a high osmotic pressure
- The largest commercial food application of reverse osmosis is the concentration of whey from cheese manufacture, either as a pre-concentration stage prior to drying or for use in the manufacture of ice cream
- A-amylases randomly hydrolyse α –(1- >4) linkages to liquefy starch and produce maltose
- Glucoamylase (or amyloglucosidase) is a saccharifying enzyme which removes successive glucose units from the non-reducing ends of starch molecules by rapid cleavage of the 1,4- α -linkages and slower cleavage of the α-1,6-linkages
- Invertase hydrolyses sucrose to glucose and fructose. It is used to remove sucrose from foods, to prevent crystallisation in molasses, and in the production of invert sugar, confectionery, liquers and frozen desserts
- Lactase (β-d-galactosidase) hydrolyses lactose to D-glucose and D-galactose. It is used to prevent lactose crystallisation in ice cream and frozen milk concentrates, in starter cultures for cheese, and to prepare foods for those suffering from lactose intolerance
- Glucose isomerase is used for the production of high-fructose corn syrup (hfcs) sweeteners from glucose

- Two products are widely used as an alternative to sucrose in the bakery and confectionery industries. HFCs-42 and HFCS-55, containing respectively 42% and 55% fructose (dry weight basis)
- The degree of hydrolysis of starch is measured by the dextrose equivalent (DE).
- Maltodextrin (DE 15-25) is valuable for its rheological properties and is used as fillers, stabilisers, thickeners and pastes in a wide variety of foods
- Cyclodextrins are molecules containing 6–8 glucose units, linked together in a ring. They can bind other molecules in their cavities and therefore stabilize, solubilize or precipitate other compounds.
- Cyclodextrins are used to encapsulate flavours and aromas. Produced from starch using the enzyme cyclodextrin glycosyl transferase (cgt-ase)
- There are three types of pectic enzymes: pectin esterase, polygalacturonase and pectin lyase
- Commercially the endo-polygalacturonase is more useful as it produces more rapid depolymerisation of pectin molecules
- Acid proteases are produced mostly by fungi, and neutral and alkaline proteases are produced by both fungi and bacteria
- Bromelain is a mixture of proteases which hydrolyse plant and animal proteins to amino acids and peptides. It is used to: tenderise meat, improve the handling of pizza doughs, chill proof beer, produce waffles, pancakes and wafers
- Rennet partially coagulates milk proteins to form casein curds in cheese production
- Chymosin was the first enzyme to become commercially available from genetically engineered *Kluyveromyces lactis* and *Escherichia coli*
- Lipases hydrolyse fats and fatty acid esters to form diglycerides and monoglycerides
- Diacetyl reductase converts the flavour compound diacetyl to flavourless acetoin to improve the flavour in beer
- Joint FAO/IAEA/WHO Expert Committee on the Wholesomeness of Irradiated Food (JECFI) who concluded that the maximum average dose of 10 kgy 'presents no toxicological hazard and no special nutritional or microbiological problems in foods'
- Cobalt-60 (60Co) or caesium-137 (137Cs) is used in most commercial plants. 60Co emits γ - rays at two wavelengths which have energies of 1.17 mev and 1.33 mev respectively
- Sterilization (or 'radappertisation')
- Reduction of pathogens (or 'radicidation')
- Prolonging shelf life (or 'radurisation')

- A dose of 48 kgy is needed for a 12D reduction of *Clostridium botulinum*
- Fresh poultry carcasses irradiated with a dose of 2.5 kgy are virtually free of *Salmonella spp*. And the shelf life is doubled when the product is held below 5°C
- Low doses, below 1 kgy, are effective for disinfestation and also extend the shelf life by delaying ripening
- Electron spin resonance (ESR) spectroscopy detects radicals produced by irradiation, which are stable in solid or dry components of foods
- The origin of High Intensity Pulsed Electric Field (HIPEF) processing is the 'electropure' process. When an electric field with a strength in the range of 12–35 kv cm^{-1} is applied to a liquid food in a short pulse (1–100 μs) pores formed in cell membranes cause swelling and rupturing of the cells
- In High pressure processing When high pressures, up to 1000 mpa (10 000 bar), are applied to packages of food that are submerged in a liquid, the pressure is distributed instantly and uniformly throughout the food (i.e. It is 'isostatic'). The high pressure causes destruction of microorganisms
- High pressure processing has no 'heating' or 'cooling' periods, and there are rapid pressurisation/de-pressurisation cycles, thus reducing processing times compared to thermal processing
- Pulsed light contains a broad spectrum of 'white' light, from UV wavelengths of 200 nm to infra-red wavelengths of 1000 nm with peak emissions between 400–500 nm. When applied to foods, the shelf life of bread, cakes, pizza and bagels, packaged in clear film, was extended to eleven days at room temperature after treatment by pulsed light
- Pulsed light has a similar spectrum to sunlight, except that it also contains some UV wavelengths that are filtered out of sunlight by the earth's atmosphere
- Ultrasound waves are similar to sound waves but have a frequency that is above 16 khz and cannot be detected by the human ear
- When ultrasonic waves hit the surface of a material, they generate a force. If the force is perpendicular to the surface, it results in a compression wave that moves through the food, whereas if the force is parallel to the surface it produces a shearing wave
- Ultrasound produces very rapid localized changes in pressure and temperature that cause shear disruption, 'cavitation' (creation of bubbles in liquid foods), thinning of cell membranes, localized heating and free radical production, which have a lethal effect on micro-organisms
- The shearing and compression effects of ultrasound cause denaturation of proteins that result in reduced enzyme activity
- Two heat-resistant enzymes which are found in most vegetables are catalase and peroxidase. Although they do not cause deterioration during storage, they are used as marker enzymes to determine the success of blanching.

- Blanching reduces the numbers of contaminating micro-organisms on the surface of foods and hence assists in subsequent preservation operations
- Blanching also softens vegetable tissues to facilitate filling into containers and removes air from intercellular spaces which increases the density of food and assists in the formation of a head-space vacuum in cans
- Sodium carbonate (0.125% w/w) or calcium oxide are often added to blancher water to protect chlorophyll and to retain the colour of green vegetables, although the increase in ph may increase losses of ascorbic acid
- Enzymic browning of cut apples and potatoes is prevented by holding the food in dilute (2% w/w) brine prior to blanching
- Calcium chloride (1–2%) is therefore added to blancher water to form insoluble calcium pectate complexes and thus to maintain firmness in the tissues
- In fruit juices, losses of vitamin C and carotene are minimised by deaeration
- In low-acid foods ($p^H > 4.5$), the heat resistant, spore forming micro-organism, *Clostridium botulinum* is the most dangerous pathogen
- Under anaerobic conditions inside a sealed container it can grow to produce a powerful exotoxin, botulin, which is sufficiently potent to be 65% fatal to humans
- *Clostridium botulinum* is ubiquitous in soil and it is therefore likely to be found in small numbers on any raw material that has contact with soil
- The level of survival is determined by the type of micro-organism that is expected to contaminate the raw material
- A 12D process is used when *Clostridium botulinum* is likely to be present in low acid foods
- Evaporation, or concentration by boiling, is the partial removal of water from liquid foods by boiling off water vapour
- Evaporation is used to pre-concentrate foods (for example fruit juice, milk and coffee) prior to drying, freezing or sterilization and hence to reduce their weight and volume
- Extrusion is a process which combines several unit operations including mixing, cooking, kneading, shearing, shaping and forming
- Extrusion cooking is a high-temperature short-time (HTST) process which reduces microbial contamination and inactivates enzymes
- Dehydration (or drying) is defined as 'the application of heat under controlled conditions to remove the majority of the water normally present in a food by evaporation'
- The main purpose of dehydration is to extend the shelf life of foods by a reduction in water activity

- Bin driers are large, cylindrical or rectangular containers fitted with a mesh base. Hot air passes up through a bed of food at relatively low velocities (for example 0.5 m s^{-1} per square metre of bin area)
- Cabinet driers (tray driers) consist of an insulated cabinet fitted with shallow mesh or perforated trays, each of which contains a thin (2–6 cm deep) layer of food. Hot air is blown at 0.5–5ms^{-1}
- In Tunnel driers Layers of food are dried on trays, which are stacked on trucks programmed to move semicontinuously through an insulated tunnel, having one or more types of air flow
- Typically a 20 m tunnel contains 12–15 trucks with a total capacity of 5000 kg of food.
- Tunnel drying widely used, especially in the USA
- Conveyor driers (belt driers) are 20 m long and 3 m wide. Food is dried on a mesh belt in beds 5–15 cm deep. The air flow is initially directed upwards through the bed of food and then downwards in later stages to prevent dried food from blowing out of the bed
- The main features of a fluidized - bed drier are a distributor to evenly distribute the air at a uniform velocity around the bed of material
- Fluidized - bed drier are used for small, particulate foods that are capable of being fluidized without excessive mechanical damage, including yeast, desiccated coconut, grain, herbs, instant coffee, sugar and tea
- Kiln driers are two-storey buildings in which a drying room with a slatted floor is located above a furnace. Hot air and the products of combustion from the furnace pass through a bed of food up to 20 cm deep
- Kiln driers are used traditionally for drying apple rings in the USA and hops in Europe
- Pneumatic driers are used for moist powders or particulate foods, usually less than 40% moisture and particle size ranges of 10–500 μm, are metered into metal ducting and suspended in hot air
- In Rotary driers, slightly inclined (up to 5°) rotating metal cylinder is fitted internally with flights to cause the food to cascade through a stream of parallel or counter-current hot air as it moves through the drier
- In Spray driers, A fine dispersion of pre-concentrated food (40–60% moisture) is first 'atomized' to form fine droplets and then sprayed into a co- or counter-current flow of heated air at 150–300°C in a large drying chamber
- Sun drying (without drying equipment) is the most widely practised agricultural processing operation in the world; more than 250 000 000 t of fruits and grains are dried by solar energy per annum
- Both solar and sun drying are simple inexpensive technologies, in terms of both capital input and operating costs

- Drum drying is used to produce potato flakes, pre-cooked cereals, molasses, some dried soups and fruit purees, and whey or distillers' solubles for animal feed formulations
- Maillard browning reactions between sugars and amino acids
- The characteristic golden brown colour associated with baked foods is due to Maillard reactions
- Caramelisation of sugars and dextrins (either present in the food or produced by hydrolysis of starches) to furfural and hydroxymethyl furfural, carbonisation of sugars, fats and proteins
- The high temperatures and low moisture contents in the surface layers also cause caramelisation of sugars and oxidation of fatty acids to aldehydes, lactones, ketones, alcohols and esters
- Amino acid proline can produce aromas of potato, mushroom or burnt egg, when heated with different sugars and at different temperatures
- Shallow (or contact) frying method is most suited to foods which have a large surface-area-to-volume ratio (for example bacon slices, eggs, burgers and other types of pattie)
- Volatile decomposition products (VDP) have a lower molecular weight than the oil and are lost in vapour from the frier
- Non-volatile decomposition products (NVDP) are formed by oxidation and polymerisation of the oil and form sediments on the sides and at the base of the frier
- Oxidation of fat-soluble vitamins in the oil results in a loss of nutritional value
- Retinol, carotenoids and tocopherols are each destroyed and contribute to the changes in flavour and colour of the oil
- In frying operations 17% loss of available lysin in fried fish, although this increased to 25% when thermally damaged oil was used
- Shallow-fried liver lost 15% thiamin and no folate
- Vitamin C losses in fried potatoes are reported to be lower than in boiling
- Dielectric and ohmic heating are used to preserve foods
- Infrared radiation is mostly used to alter the eating qualities by changing the surface colour, flavour and aroma
- Dielectric energy induces molecular friction in water molecules to produce heat,
- Ohmic heating is due to the electrical resistance of a food causes the power to be translated directly into heat. Also termed 'resistance heating' or 'electroheating'
- Infrared energy is simply absorbed and converted to heat

- Tempering is widely used for meat and fish products, which are more easily boned or ground at a temperature just below the freezing point, and for butter and other edible fats.
- If foods are tempered but not allowed to melt, the lower energy cost gives a good return on investment in dielectric equipment
- Chilling is the unit operation in which the temperature of a food is reduced to between -1°c and 8°c
- Chilled foods are grouped into three categories according to their storage temperature
    1. 1°C to + 1°C (fresh fish, meats, sausages and ground meats, smoked meats and breaded fish)
    2. 0°C to + 5°C (pasteurized canned meat, milk, cream, yoghurt, prepared salads, sandwiches, baked goods, fresh pasta, fresh soups and sauces, pizzas, pastries and unbaked dough)
    3. 0°C to + 8°C (fully cooked meats and fish pies, cooked or uncooked cured meats, butter, margarine, hard cheese, cooked rice, fruit juices and soft fruits)
- A cryogen is a refrigerant that changes phase by absorbing latent heat to cool the food.
- Cryogenic chillers use solid carbon dioxide, liquid carbon dioxide or liquid nitrogen.
- Solid carbon dioxide removes latent heat of sublimation (352 kJ kg^{-1} at - 78°C), and liquid cryogens remove latent heat of vaporization (358 kJ kg^{-1} at -196°C for liquid nitrogen; liquid carbon dioxide has a similar latent heat to the solid)
- Lipid oxidation is one of the main causes of quality loss in cook–chilled products, and cooked meats in particular rapidly develop an oxidised flavour termed 'warmed-over flavour' (WOF)
- Modified-atmosphere storage (MAS) and packaging (MAP) are the use of gases to replace air around non-respiring foods without further controls after storage or packing
- In controlled-atmosphere storage (CAS) and packaging (CAP), the composition of gas around respiring foods is monitored and constantly controlled
- In commercial operation, controlled atmosphere storage (CAS) and modified-atmosphere storage (MAS) are mostly used with apples and smaller quantities of pears and cabbage
- Modified atmosphere packaging (MAP) is used for fresh foods and an increasing number of mildly processed food

- Examples of MAP products include raw or cooked meats, poultry, fish, seafood, vegetables, fresh pasta, cheese, bakery products, sandwiches, sous vide foods, potato crisps, coffee and tea
- The normal composition of air is 78% nitrogen and 21% oxygen, with the balance made up of carbon dioxide (0.035%), other gases and water vapour
- CO_2 inhibits microbial activity in two ways: it dissolves in water in the food to form mild carbonic acid and thus lowers the pH of the product; and it has negative effects on enzymic and biochemical activities in cells of both foods and micro-organisms
- In MAS, the store is made airtight, and respiratory activity of fresh foods is allowed to change the atmosphere as oxygen is used up and CO_2 is produced
- In CAS, the concentrations of oxygen, carbon dioxide and sometimes ethylene (ethene) are monitored and regulated
- Oxygen is used in MAP to maintain the red colour of oxymyoglobin in unprocessed meats
- Shelf life of fresh red meat is extended from 3 days to 7 days at 0–2°C by packaging in an 80% O_2 / 20% CO_2 atmosphere, but this may cause problems of oxidative rancidity in fatty fish or development of off - colours in cured meats
- Spraying bread with 1% ethanol doubles the ambient shelf life, by retarding mould growth and an apparent inhibition of staling
- Active packaging systems (also termed 'intelligent' packaging or 'smart films') is a significant new area of MAP technology
- Ethylene scavengers – these are sachets of silica gel containing potassium permanganate, which oxidises ethylene to slow the ripening of fruits
- Oxygen scavengers to create low-oxygen atmospheres or slow the oxidation of lipids and films that scavenge off - odours or carbon dioxide
- Zeolite films to inactivate micro-organisms on food surfaces and sachets and films that release microbial inhibitors
- Ethanol has anti-microbial properties, especially against moulds, and ethanol generators have been used to increase the shelf life of baked products, cheeses and semi-dried fish
- Freezing is the unit operation in which the temperature of a food is reduced below its freezing point and a proportion of the water undergoes a change in state to form ice crystals
- Nucleation therefore precedes ice crystal formation. There are two types of nucleation
    1. Homogeneous nucleation (the chance orientation and combination of water molecules)

2. Heterogeneous nucleation (the formation of a nucleus around suspended particles or at a cell wall). Heterogeneous nucleation is more likely to occur in foods and takes place during supercooling

- High storage temperatures (between -4°C and -10°C) have a greater lethal effect on micro-organisms than do lower temperatures (between -15°C and -30°C)
- At normal frozen storage temperatures (-18°C), there is a slow loss of quality owing to both chemical changes and, in some foods, enzymic activity
- Main changes to frozen foods during storage are that chloroplasts and chromoplasts are broken down and chlorophyll is slowly degraded to brown pheophytin even in blanched vegetables. In fruits, changes in pH due to precipitation of salts in concentrated solutions change the colour of anthocyanins. Water-soluble vitamins (for example vitamin C and pantothenic acid) are lost at sub-freezing temperatures
- Physical changes to ice crystals (for example, changes in their shape, size or orientation) are collectively known as recrystallisation and are an important cause of quality loss in some foods
- Isomass recrystallisation - Change in surface shape or internal structure, usually resulting in a lower surface-area-to-volume ratio
- Accretive recrystallisation - Two adjacent ice crystals join together to form a larger crystal and cause an overall reduction in the number of crystals in the food
- Migratory recrystallisation - Increase in the average size and a reduction in the average number of crystals, caused by the growth of larger crystals at the expense of smaller crystals
- Migratory recrystallisation is the most important in most foods and is largely caused by fluctuations in the storage temperature
- Three main methods of coating foods: 1. Enrobing with chocolate, compound coatings, glazes, or batters 2. Dusting with spices, breadcrumbs, flour, sugar, flavourings, colourings, salt, etc. 3. Pan coating with sugar or sugarless coatings
- 'Packaging is a means of achieving safe delivery of products in sound condition to the final user at a minimum cost'
- Unit pack – Primary pack or consumer pack
- Intermediate pack – Secondary pack
- Bulk pack – Master pack, Distribution pack, Transport pack
- Flexible packaging – Aluminium, Aluminium foil, Paper, Paper board, Plastic
- Rigid packaging - Metal can, Corrugated fibreboard, Glass container
- Semi-rigid packaging - Folding carton, Line carton, Aseptic carton

- Rigid packaging material – glass
  1. Type I – Borosilicate glass
  2. Type II – Coated with sulphur
  3. Type III – Soda lime glass
- Wooden shipping containers have traditionally been used for a range of solid and liquid foods, including fruits, vegetables, tea, wines, spirits, and beers
- Three-piece 'sanitary' cans, consisting of a can body and two end pieces, are used to hermetically seal heat-sterilised food and also to package powders, syrups and cooking oils
- Glass jars and bottles are made by heating a mixture of sand (73%), the main constituent being silica (99% SiO_2), broken glass or 'cullet' (15–30% of total weight), soda ash (Na_2CO_3) and limestone ($CaCO_3$) to a temperature of 1350–1600°C
- Oriented polypropylene (OPP) is a clear glossy film with good optical properties and a high tensile strength and puncture resistance
- Biaxially oriented polypropylene (BOPP) has similar properties to oriented polypropylene but is much stronger
- PP and OPP are used for bottles, jars, crisp packets, biscuit wrappers and boil-in-bag films among many other applications
- Coextrusion is the simultaneous extrusion of two or more layers of different polymers to form a single film
- Kraft paper is a strong paper which is used for 25–50 kg multi-wall sacks for powders, flour, sugar, fruits and vegetables
- Sulphite paper is lighter and weaker than sulphate papers. It is used for grocery bags and sweet wrappers, as an inner liner for biscuits and in laminations
- A polyethylene (PE) molecule is built up by joining together many molecules of the monomer ethylene (C_2H_4)
- Industry commonly divides PE into the following broad categories based on density: HDPE 940–975 kg m^{-3}, MDPE 926–940 kg m^{-3}, LDPE 915–940 kg m^{-3}, LLDPE 915–925 kg m^{-3}, VLDPE 880–915 kg m^{-3}
- Low Density Polyethylene - Excellent barrier to water and water vapor, it is not a good barrier to gases. Used for squeezable food bottles, bread, frozen food packaging and flexible lid
- Linear Low Density Polyethylene – High clarity film produced with LLDPE manufactured with metallocene catalysts is widely used for food packaging films and blow molding of bottles. Largely used in bottle caps and shrink wraps

- VLDPE (sometimes referred to as ultralow density polyethylene or ULDPE)
- VLDPE is mostly used for the packaging of fresh produce, milk, meat, cheese and coffee as well as for the manufacture of multilayer coextruded film
- The most outstanding characteristic of EVOH (Ethylene–Vinyl Alcohol) is its ability to provide a barrier to gases and odors
- Polystyrene – When foamed its generic name is Expandable Polystyrene EPS). This Styrofoam has applications in disposable packaging and drinking cups
- Polyethylene Terephthalate (PET) used in soft drink and single use water bottles
- Polypropylene is used in Yogurt, Cream cheese/ sour cream containers
- High Density polyethylene (HDPE) is semi translucent and highly solvent resistant Found in bottles for storing water, juice or milk, margarine and butter tubs, cereal box liners and retail and grocery bags
- Polypropylene used in baby bottles
- Polyamide/Nylon used in microwave and conventional cooking applications

CHAPTER-10

PUBLIC & OCCUPATIONAL HEALTH & NUTRITION

- Health – State of complete physical, mental and social well – being and not merely an absence of disease or infirmity (WHO 1948)
- Three indicators of Human Development Index – Life Expectancy Index, Education Index, CNI Index
- Universally accepted indicator of the health status of whole population are
  1) Child mortality rate
  2) Under five proportionate Mortality rate
  3) Maternal mortality rate
  4) Disease specific mortality rate
  5) Proportional Mortality rate
- Morbidity Indicators are
  1) Incidence and Prevalence
  2) Notification rate
  3) Attendance rate at the outpatient department, health center
  4) Admission, readmission and discharge rate
  5) Duration of stay in the hospital
  6) Absence from work
- Endemic – Constant presence of disease in a particular geographical area
- Hyperendemic – Disease affects high proportion of the population
- Hypoendemic – Disease affects a moderate proportion of population
- Haloendemic – Every individual in a population is affected
- Epidemic – Unusual occurrence of a disease. Excess of its normally expected frequency of occurrence
- Pandemic – Worldwide – Involve several countries or continents
- Sporadic – Disease occurs in a irregular pattern in a community

- Exotic – Disease imported into a country. Unusual presence of a disease in a country
- Zoonosis – Communicable disease transmitted from a vertebrate animals to man. Eg) Rabies, Bovine Tuberculosis, Plague
- Contagious disease – Transmitted through contact
- Incidence – Number of new cases
- Prevalence – Number of new cases and old cases
- Eradication – Termination of infection from the root cause. Eg) Small pox
- Sullivan's index – Expectation of life free of disability. It is computed by subtracting from the life expectancy from the probable duration of bed disability and inability to perform major activities
- Rotavirus causes viral acute dehydrating diarrhoea
- Public health foundation of India, a public – private initiative was launched in 2006
- Obligate host – All stages of development of organism occurs in same host
- Definitive host – Maturation and sexual stage development of organism occurs in host
- Intermediate host – Larva stage (or asexual stage)
- The nutritional status can be assessed by two methods: 1. Direct and Indirect
- Direct – (a) Anthropometric methods (b) Biochemical methods (c) Clinical methods (d) Dietary procedures
- Indirect - (a) Under-nutrition (b) Specific deficiency (c) Over-nutrition (d) Imbalance among essential nutrients
- Weight - most common anthropometric method
- Nutrition surveys -1. Longitudinal incidence studies 2. Cross-sectional prevalence
- Longitudinal Incidence Studies - General health surveys with special emphasis on nutrition. Generally undertaken on children. Carried out for a period of at least one-year using selected members of families in a community
- Cross-sectional Prevalence Studies - These are also known as point-prevalence surveys. Undertaken in a specified short period of a time
- Protein-Energy Malnutrition (PEM) is one of the largest public health problems
- Marasmus - Greek word meaning 'to waste'. Shrivelling of the body with occasional dehydration, loss of subcutaneous fat, wasting of muscles, and low

body weight and length. Deficiency of all macronutrients – Carbohydrates, Proteins, Fats. Specifically, protein energy malnutrition

- Kwashiorkar - The child is apathetic, anaemic, anorexic, diarrhoeic and oedematous; usually brought to the doctor on account of some infective condition. Also known as edematous malnutrition. Caused by a lack of protein in the diet
- Beriberi - two types of beriberi, dry and wet
- Dry beriberi - Emaciation, generally associated with infection such as TB or dysentery. Polyneuropathy occurs followed by weakness, inability to walk, wrist drop and foot drop
- Wet beriberi - Swelling on the body. Pain and tenderness in the legs and even slight movement causes palpitation, breathlessness, which can later cause acute cardiac failure
- Pellagra - Lack of Niacin (Vitamin B3)
- Pellagra - water-soluble group of B vitamins. Commonly occur in corn eaters since, corn is devoid of niacin as well as tryptophan. Also found in people who consume only jowar as their staple, since, leucine, an amino acid, is found to interfere with niacin metabolism.
- Pellagra is characterised by feeling of unwellness, anorexia, mild gastro-intestinal upsets and nervousness; rashes appear on the skin exposed to the sun
- Pellagra is also known as the 4 D's disease, that is, diarrhoea, dermatitis, dementia, and death
- Scurvy – Lack of Vitamin C
- This diet was devoid of any fresh fruits and vegetables, which are rich in vitamin C
- The typical symptoms of scurvy are weakness, fatigue, and pain in the muscles, bones and joints
- Scurvy- The skin becomes dry, pinpoint haemorrhages appear, followed by black and blue spots on the skin. Wounds take a long time to heal, fractures appear spontaneously: anaemia develops, followed by convulsions, coma and death can occur if untreated
- The Recommended Daily Intake (RDI) of iron for men ranges between 9 mg in diets with high bioavailability to 27 mg, where bioavailability is only 5%. In premenopausal women (aged 19–50), the RDI for iron is 59 mg
- Non-haeme iron - plant foods such as cereals, pulses, legumes, grains, nuts and vegetables, has an absorption rate of 2% to 10% depending upon the balance of iron absorption inhibitors and enhancers in the meal

- Addition of vegetables and fruits containing ascorbic acid can double or triple iron absorption. Each meal should preferably contain at least 25 mg of ascorbic acid
- Rickets - Lack of Vitamin D
- Rickets - Knock-knees and bowed legs are the characteristic symptoms of rickets. The young infant develops teeth late. Bleeding time is longer, and the bones are porous. Adult rickets are also known as osteomalacia
- Goitre is characterized by abnormal growth of the thyroid gland. Protrusion of the eyeballs and low levels of thyroxine. Pregnant women, who suffer from thyroidism can give birth to children who may suffer from cretinism
- Major nutritional problems in India are Protein Energy Malnutrition (PEM), Iodine Deficiency Disorders (IDD), Vitamin A Deficiency Disorder (VAD), and Anaemia
- International Day of Families - 15 May
- World Environment Day- 5 June
- World Breastfeeding Week 1–7 August
- National Nutrition Week 1–7 September
- International Literacy Day - 8 September
- World Food Day - 16 October
- Universal Children's Day - 14 November
- Child Rights Day - 20 November
- International Day of Disabled Persons - 3 December
- International Children's Day of Broadcasting- 13 December
- The Integrated Child Development Services Programme (ICDS) of the Department of Women and Child Development was started in 1975 and has emerged as the world's most unique and largest early childhood development programme
- ICDS provides 6 services - supplementary feeding; immunization against preventable childhood diseases; health checkups and referral; health and nutrition education to adult women; and preschool education to 3- 6 year olds
- Public Distribution System (PDS) has been an important buffer against local food shortages, in many respects it has fallen short of providing food security to the poor
- National Nutritional Anaemia Control Programme aims to reduce anaemia among women of reproductive age and preschool children by providing iron-folate supplements, identifying and treating cases of severe anaemia, and promoting the consumption of iron-rich foods.

- In 1970 the National Prophylaxis Programme Against Nutritional Blindness was initiated as a centrally sponsored scheme. Under this scheme all children between ages of one and three years to be administered 200,000 IU of Vitamin A orally once in six months
- National Iodine Deficiency Disorders Control Programme (NIDDCP) – Implemented to prevent, control and eliminate these disorders and to provide assistance to the states for setting up IDD cell and IDD monitoring lab for ensuring quality control of iodated salt and for monitoring urinary iodine excretion
- Balwadi Nutrition Program – Started in 1970 for the benefit of children aged 3 – 6 years
- Mid – Day Meal program- Launched in 1961. Attract more children for admission to school and retain them so that literacy improvement of children could be brought about
- Mid–Day Meal Scheme – Launched in 1995. Revised in 2004. The main objective is the universalization of primary education by increasing enrolment, retention, and attendance and simultaneously impacting on nutrition of students up to middle level classes
- Mid – Day Meal Scheme also known as the National Program of Nutritional support to Primary Education
- Obesity – Abnormal growth of adipose tissue or an increase in fat cell number. Often expressed in terms of BMI
- BMI = Weight in kilograms/ (height in metres)^2
- Broca index is an estimation of ideal body weight using height measurement only
- BI = Height (cm) - 100
- Human Immunoglobulin- 5 Immunoglobulin – IgG, IgA, IgD, IgM, IgE
- IgG – Only Immunoglobulin can cross the placenta
- IgM – Its presence may be indicative of recent infection
- IgA – Found in body secretions
- Nipah virus infection emerging Zoonotic disease first recognised in large outbreaking Malaysia and Singapore from September 1998 to May 1999
- Fruit Bats Pteropus genus are the natural reservoir of Nipah virus
- Viruses causing Diarrhea – Rota Virus, Astro Virus, Adeno Virus, Calicivirus, Coronavirus, Norwalk Group Viruses, Entero Viruses
- Dracunculiasis- Also known as guinea worm disease
- Coal dust causes Anthracosis disease

- Silica causes Silicosis disease
- Asbestos causes Asbestosis, Cancer lung
- Iron causes Siderosis disease
- Cane fiber – Bagassosis disease
- Cotton dust- Byssinosis
- Tobacco – Tobaccosis
- Hay or grain dust – Farmer's Lung
- Immunization and fortification of food with specific nutrients are an example of primary prevention
- Early diagnosis and primary treatment of the disease are known as Secondary prevention

CHAPTER-11

Agricultural Science

- Post harvest losses varies from 8-10 %
- Insects contribute 2-4 % to post harvest losses
- Stored pests can live without food for several years
- Based on type of grains damaged, storage pests are classified into Primary storage pest and Secondary storage pest
- Primary pests attack the whole grain. The eggs are laid inside the grain, before the larvae mature inside the grain and then chew their way out. Eg:- rice weevil, pulse beetle, Rhyzopertha, Sitotroga, Trogoderma
- Secondary storage pest damage broken or already damaged grains. Eg: Saw toothed grain beetle – *Oryzaephilus surinamensis*, Long-headed flour beetle – *Latheticus oryzae* (Tenebrionidae: Coleoptera), Flat grain beetle – *Cryptolestes minutus* (Cucujidae: Coleoptera)
- Based on position of damage, storage pests are classified into External feeder and internal feeders
- External feeders - Larvae and adults feed on the grain from outside. Attacks whole grain and damage germinal portion. Examples are Red flour beetle, Indian meal moth, Fig moth, Rice moth and Khapra beetle
- Red flour beetle – *Tribolium castaneum* (Tenebrionidae: Coleoptera). Host range – grains, seeds, vegetables powders, dry fruits, oil cakes, nuts, museum specimens like dry insects and stuffed material etc
- Indian meal moth – *Plodia interpunctella* (Pyralidae : Lepidoptera). Host range – grains, dried fruits, etc.
- Fig moth – *Cauda cautella* (Pyralidae: Lepidoptera). Host range – stored grains, cashew, groundnut and wheat
- Rice moth - *Corcyra cephalonica* (Pyralidae: Lepidoptera). Host range: rice but also in other grains like sorghum, maize, gram, groundnut, and also on cotton seeds.

- Khapra beetle – *Trogoderma granarium* (Dermestidae: Coleoptera). Host range – stored wheat, groundnut, pulses, spices, and various cereals
- Internal feeders - Larvae feed entirely within the kernels or stored material. Attacks whole grain and damages germinal portion. Examples are Rice weevil, Lesser grain borer, Sweet potato weevil, Cigaratte or tobacco beetle, Drug store beetle, Pulse beetle, Tamarind beetle, Angoumois grain moth and Potato tuber moth
- Rice weevil - *Sitophilus oryzae* (Curculionidae: Coleoptera) Hosts: Rice (main), Maize and other cereals in storage
- Lesser grain borer / Paddy borer beetle *Rhyzopertha dominica* (Bostrychidae: Coleoptera). Hosts: Stored cereals (main), cassava, cereal products, flours etc.
- Sweet potato weevil – *Cylas formicarius* (Apionidae: Coleoptera)
- Cigaratte or tobacco beetle – *Lasioderma serricorne* (Anobiidae : Coleoptera). Host Range – Tobacco, Ginger, Chillies and Turmeric
- Drug store beetle – *Stegobium paniceum* (Anobiidae: Coleoptera). Host Range – turmeric, coriander, dry vegetable and animal matter
- Pulse beetle- *Callosobruchus chinensis* (Bruchidae: Coleoptera). Host Range – stored cowpea, grams
- Tamarind beetle – *Pachymeres gonagra* (Bruchidae : Coleoptera)
- Angoumois grain moth – *Sitotroga cerealella* (Gelechiidae : Lepidoptera). Host range – ripening grains of paddy, sorghum and finger millet in the standing crop and the grain in storage
- Potato tuber moth – *Pthorimaea operculella* (Gelechiidae: Lepidoptera)
- Spraying 0.05 per cent Malathion emulsion on the floor, walls and ceiling prevents pest infestation
- Fumigants like ethylene dibromide (EDB), ethylene dichloride carbon tetra chloride (EDCT), aluminium phosphide (ALP) to control stored produce pests effectively.
- Grain is generally stored either in bags or in bulk. A combined system of bag-cum-bulk storage is also practiced in some parts of the country
- Types of storage structures for storage of grains are Traditional storage structures, Improved storage structures, Modern storage structures and Farm Silos
- Traditional Storage Structures are Morai type storage structures, Bukhari type storage structures, Kothar type storage structure, Mud Kothi type storage structure, Muda type storage structure, Kanaj type storage structure, Kuthla

type storage structure, Metal/ Steel bin type storage structure and Bag type storage structure

- Improved storage structures are the storage structures for storage of food grains. In this type of storage structures there are some improvements made in traditional storage structures.
- Improved storage structures having a higher storage capacity and long term storage of food grains than traditional storage structures.
- Improved type of storage structures having capacities of 1.5 to 150 tonnes
- Improved storage structures are Pusa bin, Brick and cement bin, Bunker Storage and 'CAP' (cover and plinth) Storage structures
- Pusa bin is like other traditional storage structures made of mud. To make the storage structure moisture proof a plastic film is used in all the inner sides of the bin
- Modern Storage Structures are Silo type of storage structures, Shallow bins, Deep bins and shed
- Farm silos is a farm structure used to store and protect the animal fodder so that it is preserved in an ideal condition for farm animals. There are two types of farm silos i) Tower silos and ii) Horizontal silos
- Rodents are major non insect pests causing damage to various crops/ commodities by feeding and indirect damage by spoilage, contamination during on-farm and post-harvest stages
- House rats: House rat - *Rattus rattus*, House mouse - *Mus musculus*
- Field rats: Lesser bandicoot- *Bandicota bengalensis*, Field mouse- *Mus booduga*, White rat Indian gerbil (*Tatera indica*), Long tailed tree mouse (*Vande-leuria oleracea*), Soft furred field rat (*Millardia meltada*), Bush rat (*Golunda elliotti*)
- Most destructive of all the field rats is *Bandicota bengalensis* (Lesser bandicoot rat)
- Common species of rats found in both field as well as houses: Norway rat / Brown Rat- *Rattus norvegicus*, Large bandicoot rat- *Bandicota indica*
- Large bandicoot rat are largest domestic rat, tail length is almost equal to the body length and it damages all tuber crops
- Major behaviours of rodents are Fossoriality, Nocturnality, Exploration. Thigmotaxis. Neophobia. Bait shyness, Rodenticide resistance
- Most effective rat traps are those, which can completely conceal the rats trapped in it; eg. Moncompu trap

- Automatic traps. eg. wonder trap
- Remote-triggered trap - Work by upsetting a delicate balance when the bait stick is disturbed or when the weight is put on a treadle
- Glue trap - A form of trapping in which a sticky substance entangles the animal.
- Pot traps- These traps are extensively used for catching rice field rats. eg., Moncompu trap
- Snap traps- These are variously called "break back traps", "spring traps", "saw toothed traps" and "bamboo traps" depending upon the materials used in making them
- Acute rodenticides - rodents die within 24 hours after consuming. Eg: - Zinc Phosphide (most common), Barium carbonate, Arsenic trioxide, Thallium sulphate, Alpha Naphthyl Thio Urea, Red squill, Sodium fluoroacetate
- Chronic rodenticides - Slow acting. Eg: Anticoagulants. Eg: Warfarin, Bromadiolone
- First generation anticoagulants - Multiple dose poison and rat need to feed repeatedly for attaining lethal dosage. Eg: warfarin: Dosage : 0.025% Feeding period: 4-28 days (Longer period. Compound such as Fumarin, Difacinone, Chlorofacinone, Coumatetralyl etc (Derivatives of Coumarin and Indanediones)
- Second generation anticoagulants- Single dose. Effective against wide variety of species. Dosages: 0.0025-0.005% a.i. in baits. Bromadiolone ($C_30H_{23}BrO_4$). Best rodenticide known.
- Respiratory poisons (fumigation) – Formulation: Aluminum Phosphide 06 % Tablet. Crop & Non-Crop area field rodents. Dose- One tablet of 12 gm/ burrow.
- Pre-baiting in rodent control is conducted to prevent Bait shyness
- Common predators of rats are the cat, snake, and the owl
- Post harvest management is the branch of horticulture that deals with all operations right from harvesting or even the pre-harvest stages till the commodity reaches the consumer
- Varieties with shorter shelf-lives are generally prone to higher post harvest losses.
- Duration, intensity and quality of light affect the quality of fruits and vegetables at harvest

- Higher temperature during field conditions decreases life and quality of the produce
- Moisture stress increases the rate of transpiration over the rate of absorption and irregular irrigation leads fruits/vegetable cracking
- Higher level of moisture stress affects both yield and quality by decreasing cell enlargement
- Keeping quality of bulb crops like onion and garlic will be poor if irrigation is not stopped before three weeks of harvesting.
- Factors affecting the quality of horticultural produce are Pre-Harvest Factors, Harvest Factors and Post-Harvest Factors
- Storage potential of the fruits is largely dependent on the level of Ca and it is associated with produce texture.
- Physiological disorders of storage related to low Calcium content of the tissue are Bitter pit in apple, Cork spot in pear, Blossom end rot in tomato, Tip burn in lettuce, hollow heart in potato and Red blotch of lemons
- Fruit thinning, training, pruning and Girdling canopy manipulation techniques will help to increase the post harvest quality of the produce
- Application of GA3 @ 50-100 ppm improves PH quality of roses by anthocyanin development.
- Farmer's field, Packaging and Transportation are the different phases/stages of post harvest loss
- Pre harvest application of chemicals like Maleic hydrazide (MH) on onion field prevent them sprouting during storage
- Production of chrysanthemum under green house at 1000 – 2000 ppm of CO_2 showed an increase in stem length, fresh weight, leaf no. and longevity of cut flowers
- Harvesting factors are Stage of harvest, Time of harvest and Method of harvest
- Stages of harvest are: Mango – Tapka stage, Pineapple – Flattening of eyes, Watermelon-Dull sound, Peas- tendrometer, and Onion- the above ground portion dries up or neck fall
- Methods of Harvesting are hand harvesting, mechanical harvesting and mechanical assistance
- Cytokinin (Kinetin, BA), auxin (IAA) and gibberellins (GA3) are will delay senescence of the produce and are known to be ethylene inhibitors
- Corrugated fiberboard containers are commonly used for the packaging of produce

- **Adding value to a raw product by taking it into the next stage of production is called value addition**
- **Sauerkraut is a fermented product produced from Cabbage**

CHAPTER-12

Veterinary Science

- Abattoir - any establishment where specified or food animals are slaughtered & dressed for human consumption
- Rigor mortis - postmortem stiffening of body or irreversible inextensibility. Develops in 4-8 hr- pigs, 7 hr- goat, 8-12 hr- sheep, 8-24 hr- cattle
- Bovine – cattle, buffalo – beef
- Calf (3-9 months) – veal- immature meat of calves
- Meat of hunted animals- deer – venison
- Equine - horse – chevalin
- Porcine - pig – pork
- Caprine - goat – chevon
- Ovine – sheep – mutton
- Offal - all parts of slaughtered animal other than the carcass
- Carcass - dressed body of slaughtered animal after removal of blood, skin/hide, head, tail, feet, viscera, external genitalia in males & udder from females
- Viscera - all organs of thoracic, abdominal & pelvic cavities. Removal of viscera is called evisceration
- In reception area, ramps must be provided for unloading, which having a height of 1.2m & slope 30°
- Space requirement of tied cattle in lairage is 3.3 m^2
- Chilling temperature for offal & carcass is 3°C, 7° C
- Ideal temperature – time combination for pig scalding is 58- 62° C, 6 min
- Overall height of building should be 6m at the point of cattle bleeding
- Connecting area between lairage & stunning pen is race
- Resting place for animals before slaughter – lairage
- Nitrite - beneficial for stabilizing lean colour, for characteristic cured meat flavour, for retarding bacterial spoilage & for retarding rancidity

- Gamma rays have short wavelength - extensive use in food irradiation
- Sodium benzoate was the first chemical approved by FDA of USA as GRAS (Generally Regarded As Safe)
- Botulism is a life-threatening disease caused by the ingestion of a potent neurotoxin produced during growth of the *C. botulinum* bacteria
- *C. botulinum* produces seven different types of neurotoxins designated by the letters A through G; only types A, B, E, and F cause illness in humans
- First symptoms of botulism are nausea, vomiting, weakness, and vertigo (dizziness). These are followed by neurological symptoms: visual impairments (blurred or double vision), loss of normal throat and mouth functions (difficulty speaking and swallowing; dry mouth, throat, and tongue; and sore throat), general fatigue, lack of muscle coordination, and difficulty in breathing.
- Phenol found in smoke having bacteriostatic & antioxidant properties
- Meat curing is a method of preserving and flavoring a wide variety of proteins with salt and other flavorings and preservatives
- 2 – 2.5 % of salt generally preferred by consumers for meat curing
- **Bacon**: this fatty cured meat typically features pork belly injected with a salty brine via the wet-curing method. Always cook bacon before consumption
- **Bologna**: this common sandwich ingredient typically consists of emulsified cured pork or cured beef, stuffed into a casing, cooked, and smoked
- **Salami**: Salami is a type of salumi (Italian cured pork product) that takes the shape of a dry-cured sausage. Sopressata and Genoa salami are two popular salami varieties
- Controlled atmosphere packaging (CAP) - more regulated packaging in which gas composition in packet is maintained at a specific level throughout the storage period
- Proteolytic enzyme responsible for conditioning of meat is cathepsin
- Co-extrusion is the process of combining materials of different layers for packaging
- Maillard reaction is the non enzymatic reaction can form brown compounds & bitter taste to meat during ageing
- Standards for organic production are notified in national program for organic production (NPOP)
- Transgenic animals are obtained through genetic engineering technology
- In 2009, the FDA approved Atryn - 1st medicine produced using genetically engineered animal

- Atryn- brand name of anticoagulant antithrombin This protein with anticoagulant & anti inflammatory properties is produced in milk of goats that have been genetically modified
- In 2015, FDA of USA approved aqua advantage salmon for commercial production, sale & consumption
- Tests to detect quality of meat are copper sulphate test for staleness, peroxide test for freshness, nitrazine yellow test for pH, malachite green test for bleeding efficiency, Remington fowrie test for jaundice
- General appearance of meat are chevon - light red, mutton light/dark red, beef red, pork light red, chevalin - dark red bluish tinge and poultry - white
- Fat percentage is beef – 2.6%, buffalo – 0.9%, mutton – 13.3%, pork – 4.4%, chevon – 3.6%
- Amount of myoglobin found in chevalin is 0.7 %
- Subcutaneous fat deposition with intramuscular fat found in pork meat
- Goaty odour as in chevon
- Ammonical odour as in mutton
- Urine like odour as in pork
- Dead animals if slaughtered and flayed they are called as cold slaughtered
- Meat borne bacterial diseases are brucellosis, anthrax, erysipelas, listeriosis, leptospirosis, streptococcal meningitis, streptococcal skin infection, salmonellosis, tuberculosis and tularemia tetanus
- Meat borne viral disease is contagious pustular dermatitis (CPD)
- Meat borne parasitic disease are taeniasis - tapeworm – taenia, trichinosis, echinococcus/ hydatidosis, toxoplasmosis and sarcocystosis
- Meat borne fungal & rickettsial diseases are avian prittacosis / parrot fever, Q fever / abattoir fever, and ringworm infection
- Diseases of other origin - bovine spongiform encephalopathy (bse) prion- mad cow disease, sheep & goat – scrapie - transmissible spongiform encephalopathy (tse), human - cruzefeldt jacob disease (cjd)
- *Leptospira interrogans* - haemorrhagic jaundice
- *Listeria monocytogenes* – meningitis, meningoencephalitis, and bacteremia in susceptible patients, such as immunosuppressed patients, individuals at the extremes of age (neonates and older adults), and pregnant women
- *B. abortus* - cattle, bison
- *Salmonella typhi* - typhoid –human, *Salmonella gallinarum* - fowl typhoid

- *Mycobacterium tuberculosis* – pearle's disease
- *Francisella tularensis*– rabbit fever
- *Clostridium tetani* – lock jaw
- *Taenia solium* - pork tapeworm, *Taenia saginata* - beef tapeworm, *Taenia asiatica* - asian tapeworm
- Helminthic zoonosis - *Trichinella spiralis*
- *Sarcocystis hominis* - cattle, *Sarcocystis suihominis* – pig
- *Chlamydia psittaci* - avian chlamydiosis / ornithosis
- Q fever is a disease caused by the bacteria *Coxiella burnetii*
- *Microsporum canis* (affects cats, dogs, and to a lesser extent large animals)
- *Trichophyton mentagrophytes*, *Trichophyton verrucosum*, and *Trichophyton erinacei* (affects hedgehogs)
- *Microsporum gypseum* (soil organism that causes inflammatory lesions)
- Ornithosis transmitted to human by inhaling dust containing feathers, secretions & droppings from infected birds
- Ram - male adult sheep
- Ewe - female adult sheep
- Lamb - young sheep
- Buck - male adult goat
- Doe - female adult goat
- Boar - adult male pig uncastrated
- Sow - adult female pig
- Cow young one is calf
- Monkey young one is infant
- Fish young one is fry
- Marbling - intramuscular fat can be visibly detected when muscle surface is cut
- Cross sectional area of longissimus dorsi is considered for yield grade in cattle
- The distance between anterior point of pelvic bone to anterior edge of first rib called carcass length
- Palatability grade which reflect proportion of muscle to bone in conformation
- Egg white has 40 different proteins

- In egg, ovalbumin - main protein - 54%, phosphoglycoprotein, storage protein, ovoglobulin - excellent foaming agent, ovomucin responsible for jelly like character, lysozyme - 3.5%, antibacterial, avidin - 0.05%, it binds biotin & makes the vitamin unavailable to system
- Thickening agent - coagulation property of egg
- Phospholipids, lecithin & certain proteins in egg act as an excellent emulsifying agent – myonnaise
- Evaluation of quality of egg – candling, floating in water / water test, sensory test, white index, yolk index, haugh unit (HU)
- Haugh unit (HU) - good quality egg - 72 & above
- Yolk index – range - 0.35 - 0.45
- White index – rage - 0.08 - 0.1
- Preservation of egg by wet immersion methods are lime sealing method, water glass method
- Preservation of egg by dry methods are oiling, gaseous atmosphere, thermostabilization / heat treatment method
- Egg white contain traces of glucose & galactose which react with egg protein leading to maillard browning, this discolours the dried egg white
- Browning can be prevented by removing glucose, this is called desugaring
- Smoothing agent is the functional property of egg which inhibit formation of sugar crystals in candies
- Packaging material made up of wood pulp mould, can stacked one on top of other & placed in boxes ready for transport are filler tray
- Screw shaped egg white strand which hold yolk in centre of egg is chalaza
- In pigs, acute stress leads to a condition in which ultimate pH become low, higher drip & cooking loss called Pale, soft, exudative meat
- Ante mortem inspection- inspection of live animals or birds by a qualified veterinarian - to produce wholesome meat to the consumer
- Post mortem examination - systematic examination of dressed carcasses & their organs (blood) in hygienic manner immediately after slaughter in presence of adequate amount of light -by meat inspector
- Ostertag - father of meat inspection
- Dry ageing - traditional process of placing an entire carcass or wholesale cut (without covering or packaging) in a refrigerated room for 21 to 28 days
- Wet ageing - ageing of meat in vacuum bags under refrigerated conditions of 32-34°F

- **Significant changes in meat during ageing - protein denaturation, proteolysis and flavour enhancement**

CHAPTER-13

Dairy Science

- World Milk Day 1 June
- Every year, National Milk Day is celebrated on November 26
- Father of white revolution - Verghese Kurien (Indian Dairy Engineer and social entrepreneur)
- Operation flood launched in 1970. Operation Flood has helped dairy farmers direct their own development, placing control of the resources they create in their own hands.
- Prevention of Food Adulteration Act, 1954
- FSSAI Milk & Milk Product Order (MMPO) 1992
- Total urea content in milk shall not be more than 700 ppm
- Total sodium content in the milk shall not be more than 650mg/100 g SNF
- Specific gravity of Cow Milk = 1.028-1.030
- Instruments used for testing specific gravity are Hydrometer/ Lactometer, Pycnometer/ sg bottle, Westphal balance
- International Dairy Federation (IDF) recommends circulation of hot water 85°C for 15 minutes for milk pasteurizer sanitization
- Common sanitizer used in the dairy industry is Peracetic acid
- UV rays are commonly used for dairy plant hygiene
- Butter- Water- in-oil type of an emulsion
- Diacetyl - gives natural flavor to butter
- Methods of preparing ghee are Desi or indigenous method, Direct cream method, Creamery butter method, prestratification method and continuous method
- Milk ranges in colour from yellowish creamy white (cow milk) to creamy white (buffalo milk)
- Skim milk has a bluish colour, and whey has a greenish-yellow colour (Riboflavin)
- The sulfhydryl compounds significantly contribute to the cooked flavour of heated milks

- Flavour = smell (odour) + taste
- Casein – Exist as colloidal dispersion αs1-casein, αs2- casein, β- casein and K-casein
- Whey protein - α- Lactalbumin, β- Lactoglobulin, Immunoglobulins and BSA (Bovine Serum Albumin)
- Caseins are phosphoproteins, containing, on average, 0.85 % phosphorus, while the whey proteins contain no phosphorus.
- Methods for the determination of the fat content of milk are Soxhlet, Röse-Gottlieb, Mojonnier, Babcock and Gerber
- The principal sugar of milk is lactose.
- Methods for the determination of the Lactose content of milk are Polarimetry, Oxidation-reduction titration (lane eynon method), Colorimetry, Chromatography and Enzymatically.
- Methylene Blue Reduction Test (MBRT) - To determine bacterial load of milk
- Bactofugation - Removal of microorganisms and spores from milk using centrifugal force.
- Homogenization implies mechanical treatment to break fat globules into smaller size of 2 μm or less
- First milk pasteurization by Dr. Soxhlet- Germany
- Index organism in pasteurization - *Mycobacterium tuberculosis* (TB) and *Coxiella burnetii* (Q fever)
- Uperization (Ultra pasteurization) : In this process milk is heated with a direct steam up to 150°C for a fraction of a second
- Packaging material for Pasteurized milk - LDPE is widely used
- Detergents can be detected in milk by using indicators like bromocresole purple or methylene blue
- Detection of Vanaspati in Ghee (Furfural Test / Bauodouin Test)
- Cotton seed oil in ghee is detected by Halphen's test
- Butyro-Refractometer reading of milk fat is comparatively lower than that of most of the vegetable oils
- The general values for BR reading of milk fat (40–45) and vegetable oils and fats (above 50)
- The presence of buffalo milk in cow milk is tested by the Hansa test
- The organisms capable of fermenting lactose to form lactic acid are known as acid producers.

- Homofermenters: *Lactococcus*, few *Lactobacilli,* Heterofermenters: Few *Lactobacilli, Lueconostoc* spp
- Gas producers- *E.coli*, yeasts, and *Clostridium* spp
- Proteolytic organisms- *Bacillus* spp, *Pseudomonas* spp
- Lipolytic organisms - *Pseudomonas* spp, *Achromobacter lipolyticum*; Molds: *Geotrichum candidum, Penicillium roqueforti*
- Sweet curdling - *B. subtilis, B. cereus,* and *Enterococcus liquefaciens*
- Ropiness - *Alcaligenes viscosus*
- Fruity - *Pseudomonas fragi*
- Malty - *Lactococcus lactis* subsp. Lactis biovar maltigenes
- Fishy - *Proteus icthyosmius*
- Colour fermentations, Yellow - *Pseudomonas synxantha*, Blue - *Pseudomonas cyanogenes*, Green - *Pseudomonas fluorescens*, *Penicillium roqueforti*, Black - *Pseudomonas nigrifaciens*
- LTLT/Batch/Holding- 63°C/30minutes
- HTST (High Temperature Short time pasteurization) - 72°C/15 sec
- Stassanization - 74°C/7 sec. Introduced by Dr. Stassano of Stasbourg. The principle of its operation is heating of milk to the desired temperature by passing it through two water heated pipes, through a narrow space of 0.6 to 0.8 mm.
- Vacuum pasteurization - Pasteurization of cream/milk under reduced pressure
- Chhana or Paneer means the product obtained from any variant of milk, with or without added milk solids, by precipitation with permitted acidulants and heating. Acidulants permitted- lactic acid, citric acid, malic acid, vinegar, glucono delta lactone, sour whey
- Chhana - Used for the preparation of sweets like rasogolla (king of Bengali sweets), rasamalai, sandesh, and pantua
- Fermented dairy products are Dahi/ curd and Misti doi
- Dahi LAB (Lactic Acid Bacteria) culture commonly used @ 1-2% concentration. *L. lactis*, *L. lactis* biovar diacetylactis, *L. lactis* subsp.cremoris
- Yoghurt - a coagulated milk product obtained by lactic acid fermentation through the action of *Streptococcus thermophilus* and *Lactobacillus bulgaricus* (1:1)
- Chakka - Semi solid product- draining whey from dahi. Base material for the production of shrikhand
- Mishti doi/ Mishti dahi - Sweetened concentrated form of dahi. Cosumed in Bengal

- **Danedhar is used as the base material for preparation of kalakand**
- **As per FSSA, the maximum acidity permitted for khoa is 0.9% lactic acid**
- **Flavor producing compound of yoghurt is Acetaldehyde**

Part – 2
Tables for Quick Reference

Tables for Quick Reference

"Even though we face the difficulties of today and tomorrow, I still have a dream"

- Martin Luther King

Table1 : Iodine and Iron content in fortified salt

1) Iodized salt (when fortified with Iodine)
2) Iron fortified iodized Salt (Double Fortified Salt) when fortified with Iron and Iodine Salt shall be fortified with Iodine1 and may also be fortified with iron in combination with iodine, at the level given in the table below

SI .No	Component	Level of nutrients	Source of nutrients
1.	Iodine content		
	(a) Manufacture level (b)Distribution channel including retail level	20-30 parts per million (on dry weight basis) 15-30 parts per million (on dry weight basis)	Potassium Iodate
2.	Iron content (as Fe)	850-1100 parts per million	Ferrous sulphate or Ferrous Fumarate

Table – 2 : Fortified Oil: Vegetable Oil shall be fortified with the following micronutrients

Sl. No.	Nutrient	Level of nutrient	Source
1.	Vitamin A	6 µg RE - 9.9 µg RE per gm of oil	Retinyl acetate or Retinyl palmitate
2	Vitamin D	0.11 µg– 0.16 µg per gm of oil.	*Cholecalciferol or *Ergocalciferol (*Only from Plant Source)

Table 3 : Fortified Milk Toned, double toned, skimmed milk or standardized milk shall be fortified with the following micronutrients

Sl. No.	Nutrients	Level of nutrient per litre of toned/ double toned/skimmed milk/ Standardized Milk	Source of nutrient
1	Vitamin A	270 µg RE - 450 µg	RE Retinyl acetate or Retinyl palmitate

2	Vitamin D	5 µg -7.5 µg	*Cholecalciferol or *Ergocalciferol (*Only from Plant source)

Table 4: Fortified commodities as per FSSAI

Rice	Iron, Folic acid, Vitamin B12
Wheat flour, Maida	Iron, Folic acid, Vitamin B12
Milk	Vitamin A, Vitamin D
Edible oil	Vitamin A, Vitamin D
Salt	Iron, Iodine

Table 5: Difference between Codex and ISO

Codex	ISO
Used to develop national regulations	Voluntary
Slow to change	Standards are reviewed every five years
Describe the minimal acceptable practices	Describe current standard industrial practices

Table 6: Three Examples of colloidal food systems

Dispersed phase	Continuous phase	Name	Example
Liquid	Gas	Fog, mist, aerosol Sprays	(e.g. Spray drying)
Solid	Gas	Smoke, aerosol	Carbon dioxide fog, smoke
Gas	Liquid	Foam	Whipped cream, aeration of fermentation media, hydrogenation of oils (hydrogen in oil)
Liquid	Liquid	Emulsion	Cream, mayonnaise, margarine and low-fat spreads, salad cream, sausage meat and cakes
Solid	Liquid	Sol, colloidal solution, gel suspension	Chocolate drinks, fruit juice
Gas	Solid	Solid foam	Meringue, ice cream

Table 7: Maximum levels of carbon dioxide and minimum levels of oxygen for storage of selected fruits and vegetables

Food	CO_2 (%)	O_2 (%)
Apple (Golden Delicious)	2	2
Asparagus (5°C)	10	10
Avocado	5	3
Banana	5	–
Broccoli	15	1
Cabbage	5	2

Table 8: Advantages and limitations of MAP

Advantages	Limitations
Increased shelf life of 50–400%	Added cost
Extended storage results in reduced economic losses and wider distribution radius	Temperature control required Different gas compositions for each type of product
Fewer distribution deliveries leads to lower costs	Requirement for special equipment and operator training
Little or no need for chemical preservatives	Increased pack volume has impact on transport and retail display costs
Easier separation of sliced foods (except vacuum packing)	Benefits are lost once the pack is opened or leaks
Good presentation of products	Product safety to be established for some foods

Adopted from Davies (1995), Farber (1991) and Blakistone (1998b).

Table 9: Examples of active packaging systems

Method	Variations	Examples of products
Oxygen scavenger	Powdered iron oxide Ferrous carbonate Iron/sulphur Platinum catalyst Glucose-oxidase enzyme Alcohol oxidase enzyme	Cookies, cured meats, pizza crusts, bread, rice cakes
Carbon dioxide scavenger/ emitter	Powdered iron oxide/calcium hydroxide Ferrous carbonate/metal halide	Coffee, fresh meats/fish
Preservative	BHA/BHT (Appendix C) Sorbates Mercurial compounds Zeolite system	Meats, fish, bread, cereals, cheese
Ethanol emitter	Ethanol spray Encapsulated ethanol	Cakes, bread, buns, tarts, fish
Moisture absorber	PVA blanket	Fish, meats, poultry
Temperature or humidity control	Non-woven plastics PET containers Foams	Prepared entre´es, meats, poultry, fish

Adopted From Day (1992)

Table 10: Vitamins & their deficiency diseases

Vitamins	Deficiency diseases
Vitamin A (retinol)	• Night blindness • Bitot's spot • Keratomalacia • Xerophthalmia • Conjunctival xerosis
Vitamin D (1,25 dihydroxycholecalciferol)	• Rickets • Osteomalacia
Vitamin E (tocopherol)	• Nerve & Muscle weakness
Vitamin K	• Prolonged blood clotting time

Vitamin B1 (thiamine)	• Beri beri • Wernicke's encephalopathy
Vitamin B2 (riboflavin)	• Angular stomatitis
Vitamin B3 (niacin)	• Pellegra
Vitamin B5 (pantothenic acid)	• Burning foot syndrome • Paresthesia
Vitamin B6 (pyridoxine)	• Peripheral neuritis
Vitamin B7 (biotin)	• Alopecia(hair loss), skin rashes • Brittle nails
Vitamin B9 (folate or folic acid)	• Macrocytic anemia
Vitamin B12 (cyanocobalamin)	• Pernicious anemia
Vitamin C (ascorbic acid)	• Scurvy

Table 11: Typical operations and the food product

Unit operation	Product
Blanching	Vegetables
Churning	Butter
Conching	Chocolate
Curing	Meat
Degumming	Oil
Malting	Beer
Pearling	Sorghum
Proofing	Bread
Refining	Chocolate
Rolling, Withering	Tea
Smoking	Meat
Winnowing	Cocoa

Table 12: Microorganisms used in different products

Culture used	Function
Top yeast – *Saccharomyces cerevisiae* Bottom yeast – *Saccharomyces carlsbergensis*	Yeasts for malt beverages
Penicillium roqueforti	Blue cheese
Propionibacterium freudenreichii	Swiss cheese to improve flavour and assist eye formation
Candida crusei	Cocoa
Aspergillus oryzae	Soysauce, Miso
Rhizopus oryzae	Tempeh
Aspergillus niger	Citric acid
Leuconostoc mesenteroides	Dextran

Table 13: Important commercial products of yeast

Types of yeast	Product	Uses
Saccharomyces cerevisiae	Beer, Wine, Bread, Baker's yeast	Baking Industry and Brewing Industry
Saccharomyces rouxii	Soy sauce	Food condiment
Saccharomyces cerevisiae	Ethanol	Fuel, Solvent
Erymothecium ashybi	Riboflavin	Vitamin Supplement

Table 14 : Common adulterants used

Food materials	Common Adulterants
Cereals such as wheat and rice	Mud, Grits, Soapstone bits
Dhal	Coal tar dyes, Khesari dhal
Turmeric powder	Lead chromate powder
Dhania powder	Starch, Cow dung or horse dung powder
Milk	Extraction of fat, Addition of starch and water
Ghee	Vanaspati, Mashed potatoes, Sweet potatoes
Butter	Starch, Animal fat
Edible oils	Mineral oil, Argemone oil
Ice-creams	Cellulose, Starch, Non-permitted colours
Fresh green packed peas	Green dye
Mustard seeds	Seeds of prickly poppy, argemone
Black pepper	Dried seeds of papaya
Honey	High fructose syrup, Cane sugar, Jaggery
Sweet wines	Diethylene glycol
Alcoholic liquors	Methanol
Wheat flour	Excessive sand, Dirt, Bran & Chalk powder
Cumin seeds	Grass seeds coloured with charcol dust
Chilly powder	Saw dust, Brick powder
Tea dust/leaves	Black gram husk, Tamarind seeds powder, Saw dust, Used tea dust
Coffee powder	Chicory, Date husk, Tamarind husk
Asafoetida (hing)	Sand, Grit, Resins, Gums, Soap stones

Table 15 : Tests to detect common adulteration

Honey	Aniline chloride test (starch mixed honey turns orange red in colour if mixed aniline chloride)
Ghee	Iodine solution test (boil sample and add a drop of Iodine solution; sample turns blue if starch was mixed; colour disappears if cooled and reappears on heating again
Black pepper	Papaya seeds float on carbon tetra chloride solution while pure black pepper seeds settles down

Coriander powder	Soak in water. Dung will float and can be detected by its fowl smell
Turmeric powder	Dissolve sample in 1:7 sulphuric acid and filter it. Add 1 to 2 drops of 0.1% diphenylcarbazide; A pink colour indicates presence of lead chromate
Asafoetida (Hing)	Shake a small quantity with water. Soapstone or other earthly matter will settle at bottom
Pulses	Heat with diluted HCl on simmer for 15 minutes. Pink colour indicates presence of khesari dhal
Chilly powder	Add sample in a beaker of Chloroform + Carbon tetrachloride. Brick powder will settle at the bottom
Wheat flour	Shake sample with dilute Hydrochloride; effervescence indicates chalk
Cumin seeds (jeera)	Rub the cumin seeds on palms. If palm turns black, adulteration is indicated

Table 16: Major group of chemicals used in food preservation

Preservatives	Maximum use	Organisms affected
Propionic acid/ Propionates	0.32%	Molds
Sorbic acid/ Sorbates	0.2%	Molds
Benzoic acid/ Benzoates	0.1%	Yeast and molds
Parabens	0.1%	Yeast and molds
Dehydroacetic acid	65 ppm	Insects
Sodium nitrite	120 ppm	Clostridia
Caprylic acid	-----	Molds

Table 17: Major types of cheese

Cheese	Types
Soft, Unripened	Cottage, Cream, Mozzarella (Italy)
Soft, ripened	Brie (France), Camembert (France)
Semisoft	Blue Roquefort (France), Brick Muenster (USA), Limburger (Belgium)
Hard, Ripened	Cheddar, Colby (Britain), Swiss (Switzerland)
Very hard, ripened	Parmesan (Italy)

Table 18: Fermented food products

Foods	Raw ingredients	Fermenting microorganisms	Area
Coffee	Coffee beans	*Erwinia dissolvens*	Brazil, Congo
Gari	Cassava	*Coynebacterium manihot*	West africa
Kenkey	Corn	*Aspergillus sp*	Ghana, Nigeria
Kimchi	Cabbage	Lactic acid bacteria	Korea
Miso	Soybeans	*Aspergillus oryzae*	Japan
Ogi	Corn	*Lactobacillus plantarum*	Nigeria
Olives	Green olives	*Leuconostoc mesenteroides*	World wide

Sufu	Soybeans	*Actinimucor elegans*	China
Tao – si	Soybeans	*A. oryzae*	Philippines
Tempeh	Soybeans	*Rhizopus oligosporus*	Indonesia, New guinea, Surnam
Ontjom	Peanut presscake	*Neurospora sitophila*	Indonesia
Peujeum	Cassava	Molds	Indonesia
Pickles	Cucumbers	*Pediococcus cerevisiae*	Worldwide
Poi	Taro roots	Lactic acid bacteria	Hawaii
Sauerkraut	Cabbage	*L. mesenteroides*	Worldwide
Soy sauce	Soybeans	*Aspergillus oryzae*	Japan

Table 19: Fat & SNF of Milk

Product	Fat	SNF
Full cream milk	6%	9%
Standardized milk	4.5%	8.5%
Toned milk	3.0%	8.5%
Double toned milk	1.5%	9%
Skimmed milk	0.5%	8.7%

Table 20: Quantity of sample to be sent to the Food Analyst:- The quantity of sample of food to be sent to the Food Analyst /Director for analysis shall be as specified in the table below

Sr. No	Article of Food	Approximate Quantity to be supplied
1	Milk	500 ml
2	Sterilized Milk / UHT Milk	500 ml
3	Malai / Dahi	200 gms
4	Yoghurt / Sweetened Dahi	500 gms
5	Chhana / Paneer / Khoya / Shrikhand	250 gms
6	Cheese/Cheese spread	200 gms
7	Evaporated Milk/Condensed Milk	200 gms
8	Ice-Cream/Softy/Kulfi/Icecandy/Icelolly	300 gms.
9	Milk Powder/Skimmed Milk Powder	250 gms
10	Infant Food/Weaning Food	500 gms
11	Malt Food/Malted Milk Food	300 gms
12	Butter/Butter Oil/Ghee/Margarine/ Cream/Bakery Shortening	200 gms
13	Vanaspati, Edible Oils/Fats	400 gms
14	Carbonated Water	3 litre
15	Baking Powder	100 gms

16	Arrow root/Sago	250 gms
17	Corn flakes/Macaroni Products/Corn Flour/Custard Powder	200 gms
18	Spices, Condiments and Mixed Masala (Whole)	500 gms
19	Spices, Condiments and Mixed Masala (Powder)	500 gms
20	Nutmeg/Mace	250 gms
21	Asafoetida	100 gms
22	Compounded Asafoetida	150 gms
23	Saffron	20 gms
24	Gur/jaggery, Icing Sugar, Honey, Synthetic Syrup, Bura	250 gms
25	Cane Sugar/Refined Sugar/Cube Sugar, Dextrose, Misri/Dried Glucose Syrup	200 gms
26	Artificial Sweetener	100 gm. Gms
27	Fruit Juice/Fruit Drink/Fruit Squash	1 ltr
28	Tomato Sauce/Ketch up/Tomato Paste, Jam/Jelly/ Marmalade/Tomato Puree/Vegetable Sauce	300 gms
29	Non Fruit Jellies	200 gms
30	Pickles and Chutneys	250 gms
31	Oilseeds / Nuts /Dry Fruits	250 gms
32	Tea/Roasted Coffee/Roasted Chicory	500 gms
33	Instant Tea/Instant Coffee/Instant Coffee-Chicory Mixture	100 gms
34	Sugar Confectionery/Chewing Gum/Bubble Gum	200 gms
35	Chocolates	200 gms
36	Edible Salt	200 gms
37	Iodised Salt/Iron Fortified Salt	200 gms
38	Food Grains and Pulses (Whole and Split)	1 kg
39	Atta/Maida/Suji/Besan/Other Milled Product/ Paushtik Fortified Atta/Maida	500 gms
40	Biscuits and Rusks	200 gms
41	Bread/Cakes/Pasties	250 gms
42	Gelatin.	150 gms
43	Catechu	150 gms
44	Vinegar/Synthetic Vinegar	300 gms
45	Food Colour	25 gms
46	Food colour preparation (Solid/Liquid)	25 gm Solid/100 ml liquid
47	Natural Mineral Water/Packaged Drinking Water	4000ml in three minimum original sealed packs
48	Silver Leafs	2 gm
49	Prepared Food	500 gms
50	Proprietary Food, (Non Standardized Foods)	500 gms

51	Canned Foods	6 sealed cans
52	Food not specified	500 gms

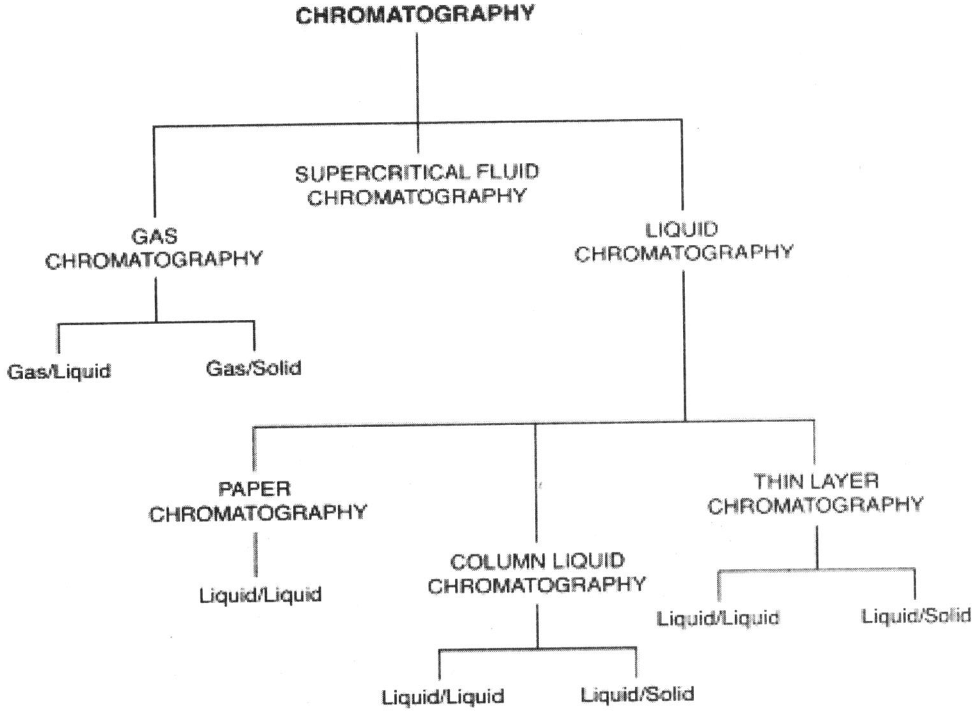

Scheme for subdividing the field of chromatography, according to various applied techniques

Items exempted from the provisions of the Packaged Commodities Rules are packages containing

- The net weight or measure of the commodity in 10 g or 10 ml or less, if sold by weight or measure.
- Fast food items packed by restaurant/hotel scheduled and non-scheduled formulations covered under the Drugs (Price Control) Order,1995
- Agricultural farm produces in packages of above 50 kg

Food Safety and Standards (Prohibition and Restriction on Sales) Regulations, 2011 has prescribed mandatory certification under the BIS Act for the following products

- Infant formula (IS14433)
- Milk cereal based weaning food (IS1656)
- Processed cereal based weaning food (IS11536)
- Follow up formula (IS15757)

- Packaged drinking water (IS14543)
- Packaged mineral water (IS13428)
- Milk Powder (IS1165)
- Skimmed Milk Powder (IS13334)
- Partly Skimmed Milk Powder (IS14542)
- Condensed Milk, Partly Skimmed and Skimmed Condensed Milk (IS1166)

Codex Alimentarius has

- Formulated 237 food standards for commodities
- Formulated 41 codes of hygienic or technological practice
- Evaluated 185 pesticides
- Prescribed limits for pesticide residues developed
- Guidelines for 25 contaminants
- Evaluated 1005 food additives
- and evaluated 54 veterinary drugs

Table 21: Lowest aw Values Permitting Growth of Spoilage Organisms

Group of microorganisms	Minimal aw value
Many bacteria	0.91
Many yeasts	0.88
Many molds	0.80
Halophilic bacteria	0.75
Xerophilic fungi	0.65
Osmophilic yeasts	0.60

Table 22: Bacteria Used as Test Organisms

Bacteria used	Processing of test purpose
Clostridium sporogenes (P.A. 3679)	Inoculated pack studies
*Bacillus subtilis var niger** (syn. *B. globigii*, ATCC 9372)	Hot air and ethylene oxide studies
Bacillus pumilus (ATCC 27142)	Cobalt or gamma radiation sterilization
Bacillus stearothemophilus (ATCC 7953)	Steam sterilization
Bacillus subtilis (ATCC 6633)	Steam sterilization

Table 23: Types of Dryer used for Various Foods, Food by-products, and Wastes

Product	Type of dryer
Vegetables, confectionery, fruits, pectin	Compartment and tunnel tray
Grass, grain, vegetables, fruit, nuts, breakfast cereals	Conveyor band
Grass, grain, apple pomace, lactose, poultry manure, peat, starch(vacuum)	Rotary

Coffee, milk, tea, fruit purees	Spray
Milk, starch, predigested infant foods, soups, brewery and distillery by-products	Film drum
Starch, fruit pulp, distillery waste products, crops	Pneumatic
Coffee, essences, meat extracts, malted and other confectioneries	Freeze dryers and vacuum dryers

Table 24: Different Groups of Food Additives

Groups	Examples
Preservatives	Chemical preservatives
Colors	Natural, Synthetic
Flavors	Nature identical extracts
Sweeteners,	Saccharin, Aspartame, Polyols
Emulsifiers and Stabilizers	Lecithin
Antioxidants	Vitamin E, BHA, BHT
Flour improvers	Vitamin C, Cysteine, Chlorine
Humecants and Anticaking agents	Polyhydroxy alcohols, Calcium silicate
Leavening agents	Baking soda, Ammonium carbonate
Chelating agents	Polycarboxylic acids
Curing agents	Sodium nitrite, Polyphosphates
Nutrient supplements	Thiamine, Nicotinic acid, Iron, Calcium
Processing aids	Acids, Acidity regulators, Gelling agents, Anti-foaming agents

Table 25: Preservatives

Principal preservative	Significance
Sodium chloride	Antimicrobial, dehydrating agent, used as brine
Sugar	Preservation of foods due to the high osmotic pressure
Sulfur dioxide	Prevents the growth of undesirable microbes during wine making, prevents browning of dried and cut fruits
Nitrate and Nitrite	Color stabilizer in the curing of meat and antimicrobial in action
Sorbic acid	Sodium and potassium salts inhibit the growth of moulds and yeast in cheese and bakery products, fruit juices, wines and pickles
Acetic acid	Vinegar (4% acetic acid) is used to preserve pickled vegetables, acetates of sodium, potassium and calcium are used to prevent ropiness and growth of moulds
Propionic acid	Sodium and calcium salts are effective against moulds and some bacteria; Controls *Bacillus mesentericus* causing ropy bread
Benzoic acid	Active agent against yeast and bacteria, well suited for the preservation of acid foods such as fruit juices, carbonated beverages, pickles and sauerkraut

Parabens	Effective inhibitors of molds and yeast, they are alkyl esters of p-hydroxybenzoic acid; Methyl, ethyl, propyl and heptyl esters are used
Epoxides	Antimicrobial cyclic esters, used as preservatives—ethylene oxide and propylene oxide; to reduce load of microbes in spices
Antibiotics	Antimicrobial agents used in the control of bacteria in fish and poultry products; Chlorotetracycline and oxytetracycline
Diethyl pyrocabonate	Used as an antimicrobial agent in fruit juices, wines and carbonated beverages

Table 26: Maximum Levels of Antimicrobials Permitted in Foods (Source: From Code of Federal Regulations, Title 21, various subtitles, compiled January 1986)

Preservative	Concentration allowed
Benzoic acid	0.1%, covered by good manufacturing practices (GMPs)
Methylparaben	0.1%, covered by GMPs
Propylparaben	0.1%, covered by GMPs
Ethylparaben	Not authorized for use
Sodium nitrate	500 ppm
Sodium nitrite	200 ppm
Sorbates	Covered by GMPs
Acetates (acetic acid)	Covered by GMPs with concentrations from 0.25 to 9.0%
Propylene oxide	300 ppm cocoa, gums, starch, spices, processed nutmeats (except peanuts)
Ethylene oxide	Residues not to exceed 50 ppm
Sulfites	Covered by GMPs
Natamycin	200 to 300 ppm as a dip, spray, or solution

Table 27: Conditions of Controlled-atmosphere Storage for Several Fruits and Vegetables

Item	CO_2 %	O_2%
Apples	1.5–10.0	2.5
Lettuce	2.5	2.5
Cabbage	2.5	5.0
Onions	5 –10.0	3.0
Peaches	5.0	0

Table 28: FOOD SAFETY AND STANDARDS (PACKAGING AND LABELLING) REGULATIONS, 2011 (Size of the logo)

Sl No	Area of principal display panel	Minimum size of diameters in mm
1	Upto 100 cms. Square	3

2	Above 100 cms. square upto 500 cms square.	4
3	Above 500 cms square upto 2500 cms square	6
4	Above 2500 cms. Square	8

Table 29: Techniques of Major Interest to the Food Researcher and the Properties they Measure

Techniques	Abbreviation	Property measured
Thermogravimetric analysis	TGA	Weight change
Differential Scanning Calorimetry	DSC	Heat flow
Modulated Temperature DSC	MDSC	Heat flow and heat capacity
Thermomechanical analysis	TMA	Dimensional change
Dynamic mechanical analysis	DMA	Stiffness and energy dissipation
Rheology	Rheometer	Viscosity/flow behavior
Moisture sorption analysis	MSA	Moisture sorption

Table 30: WHO classification of BMI for adult

Classification	BMI
Under weight	<18.50
Normal range	18.50 – 24.99
Overweight	>25.00
Pre obese	25.00-29.99
Obese class I	30.00- 34.99
Obese class II	35.00 – 39.99
Obese class III	>40.00

SFE Applications in Food Products

- Paprika color (oleoresin) extraction from meats and pickles
- Decaffeination of coffee and tea
- Extraction of vegetable oils and fats
- Extraction of herbal medicines Flavors, fragrances, aromas, and perfumes
- Food colors from botanicals
- Antioxidants from plant materials
- Denicotinization of tobacco
- Stabilization of fruit juices
- Hops extraction for bitter
- De-oiling of fast foods
- Essential oil extraction

- Thyme oil extraction from meat and pharmaceutical products

Table 31: Minerals and its deficiencies

Minerals	Deficiencies
Calcium	• Tetany, osteoporosis
Phosphorus	• Neuromuscular, skeletal & renal manifestations
Iron	• Anemia
Copper	• Menke's disease, neutropenia
Zinc	• Poor wound healing, Growth retardation
Iodine	• Endemic goiter, myxedema, cretinism
Fluoride	• Dental caries
Magnesium	• Depression, muscle weakness
Manganese Chromium	• Bone deformities • Glucose intolerance
Selenium	• Liver necrosis
Cobalt	• Pernicious anemia
Molybdenum	• Affects growth, causes mental retardation

Table 32: Total Soluble solids

Tomato paste	25%
Tomato ketchup	25%
Fruit syrup	65%
Fruit jam	65%
Fruit jelly	65%
Fruit cordial	30%
Fruit nectar	15%
Fruit juice	10%
Tomato puree	9%
Grape fruit juice	9%

Table 33: Color coding for all gas cylinders

Oxygen	White shoulder/ black body
Nitrous oxide	Light blue
Medical air	Black and white
Suction	Yellow
Nitrogen	Black
Carbon dioxide	Grey
Helium	Brown

Table 34: Conversion from Celsius (^{0}C) to Farenheit (^{0}F)

The formula is (^{0}C×9/5) + 32 = ^{0}F or (^{0}F – 32) ×5/9 = ^{0}C
Let us convert 37^{0}C to Farenheit 37^{0}C × 9/5 + 32 = 98.6^{0}F
Let us convert 98.6^{0}F to Celsius (98.6^{0}F -32) ×5/9 = 37^{0}C

Table 35: Classification of carbohydrates

Monosaccharides (One sugar molecule)	Aldoses (eg) Glucose, Ribose Ketoses (eg) Fructose, Ribulose
Disaccharides (2 Sugar molecules)	Reducing – Maltose, Lactose, Isomaltose Non reducing – Sucrose
Oligosaccharides (2 – 10 sugar molecules)	Raffinose, Stachyose
Polysaccharides (More than 10 sugar molecules)	Starch, Glycogen, Cellulose

Table 36: Digestive enzymes and its action on carbohydrates

Enzymes	Site of action	Action
Salivary amylase	Mouth	Breaks starch/ Glycogen into partially hydrolyzed dextrins, oligosaccharides, isomaltose, and maltose
Pancreatic amylase	Small intestine	Breaks partially hydrolysed dextrins/oligosaccharides into dextrins, maltose, isomaltose, maltotriose
α- dextrinase	Small intestine	Breaks α – limit dextrins into maltotriose, maltotriose
Disaccharidases	Small intestine	-
Sucrase	Small intestine	Breaks sucrose into glucose and fructose
Lactase	Small intestine	Breaks lactase into glucose and galactose
Maltase	Small intestine	Maltose into glucose
Isomaltase	Small intestine	Isomaltose into glucose

Table 37: Lipids classification

Simple lipids	Compound lipids	Derived lipids
Esters of fatty acids + alcohol	Fatty acids+ alcohol+ amphipathic group	Derived from the hydrolysis of simple and compound lipids
Eg) Fats and oils, waxes	Eg) Phospholipids, Glycolipids, Proteolipids (Lipoproteins)	Eg) Fatty acids, Alcohols (Glycerol, sterols, etc.)

Table 38: Classification of proteins

Simple proteins	Conjugated proteins	Derived proteins
Albumins	Glycoproteins	Primary derived proteins (Denatured or coagulated proteins)
Globulins	Lipoproteins	Secondary derived proteins (by cleavage of the peptide bonds)
Glutelins	Nucleoproteins	
Prolamines	Phosphoproteins	
Sclero-proteins	Metalloproteins	

Table 39: Calorific value of macronutrients per gram

Macronutrients	Kilocalorie (kcal) / gram
Carbohydrates	4
Proteins	4
Fat	9

Table 40: Classification of vitamins

Water soluble vitamins	Fat soluble vitamins
Vitamin C (Ascorbic acid)	Vitamin A (Retinol)
Vitamin B1 (Thiamine)	Vitamin D
Vitamin B2 (Riboflavin)	• D1 – Ergocalciferol • D2 – Cholicalciferol
Vitamin B3 (Niacin)	Vitamin E (Tocoferol)
Vitamin B5 (Pantothenic acid)	Vitamin K (Menadione)
Vitamin B6 (Pyridoxine)	
Vitamin B7 (Biotin)	
Vitamin B9 (Folic acid)	
Vitamin B12 (Cyanocobalamin)	

Table 41: Molecules transported by transport proteins

Transport proteins	Molecules transported
Albumin	Copper, Iron, bilirubin, free fatty acids, Steroids, heme
Transferrin, ferritin, hemosiderin	Iron
Ceruloplasmin	Transport of copper
Haptoglobin, Hemopexin	Free hemoglobin
Thyroid binding globulin	T thyroid hormone
Cortisol binding globulin	Cortisol
Sex hormone binding globulin	Androgens, Estrogens

Table 42: Communicable diseases

Disease	Causative agent	Mode of transmission
Small pox	Variola virus	Respiratory
Chicken pox	Varicella – zoster	Person to person by droplet
Measles (Rubeola)	Myxoviruses	Droplet
Rubella (Germen measles)	RNA virus of toga virus family	Droplet
Mumps	Genus Rubula virus of the family paramyxoviridae	Droplet
Influenza	Type A, Type B, Type C Viruses in the orthomyxoviridae family	Droplet
Diphteria	*Corynebacterium diphtheria*	Droplet
Whooping cough	*Bordetella pertussis*	Droplet and direct contact
Meningococcal meningitidis	*Neisseria meningitides*	Droplet
Severe Acute Respiratory Syndrome (SARS)	New strains of Corona virus	Close contact with patients infected material
Tuberculosis	*Mycobacterium tuberculosis*	Droplet
Poliomyelitis	Polio virus	Fecal – oral route. Less commonly through droplet
Hepatitis A	Hepatitis A virus	Fecal – oral route
Hepatitis B	Hepatitis B virus	Parenteral route, perinatal transmission, sexual transmission
Hepatitis C	Hepatitis C virus	Parenteral transmission
Hepatitis D	Hepatitis D virus	Parenteral transmission
Hepatitis E	Hepatitis E Virus	Waterborne disease(Feco - oral route)
Diarrhea	Virus and bacteria	Fecal – oral route
Cholera	*Vibrio cholera*	Fecally contaminated water, contaminated food, direct contact
Typhoid fever (Enteric fever)	*Salmonella typhi*	Fecal – oral route or Urine – Oral route

Table 43: Organisms causing diarrhea

Viruses	Rota viruses (Most common cause of diarrhea in infants and children) Astro Viruses Adeno viruses Calci viruses Corona viruses Norwalk group viruses Entero viruses

Bacteria	*Campylobacter jejuni* *Escherichia coli* *Shigella* *Salmonella* *Vibrio cholera* *Vibrio parahaemolyticus* *Bacillus cereus*
Others	*Entamoeba histolytica* *Giardia intestinalis* Trichuriasis *Cryptosporidium spp* Intestinal worms

Table 44: Occupational hazard (Diseases due to physical agent)

Physical agent	Disease
Heat	Hyperpyrexia, heat exhaustion, heat syncope, heat cramp, burns
Cold	Trench foot, Frost bite, Chilblains
Light	Occupational cataract, miner's nystagmus
Noise	Occupational deafness
Radiation	Cancer, leukemia, aplastic anemia, pancytopenia
Mechanical factors	Injuries, Accidents
Radiation	Burns

Table 45: Occupational hazard (Diseases due to Chemical agent)

Agent	Disease
Gases	CO2, CO, HCN, CS_2, NH_3, N_2, H_2S, HCl, SO_2, these gases cause poisoning
Coal dust	Anthracosis
Silica	Silicosis
Asbestos	Asbestosis, Cancer lung
Iron	Siderosis
Cane fiber	Bagassosis
Cotton dust	Byssinosis
Tobacco	Tobaccosis
Hay or grain dust	Farmer's lung

Table 46: Classification of protein energy malnutrition

ICMR classification	Gomex classification
Normal – 80% and above	>90% - Normal
Grade I - 70-80%	75 – 89% - 1st degree
Grade II – 60 – 70%	60- 74% - 2nd degree

Table 50: Nutrient claims used on labels

Sugar free	**Less than 0.5g per serving**
Cholesterol free	Less than 2mg cholesterol & 2gram or less of saturated fat per serving
High fibre	5 grams more per serving
Calorie free	Fewer than 5 calories per serving
Fat free	Less than 0.5g of fat per serving
Sodium free	Less than 5 mg per serving

Table 51: Adulterants and their toxic effects

Adulterant	Foods commonly involved	Disease or health effects
Argemone seeds	Mustard seeds	Epidemic dropsy, Glaucoma
Argemone oil	Edible oils and fats	Cardiac arrest
Mineral oil	Edible oils and fats, black pepper	Cancer
Orthotricresyl phosphate	Edible oils and fats	Flaccid paralysis
Lathyrus sativus	Khesari dal, or mixed with other pulses	Lathyrism
Lead chromate	Turmeric whole and powdered, mixed spices	Anaemia, abortion, paralysis, brain damage
Arsenic	Fruits such as apples sprayed with lead arsenate (pesticide)	Dizziness, chills, cramps, paralysis, death
Copper	Acid foods in contact with tarnished copperware	Vomitting, diarrhea, astringent taste in mouth, abdominal pain
Mercury	Mercury fungicide treated seed grains or mercury contaminated fish	Brain damage, paralysis, death
Aflatoxins	*Aspergillus flavus* – contaminated foods such as groundnuts, cottonseed, etc	Liver damage and cancer
Machupo virus	Foods contaminated with rodent's urine. Such as cereals	Bolivian haemorrhagic fever
Gossypol	Cottonseed flour and cake	Cancer
Polychlorinated Biphenyl's	Fatty foods contaminated with PCB's from packaging or processing	Severe ache, eye discharge, Skin darkening, Liver damage, reproduction abnormalities
Nitrates and nitrites	Drinking water, spinach and meat products	Methhaemoglobinaemia, cancer and tumours in the liver, kidney, trachea, Oesophagus and lungs etc.
Pesticide residues	All types of foods	Acute or chronic poisoning with damage to nerves and vital organs like liver, kidney, etc.
Antibiotics	Meats from antibiotic – fed animals	Multiple drug resistance, hardening of arteries, heart disease

Table 52: Consolidated table for Penalties with Monetary fine plus Imprisonment

Section	Offence	Liability	Penalty in rupees (max.)
50	Penalty for selling food not of the nature or substance or quality demanded	Seller If Petty food manufacturer registered as seller too {Sec 31(2)}	5 lakh 25 thousand {Sec 31(2)}
51	Penalty for sub-standard food	Manufacturer / Seller, Distributor / Storage / Importer	5 lakh
52	Penalty for misbranded food	Manufacturer / Seller, Distributor / Storage / Importer	3 lakh
53	Penalty for misleading advertisement	Person who publishes, or is a party to the publication of a misleading advertisement	10 lakh
54	Penalty for food containing extraneous matter	Manufacturer / Seller, Distributor / Storage / Importer	1 lakh
55	Penalty for failure to comply with the directions of Food Safety Officer	FBO or Importer	2 lakh
56	Penalty for unhygienic or unsanitary processing or manufacturing of food	Manufacturer or Processor	1 lakh
57	Penalty for possessing adulterant. If adulterant (i) not injurious to health (ii) injurious to health	Manufacture, sales, distribution or import of any adulterant	i. 2 lakh ii. 10 lakh
58	Penalty for contraventions for which no specific penalty is provided	Any individual / person	2 lakh
59	Punishment for unsafe food. If unsafe food cause no injury, non-grievous injury, grievous injury, death	Manufacturer / Seller, Distributor/ Storage, Importer	(i) 6 Months / 1 lakh (ii) 1 Year / 3 lakh (iii) 6 Years / 5 Lakh (iv) not less than 7 years but extended up to lifetime & fine shall not be less than 10 lakh
60	Punishment for interfering with seized item	Any person	06 months and 2 lakh
61	Punishment for false information	Any person	03 months and 2 lakh
62	Punishment for obstructing or impersonating a Food Safety Officer	Any person	03 months and 1 lakh

63	Punishment for carrying out a business without license	FBO-Manufacturer, Packer, Distributor etc. [Note:-Only Exemption from licensing under sub-section (2) of section 31 of this Act)]	06 months and 5 lakh
64	Punishment for subsequent offences	Any person	(i) twice the punishment as imposed on a first conviction, (ii) fine on daily basis which may extend up to one lakh rupees (iii) cancellation of license
65	Compensation in case injury of death of consumer	FBO-Manufacturer, Packer, Distributor etc	(a) not less than five lakh rupees in case of death; (b) not exceeding three lakh rupees in case of grievous injury; and (c) not exceeding one lakh rupees, in all other case of injury: Also may be, (a) order for cancellation of licence, re-call of food from market, forfeiture of establishment & property in case of grievous injury or death of consumer; (b) issue prohibition orders in other cases
66	Offences by companies	Company and nominated for food safety / or In-charge / or responsible person of company / establishment / branch	Penalty or Punishment accordingly to contravention as per act
67	Penalty for contravention of provisions of this Act in case of import of articles of food to be in addition to penalties provided under any other Act.	FBO / Importer	(1) Any penalty as per Foreign Trade (Development and Regulation) Act, 1992 (22 of 1992) and the Customs Act, 1962 (52 of 1962). (2) Penalty or Punishment accordingly to contravention as per this act (FSS act 2006)

Table 53: Maximum limits of the Aflatoxins in various food conditions as per the regulation

S. No.	Name of the contaminants	Article of food	Limit µg/kg
1	Aflatoxin	All articles of food	30
2	Aflatoxin M1	Milk	0.5
3	Patulin	Apple juice & apple juice ingredients in other beverages	50
4	Ochratoxin A	Wheat, barley & rye	20

Table 54: All the vertical and horizontal SPs (Scientific Panels) are listed below

Horizontal panels	Vertical Panels
❖ Food additives, Flavourings, Processing aids & Materials in contact with food ❖ Pesticide residues ❖ Antibiotic residues ❖ Genetically Modified Organisms and foods ❖ Biological hazards ❖ Contaminants in the food chain ❖ Labelling and claims/Advertisements ❖ Method of Sampling and Analysis ❖ Nutrition and fortification ❖ Packaging	❖ Functional foods, Nutraceuticals, Dietetic products and other similar products ❖ Fish and fisheries products ❖ Cereals, Pulses & Legume and their products (including Bakery) ❖ Fruits and Vegetables and their products (including dried fruits and nuts) ❖ Meat and Meat products, including poultry ❖ Milk and milk products ❖ Oils and Fats ❖ Sweets, Confectionery, Sweeteners Sugar & honey ❖ Water (including flavoured water) & Beverages (non alcoholic) ❖ Spices and Culinary herbs ❖ Alcoholic Beverages

Table 55: Example Applications of HPLC in the Analysis of Various Food Constituents

Analyte	Seperation-mode	Method of detection
Mono and Oligosaccharides	Ion exchange; normal or reversed phase	Electrochemical; refractive index: postcolumn analysis
Vitamin E	Normal or reversed phase	Fluorescense; Electrochemical; UV
Aminoacids	Ion exchange; Reversed – phase	Post or precolumn derivatization
Pesticides	Normal or reversed phase	UV; fluorescensce; mass spectrometry
Mycotoxins	Reversed phase; Immunoaffinity	UV; fluorescence
Antibiotics	Reversed phase	UV
Melamine	Reversed phase, ion exchange	UV; Mass spectrometry
Sulfites	Ion exchange	UV; electrochemical

Table 56: Most Common Detectors for Gas Chromatography

Characteristic	Thermal conductivity Detector	Flame Ionization Detector	Electron Capture Detector	Flame photometric Detector	Photoionization Detector
Specificity	Very little; detects almost anything, including H2O; called the 'Universal Detector'	Most organics	Halogenated compounds and those with nitro or conjugated double bonds	Organic compounds with S or P (determined by which filter is used)	Depends on Ionization energy of lamp relative to bond energy of solutes

Table 57: Naturally occurring pigments in foods

Pigment	Typical source	Oil or water soluble	Stability to heat	Stability to light	Stability to Oxygen	pH change
Anthocyanins	Fruits	Water soluble	High	High	High	Low
Betalines	Beetroot	Water soluble	Moderate	High	High	High
Bixin	Seed coat of *Bixa orellana*	Oil soluble	Moderate to low	Low	High	-
Canxanthin		Oil soluble	Moderate	Moderate	Moderate	Moderate
Caramel	Heated sugar	Water soluble	High	High	High	High
Carotenes	Leaves	Oil soluble	Moderate to low	Low	Low	High
Chlorophylls	Leaves	Water soluble	High	High	High	Low
Cochineal	Insect (*Dactylopius coccus*)	Water soluble	High	High	-	Moderate to high
Curcumin	Turmeric	Water soluble	Low	Low	Low	-
Norbixin	See bixin	Water soluble	Moderate to low	Low	High	-
Oxymyoglobin	Animals	Water soluble	Low	-	High	Low
Polyphenols	Tea leaf	Water soluble	High	High	High	High
Quinones	Roots, Bark	Water soluble	High	Moderate	-	Moderate
Xanthophylls	Fruits	Water soluble	Moderate	High	High	Low

From the data of Zapsalis and Beck (1985) and Coulate (1984)

Table 58: Audits can be classified in 3 ways based on the auditor/auditee relationship

First Party	Second Party	Third Party
This type of audit is a self-assessment, to internally verify that procedures and management strategies reflect the requirements of a standard and reflect business objectives	Also known as proprietary audits, a primary organization evaluates the performance of a supplier or contractor	Independent auditors from outside the organization conduct audits, often for purposes of certification

Table 59: Gas Mixtures

Gas	Shoulder colours
Inert	Bright green
Fire intensifier/ oxidizing	Light blue
Flammable	Red
Toxic	Yellow

Table 60: Examples of color code used in India for identification of gas cylinders

S. No	Gas	Colour code
1	**Argon**	Peacock Blue
2	Nitrogen	French grey with a black band on the shoulder of the cylinder
3	Helium	Light Brown
4	Carbon Dioxide	Black with a silver band on the shoulder of the cylinder
5	Oxygen	Black
6	Zero Air (Ambient air filtered to contain less than 0.1 parts per million (PPM) of total hydrocarbons.)	French Grey
7	Hydrogen	Signal red
8	Dissolved Acetylene	Maroon

Table 61: Radioactive isotope Uses

No	Radioactive Isotopes	Uses
1	Calcium - 47	Studying cellular function & bone formation
2	Carbon - 14	Metabolism
3	Cesium -137	Cancer treatment
4	Chromium -51	RBC Studies
5	Cobalt -57	Diagnosis of perinicious Anemia

6	Cobalt -60	Sterilization of surgical instruments
7	Copper -67	Treat Cancer
8	Iodine -123, 125	Diagnose Thyroid Disorders
9	Iodine -131	Treat thyroid disorders
10	Phosphorus -32,33	Molecular biology & genetic research
11	Selinium -75	Protein studies
12	Sulphur -35	Molecular biology & genetic research
13	Technetium -99m	Organ imaging & blood flow studies
14	Tritium	Drug metabolism
15	Xenon	Lung ventilation & blood flow

Table 62: Laboratory waste managment

BIN Type	Waste type
Red Bin Biohazard – Laboratory waste	Tips, tubes, gloves, SDS PAGE gel, serological pipette, TC Flask, Plastic petridish, tubes 15ml and 50 ml
Blue Bin Broken glass ware	Disinfected/Treated broken glass wares, Any glass equipment containers, pipettes
Halogenated Solvent Waste White Canister, 5 ltrs	Chloroform, Dichloromethane. Carbontetrachloride, Tetrachloethylene, Perchloroethylene
Non Halogenated Solvent Waste White Canister, 5 ltrs	Acetone, Acetonitrile, Diethylether, Ethanol, Hexane, THF, Methanol, Toluene, Methyl tert-butyl ether (MTBE), Dimethyl Sulfoxide (DMSO), Dimethyl Formamide (DMF)
White round container	Sharps, Slides, Coverslips, Blades, etc..
White square container	Ethidium bromide Gel, Gloves, tubes and tips which contaminated with EtBr
Large grey bin Ethidium Bromide (Imaging stations)	Buffers containing Ethidium Bromide
Paper recycle	Waste papers
Green Bin	Books, Papers, Catalogues
Cyan Bin E-Waste (Ground floor Kitchen)	Battery, CDs, Pendrive, Catridge, Floppy, etc
Small grey bin Phenol/ Chloroform solid waste (Ground/ Second floor fume hoods)	Eppendorf tubes, Falcon tubes, tips contaminated with phenol
New bins for fly labs for broken bottles and vials with media	Broken fly vials with media in them

Table 63: Table showing differences between Kwashiorkor and Marasmus

Manifestation	Kwashiorkor	Marasmus
Oedema	Present	Absent
Weight – for - age	<80% of standard	<60% of standard
Hair changes	Present	Absent
Skin changes	Present	Absent
Moon face	Present	Absent
Hanging skin folds	Absent	Present

Table 64: Protein Quality rankings

Protein type	Protein efficiency ratio	Biological value	Net protein utilization	Protein digestability corrected Aminoacid Score
Beef	2.9	80	73	0.92
Black beans	0		0	0.75
Casein	2.5	77	76	1.00
Egg	3.9	100	94	1.00
Milk	2.5	91	82	1.00
Peanuts	1.8			0.52
Soy protein	2.2	74	61	1.00
Wheat gluten	0.8	64	67	0.25
Whey protein	3.2	104	92	1.00

Adapted from U.S. Dairy Export council, Reference Manual for U.S. Whey products 2nd edition, 1999 and Sarwar, 1997.

Plastics

■ In your quest to go green, use this guide to use and sort plastic. The number, usually found with a triangle symbol on a container, indicates the type of resin used to produce the plastic. Call **1-800-CLEANUP** for recycling information in your state.

1 PETE

Number 1 • *PETE or PET (polyethylene terephthalate)*

IS USED IN . . . . microwavable food trays; salad dressing, soft drink, water, and beer bottles

STATUS . . . . hard to clean; absorbs bacteria and flavors; avoid reusing

IS RECYCLED TO MAKE . . carpet, furniture, new containers, Polar fleece

2 HDPE

Number 2 • *HDPE (high-density polyethylene)*

IS USED IN . . . . household cleaner and shampoo bottles, milk jugs, yogurt tubs

STATUS . . . . transmits no known chemicals into food

IS RECYCLED TO MAKE . . detergent bottles, fencing, floor tiles, pens

3 V

Number 3 • *V or PVC (vinyl)*

IS USED IN . . . . cooking oil bottles, clear food packaging, mouthwash bottles

STATUS . . . . is believed to contain phalates that interfere with hormonal development; avoid

IS RECYCLED TO MAKE . . cables, mudflaps, paneling, roadway gutters

4 LDPE

Number 4 • *LDPE (low-density polyethylene)*

IS USED IN . . . . bread and shopping bags, carpet, clothing, furniture

STATUS . . . . transmits no known chemicals into food

IS RECYCLED TO MAKE . . envelopes, floor tiles, lumber, trash-can liners

5 PP

Number 5 • *PP (polypropylene)*

IS USED IN . . . . ketchup bottles, medicine and syrup bottles, drinking straws

STATUS . . . . transmits no known chemicals into food

IS RECYCLED TO MAKE . . battery cables, brooms, ice scrapers, rakes

6 PS

Number 6 • *PS (polystyrene)*

IS USED IN . . . . disposable cups and plates, egg cartons, take-out containers

STATUS . . . . is believed to leach styrene, a possible human carcinogen, into food; avoid

IS RECYCLED TO MAKE . . foam packaging, insulation, light switchplates, rulers

7 OTHER

Number 7 • *Other (miscellaneous)*

IS USED IN . . . . 3- and 5-gallon water jugs, nylon, some food containers

STATUS . . . . contains bisphenol A, which has been linked to heart disease and obesity; avoid

IS RECYCLED TO MAKE . . custom-made products

Part – 3

Important Points to Ponder

- Warming up a food may mean anything from a small increase in temperature up to heating to 100°C.
- C-enamel contains zinc oxide, so that the white ZnS is formed instead of the dark FeS when low acid sulfur-bearing foods such as [illegible] are canned, and darkening of the interior of the can is thus avoided. This enamel is not usable for [illegible], the fat would loosen and flake the enamel.
- In the cold-pack method of home canning, the food is not heated before being placed into the jar or other container.
- In hot-pack method, where the food is precooked, is hot when transferred to the container and is immediately heat-processed.
- For dehydrofreezing, fruits and vegetables are dried to about half their moisture content before freezing.
- A roentgen (R) is the quantity of gamma or X-radiation which produces one electrostatic unit of electric charge [illegible] in a cubic centimeter of air under standard conditions.
- Radappertization [illegible] "radiation sterilization" [illegible] to apply high dose treatments with [illegible].
- Radurization refers to "radiation pasteurization" low-dose treatments, where the intent is to extend a product's shelf life.
- Radicidation also is a low-dose radiation pasteurization treatment, but with the specific intent being the elimination of [illegible] pathogen.
- Picowave is a term used to label foods treated with low-level gamma radiation.
- An electron volt (eV) is the energy gained by an electron in moving through a potential difference of 1 volt. A MeV is 1 million electron volts.
- Egg has various ways of protecting itself from microbial invasion. The shell and the thin surface layer of proteinaceous material known as the cuticle or bloom are the first line of defense and serve to retard entry.
- A thermostabilization method of dipping eggs into hot water reduces evaporation of moisture from the egg by a slight coagulation of the outermost portion of the albumen.
- Most shell eggs are preserved by chilling. They are selected for storage on the basis of their general appearance and the result of candling.
- Green rots, caused chiefly by *Pseudomonas fluorescens*, a bacterium that grows at 0°C; the rot is so named because of the bright-green color of the white during early stages of development.
- Colorless rots, which may be caused by *Pseudomonas*, *Acinetobacter*, *Alcaligenes*, certain coliform bacteria, or other types of bacteria.

Important Points to Ponder

"The future depends on what we do in the present" **- Mahatma Gandhi**

- When ice crystals evaporate from an area at the surface, a defect called freezer burn is produced on fruits, vegetables, meat, poultry, and fish
- The unfrozen, concentrated solution of sugars, salts, etc., may ooze from packages of fruits or concentrates during storage as a viscous material called the metacryotic liquid
- The pink or reddish liquid that comes from meat on thawing is called drip, or bleeding, and the liquid oozing from fruits or vegetables on thawing is termed leakage
- Many vegetables can be dried by a process called explosive puffing
- Low-acid foods, with a pH above 5.3, including such foods as peas, corn, lima beans, meats, fish, poultry, and milk (although Cameron included only vegetables and fruits in his original grouping)
- Medium-acid foods, with a pH between 5.3 and 4.5, including such foods as spinach, asparagus, beets, and pumpkin.
- Acid foods, with a pH between 4.5 and 3.7, including such foods as tomatoes, pears, and pineapple
- High-acid foods, with a pH of 3.7 and below, including such foods as berries and sauerkraut
- Three principal types of asexual spores are conidia (singular conidium), arthrospores, or oidia (singular oidium) and sporangiospores
- The swollen tip of the sporangiospore, the columella, which usually projects into the sporangium, assumes shapes typical of species of mold
- Some molds have conidia in chains, squeezed off one by one from a special cell, a sterigma (plural sterigmata) or phialide, at the tip of the conidiophore
- Sexual Spores are oospores, zygospores and Ascospores
- Simmering is incipient or gentle boiling, with the temperature about 100^0 C
- Frying gets the outside of the food very hot, but the center ordinarily does not reach100^0 C

- Warming up a food may mean anything from a small increase in temperature up to heating to 100^{0}C
- C enamel contains zinc oxide, so that the white ZNS is formed instead of the dark FeS when low acid, sulfur-bearing foods such as corn are canned, and darkening of the interior of the can is thus avoided. This enamel is not usable for meat, for the fat would loosen and flake the enamel
- In the cold-pack method of home canning, the food is not heated before being placed into the jar or other container
- In hot-pack method, where the food is precooked, is hot when transferred to the container, and is immediately heat-processed
- For dehydrofreezing, fruits and vegetables have about half their moisture removed before freezing
- A roentgen (R) is the quantity of gamma or x-radiation which produces one electrostatic unit of electric charge of either sign in a cubic centimeter of air under standard conditions
- Radappertization is a term used to define "radiation sterilization" which would imply high dose treatments, with the resulting product being shelf-stable
- Radurization refers to "radiation pasteurization" low-dose treatments, where the intent is to extend a product's shelf life
- Radicidation also is a low-dose "radiation pasteurization" treatment, but with the specific intent being the elimination of a particular pathogen
- Picowaved is a term used to label foods treated with low-level ionizing radiation
- An electronvolt (eV) is the energy gained by an electron in moving through a potential difference of 1 volt. A mev is 1 million electronvolts
- Egg has various ways of protecting itself from microbial invasion. The shell and the thin surface layer of proteinaceous material known as the cuticle or bloom are the first line of defense and serve to retard entry
- A thermostabilization method of dipping eggs into hot water reduces evaporation of moisture from the egg by a slight coagulation of the outermost part of the egg albumen
- Most shell eggs are preserved by chilling. They are selected for storage on the basis of their general appearance and the result of candling
- Green rots, caused chiefly by *Pseudomonas fluorescens*, a bacterium that grows at 0 C; the rot is so named because of the bright-green color of the white during early stages of development
- Colorless rots, which may be caused by *Pseudomonas, Acinetobacter, Alcaligenes*, certain coliform bacteria, or other types of bacteria

- *Proteus melanovogenes* causes an especially black coloration in the yolk and a dark color in the white
- Pink rots are caused by strains of *Pseudomonas*
- Red rots, caused by species of *Serratia*
- If the trachea is left intact, it is referred to as an outside cut; a kosher cut severs the trachea
- Rapid heating of cream is accomplished by injecting steam or by a combination of steam injection and evacuation in a process known as vacreation
- Burnt or Caramel Flavor Certain strains of *Streptococcus lactis var. Maltigenes* produce this flavor, which resembles the cooked flavor of overheated milk
- Blue Milk *Pseudomonas syncyanea* produces a bluish-gray to brownish color in milk in pure culture but when growing with an acid former like *Streptococcus lactis* causes a deep-blue color
- Yellow Milk *Pseudomonas synxantha* may cause a yellow color in the cream layer of milk, coincident to lipolysis and proteolysis
- Species of *Flavobacterium* can also give yellowness
- Red milk usually is caused by species of *Serratia,* e.g., *S. marcescens*
- *Brevibacterium erythrogenes* produces a red layer at the top of the milk, followed by proteolysis
- *Micrococcus roseus* may grow and produce a red sediment, and yeast may produce pink or red colonies on the surface of sour milk or cream
- A brown color may result from *Pseudomonas putrefaciens* or by the enzymic oxidation of tyrosine by *P. fluorescens*
- Normally the ends of a can of food are termed flat, which means that they are actually slightly concave; and a partial vacuum exists in the container
- A flipper has flat ends, one of which will become convex when the side of the can is struck sharply or the temperature of the contents is increased
- A springer has both ends of the can bulged, but one or both ends will stay concave if pushed in; or if a swollen end is pushed in, an opposite flat end will pop out
- A soft swell has both ends of the can bulged, but the gas pressure is low enough to permit the ends to be dented by manual pressure
- A hard swell has such high gas pressure from within that the ends are too hard to dent by hand
- A breather is a can with a minute leak that permits air to move in or out but does not necessarily allow microorganisms to enter
- Extensive oxidation, usually following hydrolysis and the release of fatty acids, can result in ketonic rancidity

- Flavor reversion is defined as the appearance of objectionable flavors from less oxidation than is needed to produce rancidity
- The top yeasts used are strains of *Saccharomyces cerevisiae*, and the bottom yeast used is *S. uvarum (carlsbergensis)*
- For wine making, a special strain of *Saccharomyces cerevisiae var. Ellipsoideus*, adapted to the making of the specific type of wine, is selected
- Dhokla are prepared from black-gram paste fermented for 3 to 10 days
- Nan, bhatura, and kulcha are types of staple foods made from fermented wheat dough and shaped as flattened breads
- Sinki is a form of fermented radish
- Kinema is a soybean-based fermented food
- Malt liquor may have a higher alcohol content than does regular beer
- Bock beer is a very dark beer with a high alcohol content
- Brewing involves the addition of higher concentrations of malt and hops followed by longer aging.
- Pilsener is a lager-type beer, light in color, containing little remaining fermentable carbohydrate.
- Ale usually is made with a top yeast, a strain of *Saccharomyces cerevisiae,* instead of the bottom yeast employed for beer, although a bottom yeast sometimes is used
- Weiss beer, porter, and stout are ales in that top yeasts are employed in their manufacture.
- Sake is a yellow rice beer or wine of Japanese origin with an alcohol content of about 14 to 17 percent
- Pulque is a Latin-American beer-like beverage containing about 6 percent alcohol that results from a natural yeast fermentation of the juice of the agave, or century plant
- Ginger beer is a mildly alcoholic, acid beverage made by the fermentation of a sugar solution flavored with ginger
- Most wines are still wines - i.e., they retain none of the carbon dioxide produced during the fermentation - in contrast to sparkling wines, which contain considerable amounts. Other wines may be artificially carbonated
- Dry wines contain little or no unfermented sugar, as contrasted to sweet wines, which have sugar left or added
- Wines usually contain from 11 to 16 percent alcohol by volume but may go as low as 7 percent
- Fortified wines, however, to which the distillate of wine called "wine spirits" or "brandy" has been added, contain about 19 to 21 percent of alcohol by volume

- Table wines have a comparatively low content of alcohol and little or no sugar, while dessert wines are fortified, sweet wines
- Lactic acid bacteria are the principal causes of the bacterial spoilage of must and wines
- In Wine, most commonly occurring is tourne (turned or soured) spoilage, in which acid is formed from sugars, glucose, and fructose in the wine, chiefly by heterofermentative *Lactobacillus species*, such as *L. brevis, L. hilgardii, L. trichodes* and perhaps *L. buchneri*
- When the fermentation of fructose results in the bitter product mannitol, the fermentation sometimes is termed "mannitic", bitterness (amertume) also may result from the fermentation of the glycerol in the wine
- Gassiness resulting from any cause, such as from the liberation of carbon dioxide by heterofermentative lactics, is called pousse
- Honey wine, or mead, is made from diluted honey to which minerals and nitrogenous food for the yeasts have been added.
- Dandelion wine is a homemade product made by alcoholic fermentation of a water extract of flowers of the dandelion to which sugar, flavoring substances, and yeast have been added
- Rum is the distillate from alcoholically fermented sugarcane juice, sirup, or molasses.
- Whiskeys are distilled from saccharified and fermented grain mashes, e.g., rye whiskey from rye mash, bourbon or corn whiskeys from corn mash, wheat whiskey from wheat mash, etc
- Rums and whiskeys are made from mashes fermented by special distillers' yeasts, strains of *Saccharomyces cerevisiae var. Ellipsoideus*, which give high yields of alcohol
- Black pickles may owe their color to the formation of hydrogen sulfide by bacteria (or less commonly by chemical reaction) and combination with iron in the water to yield black
- Catalase, the enzyme that converts hydrogen peroxide to water and oxygen is commercially prepared from *Aspergillus niger, Penicilium vitale,* and *Micrococcus lysodelilaticus*
- Glucose isomerase converts glucose to fructose and is used in the corn milling industry.
- Lactase from *Saccharomyces fragilis* may find use in hydrolysis of the lactose in whey to glucose and galactose, which are less laxative sugars
- The strength of the sewage or food waste containing organic matter is expressed in terms of biochemical oxygen demand (BOD), which is the quantity of oxygen

used by aerobic microorganisms and reducing compounds in the stabilization of decomposable matter during a selected time at a certain temperature. A period of 5 days at 20°C is generally used, and results are expressed as 5-day BOD

- DOUBLE TONED MILK means the product prepared by admixture of cow or buffalo milk or both with fresh skimmed milk, or by admixture of cow or buffalo milk or both that has been standardized to fat and solids-not-fat percentage
- "Hydrogenation" means the process of addition of hydrogen to an edible vegetable oil using a catalyst to produce a fat with semi-solid consistency
- Flavoured Milk, by whatever name called, may contain nuts (whole, fragmented or ground) chocolate, coffee or any other edible flavour, edible food colours and cane sugar
- Full Cream Milk means milk or a combination of buffalo or cow milk or a product prepared by combination of both that has been standardized to fat and solids-not-fat percentage
- "Margarine" means an emulsion of edible oils and fats with water
- The terms "Pasteurisation", "Pasteurised" and similar terms shall be taken to refer to the process of heating every particle of milk of different classes to at least 63° C and holding at such temperature continuously for at least 30 minutes or heating it to at least 71.5°C and holding at such temperature continuously for at least 15 seconds or an approved temperature time combination that will serve to give a negative Phosphatase Test.
- All pasteurised milk of different classes shall be cooled immediately to a temperature of 10°C, or less
- RECOMBINED MILK means the homogenised product prepared from milk fat, non-fat-milk solids and water. Recombined milk shall be pasteurised and shall show a negative Phosphatase test
- "Refined vegetable oil" means any vegetable oil which is obtained by expression or solvent extraction of vegetable oil bearing materials, deacidified with alkali and/or by physical refining and/or by miscella refining using permitted food grade solvents and/or degumming followed by bleaching with absorbent earth and/or activated carbon and deodorized with steam without using any other chemical agents
- SKIMMED MILK means the product prepared from milk from which almost all the milk fat has been removed mechanically
- The term "sterilisation when used in association with milk, means heating milk in sealed container continuously to a temperature of either 115° C for 15 minutes or at least 130° C for a period of one second or more in a continuous flow and then packed under aseptic condition in hermatically sealed containers to ensure preservation at room temperature for a period not less than 15 days from the date of manufacture

- STANDARDISED MILK means cow milk or buffalo milk or sheep milk or goat milk or a combination of any of these milk that has been standardised to fat and solids-not-fat percentage
- Malai means the product rich in butter fat prepared by boiling and cooling cow or buffalo milk or a combination thereof. It shall contain not less than 25.0 per cent milk fat
- Chhana or paneer means the product obtained from the cow or buffalo milk or a combination thereof by precipitation with sour milk, lactic acid or citric acid. It shall not contain more than 70.0 per cent moisture and the milk fat content shall not be less than 50.0 per cent of the dry matter
- Evaporated Milk means the product obtained by partial removal of water from milk of cow and/ or buffalo by heat or any other process which leads to a product of the same composition and characteristics
- Sweetened Condensed Milk means the product obtained by partial removal of water from milk of Cow and/ or Buffalo with the addition of sugar or a combination of sucrose with other sugars or by any other process which leads to a product of the same composition and characteristics
- Cordial means a clear product free from any cellular matter, obtained by blending unfermented but fermentable clarified fruit juice with nutritive sweeteners & water with or without salt and peel oil and any other ingredients suitable to the products
- Synthetic syrup or sharbat means the syrup obtained by blending syrup made from sugar, dextrose or liquid glucose.
- Murabba means the product, prepared from suitable, sound whole or cut grated fruits, rhizome or vegetables, appropriately prepared, suitable for the purpose, singly or in combination, by impregnating it, with nutritive sweeteners to a concentration adequate to preserve it
- Marmalades means a product prepared by boiling sound fruits with peel, pulp and Juice, with or without water, added nutritive sweeteners and concentrating to such a consistency that gelatinisation takes place on cooling of the product. It shall not be syrupy, sticky or gummy and shall be clear and transparent
- Besan means the product obtained by grinding dehusked Bengal gram (*Cicer arietinum*) and shall not contain any added colouring matter or any other foreign ingredient
- Artificial sweetner - Saccharin Sodium in Carbonated Water of Maximum limit is 100 ppm
- Artificial sweetner- Aspartame (methylester) in Carbonated Water of Maximum limit is 700 ppm
- Artificial sweetners - Acesulfame Potassium and Sucralose in Carbonated water of Maximum limit is 300 ppm

- Artificial sweetner Neotame in Carbonated water of Maximum limit is 33 ppm
- Emulsifying and stabilising agents added to Fruit Products are Pectin, Sodium alginate, Calcium alginate, Alginic acid and Propylene glycol alginate
- "Sequestering agents" means substances which prevent adverse effect of metals catalysing the oxidative break-down of foods forming chelates; thus inhibiting decolourisation, off taste and rancidity
- "Buffering agents" means materials used to counter acidic and alkaline changes during storage or processing steps, thus improving the flavour and increasing the stability of foods
- Lactulose syrup may be used in special milk based infant food formulations, which is to be taken under medical advice upto a maximum level of 0.5 per cent of final food subject to label declaration
- Dimethyl Dicarbonate may be used in fruit drinks, ready to drink tea beverages, isotonic/sports drinks and flavoured water upto 250 mg/litre subject to a maximum methanol content in final product as 200 mg/litre
- Acidity regulators- Sodium fumarate, Potassium malate, Sodium hydroxide , Acetic acid or Lactic acid, Citric acid, Malic acid, Tartaric acid
- Flour treatment agents- Ammonium chloride, L- cystein mono hydrochloride, Ammonium phosphate and Benzoyl peroxide
- Synthetic colors - Ponceau 4R, Carmoisine, Erythrosine, Tartrazine, Sunset Yellow FCF, Indigo carmine, Brilliant blue FCF and Fast green FCF
- Leavening agents- Baking powder, Ammonium bi-carbonate and Ammonium carbonate
- Dough conditioners - Sodium bisulphite and Sodium metabisulphite
- Polyols - Sorbitol, Manitol , Xylitol, Isomalt, Lactitol and Maltitol
- Artificial sweeteners- Aspertame, Acesulphame K , Saccharin Sodium and Sucralose
- Glazing agents – Shellac, Beeswax , Candelilla wax, Gum arabic and Pectin
- Bulking agents - Polydextrose A and N
- "Balance shelf-life" means the period between the date of import (Import General Manifest) and "Best Before" or "Date of expiry" as the case may be
- "Customs airport" means any airport appointed under clause (a) of section 7 of the Customs Act, 1962 (52 of 1962)
- "Custom House Agent" shall have the meaning assigned to it in clause (c) of section 2 of the Custom House Agent Regulations, 2004
- "Customs port" means any port appointed under clause (a) of section 7 of the Customs Act, 1962 (52 of 1962) to be a customs port and includes a place appointed under clause (aa) of that section to be an inland container depot

- "No objection certificate" means a certificate issued to the customs authorities and the food importer by the Authorised Officer, or any other officer specifically authorised for this purpose, by the Food Authority for complying with the provisions of the Act and the rules and regulations made there under, of the consignment of the Food Importer
- "Shelf life" means the period between the date of manufacture and the "Best Before" or "Date of expiry" whichever is earlier as printed on the label
- "Stuffing list" means a list of food items and its actual physical arrangement inside the container or cartons or pallets or skids
- "Transit Country List" means the list of countries through which the imported articles of food transits before it reaches the Indian territory
- "Recall alert" means any alert issued to the public by the Chief Executive Officer, Food Safety and Standards Authority of India or the Commissioner of Food Safety of the State or Union territory or the Food Business Operator under intimation to Chief Executive Officer, Food Safety and Standards Authority of India and the concerned Commissioner(s) of Food Safety of the State(s) about the food under recall
- "Traceability" means the ability to follow the movement of a food article through specified stage(s) of its production, processing and distribution;
- "Unsafe food" means food as defined under clause (zz) of sub- section (1) of section 3 of the Act
- The food business operator may request termination of recall by submitting a written request to the Chief Executive Officer, Food Safety and Standards Authority of India along with recall status report or post-recall report certifying that the recall was effective. The request may be made in the form specified in Schedule-III
- Fenny or Feni is a distilled liquor made from the fermented juice of cashew apple or coconut toddy
- Gin is a distilled alcoholic beverage made from neutral spirit of agricultural origin flavoured with juniper berries and or other flavoring agents of botanical origin
- Rum is an alcoholic distillate obtained from fermented juice of sugarcane, sugarcane molasses, or any other sugarcane product, and shall not contain any colouring matter other than caramel
- Vodka is a distilled alcoholic beverage made from the neutral spirit obtained from fermented mash of rye, potato, cassava, grains or any other carbohydrates of agricultural origin
- Whisky is an alcoholic beverage made by distilling the fermented extract of malted cereal grains such as corn, rye, barley, or using neutral grain spirit or rectified grain spirit, or neutral spirit of agricultural origin, or their mixture

- Pot-still distilled spirit is an alcoholic beverage obtained from multiple distillations of fermented molasses, jaggery (Gur), mash of cereals, potato, cassava, fruits (like grape), juice or sap of coconut and palm trees, agave plant, sugarcane juice, cashew apple, mahua flowers, or any other source of fermentable carbohydrates of agriculture origin
- Dry wine: Dry wine is a wine that contains 0.4 upto 0.9 per cent. Sugar
- Medium dry wine: Medium dry wine is a wine that contains more than 0.9 upto 1.2 per cent. Sugar
- Medium sweet wine: Medium sweet wine is a wine that contains more than 1.2 upto 4.5 per cent. Sugar
- Sweet wine: Sweet wine is a wine that contains more than 4.5 per cent. Sugar
- Sparkling wine has a carbon dioxide content of minimum 7.0 g/l or 3.5 bars pressure, at 20 $^{\circ}$ C, resulting solely from either the primary or the secondary fermentation of the wine within a closed container, tank or bottle
- Brut: It has sugar content below 1.2 per cent
- Fortified wine: Fortified wine is a wine with high alcohol content achieved by the addition of alcohol (brandy or wine spirits or neutral spirit of agricultural origin) provided a minimum 7 .0 per cent comes from fermentation of grapes, grape must and fruits and used as aperitif or dessert wine. Fortified wine may be red or white, dry or sweet
- Vermouth is a wine having the taste, aroma and characteristics derived from the addition of extract of herbs and spices, attributed to vermouth, and shall be so designate
- Beer is a fermented alcoholic beverage made from barley malt or other malted grains, sometimes with added adjuncts like wheat, maize, corn, rice or other cereal crops, and with hops or hop extracts to impart a bitter taste and flavour
- Depending upon the ethyl alcohol content, beer maybe classified as under: (i) Regular or Mild–Abv more than 0.5 percent upto 5.0 per cent (ii) Strong – Abv more than 5.0 per cent upto 8.0 per cent
- Lager: Lager beer is prepared by using bottom fermenting yeast and matured at low temperature. It can be found in colours from light to dark. Pilsner is a type of lager beer which is light in colour and has a medium hop flavour
- Ale: Ale beer is prepared by using top fermenting yeast and is usually lighter in colour. It is also prepared from pale malt and has a medium body
- Wheat beer: Wheat beer is brewed with a large proportion of wheat and may also contain a significant proportion of malted barley
- Wheat beer is usually top-fermented. Wheat beer is sometimes hazy or cloudy with a touch of spicy notes

- Stout and porter: Stouts and porters are dark beers made using roasted malts or roasted barley and typically brewed with slow fermenting yeast
- Draught beer: Draught beer is a beer of all types i.e., lager, ale, stout and porter or wheat, and may or may not be pasteurized. It is served from a cask
- Fortification means deliberately increasing the content of essential micronutrients in a food so as to improve the nutritional quality of food and to provide public health benefit with minimal risk to health
- "Fortificant" means a substance added to food to provide micronutrients but does not include nutraceuticals or foods for Special Dietary Uses
- "Micronutrients" means essential dietary nutrients including vitamins, minerals or trace elements that are required in very small quantities and are vital to development, disease prevention and wellbeing of human beings
- "Quality assurance" means the systematic measures applied and steps taken by manufacturers and packers of fortified food throughout the manufacturing or packing process to ensure that the finished food complies with the provisions of the Act and regulations and standards specified there under
- "Staple foods" means articles of food intended for mass consumption on a daily basis and include rice, wheat, wheat flour, atta, maida, oil, salt, milk, and such other articles of food as may be designated staple foods under these regulations
- Every package of fortified food shall carry the words "fortified with (name of the fortificant)" and the logo, specified in Schedule-II of these regulation, on its label. It may also carry a tag line "Sampoorna Poshan Swasth Jeevan" under the logo
- Every package of food, fortified with Iron shall carry a statement "People with Thalassemia may take under medical supervision"
- "Accreditation" means a third party attestation of the competence of a food laboratory to carry out its function effectively
- "Adequacy audit" means an audit conducted on site prior to notifying a laboratory to ensure that essential requirements of testing and other related facilities are available in a food laboratory
- "Notified food laboratory" means a food laboratory notified by the Food Authority under sub-section (1) of section 43
- "Referral food laboratory" means a food laboratory established or recognized by notification by the Food Authority under sub section (2) of section 43
- A scheduled audit which shall be at least once every year
- Non-specified food" means any food other than proprietary food or food ingredients, including additives, processing aids and enzymes for which standards have not been specified in any regulation made under the Act
- "Participatory Guarantee System for India" means a quality assurance initiative

by the Department of Agriculture Co-operation and Farmer's Welfare, Ministry of Agriculture and Farmer's Welfare, Government of India for organic production which emphasizes the participation of producers, consumers and other stakeholders and operate outside the framework of third party certification

- "Claim" means any representation which states, suggests or implies that a food has particular qualities relating to its origin, nutritional properties, nature, processing and composition
- "Food Authority" means the Food Safety and Standards Authority of India established under section 4 of the Food Safety and Standards Act, 2006
- "National Programme for Organic Production" means a programme of the Government of India which provides an institutional mechanism for implementation of the National Standards for Organic Production with a third party certification control system as notified by the Director General of Foreign Trade under the Foreign Trade (Development and Regulation) Act, 1992(22 of 1992)
- "Organic food" means food products that have been produced in accordance with specified standards for organic food production
- Labelling on the package of organic food shall convey full and accurate information on the organic status of the product
- "Multilayer/composite food packaging" means a food packaging material composed of two or more layers of same or different types of packaging materials specified under these regulations
- "Overall migration limit" means the maximum permitted amount of non-volatile substances released from a material or article into food simulants
- "Package or container" means a pre-packaged box, bottle, casket, tin, barrel, case, pouch, receptacle, sack, bag, wrapper or such other things in which an article of food is packed
- "Packaging material" means materials such as cardboard, paper, glass, metal, plastic, multi-layer packaging material used for packaging of food products
- "Primary food packaging" means packaging material in direct contact with food products
- "Secondary food packaging" means packaging material which encloses the primary food packaging and does not come in direct contact with food products
- "Specific migration limit" means the maximum permitted amount of a given substance released from a material or article into food or food stimulants
- Tin containers once used, shall not be re-used for packaging of food
- Plastic containers of capacity 5 litre and above and Glass bottles, which are reused for packaging of food, shall be suitably durable, easy to clean or disinfect

- Printing inks for use on food packages shall conform to IS: 15495
- Newspaper or any such material shall not be used for storing and wrapping of food
- Every food business operator shall obtain the certificate of conformity issued by NABL accredited laboratory against these regulations for the packaging material which comes in direct contact with food or layers likely to come in contact with food to be use
- Provided that Drinking Water (both Packaged and Mineral Water) shall be packed in colourless, transparent and tamper-proof bottles or containers made of polyethylene (PE) conforming to IS: 10146 or polyvinyl chloride (PVC) conforming to IS: 10151 or polyalkylene terephthalate (PET and PBT) conforming to IS: 12252 or polypropylene (PP) conforming to IS: 10910 or food grade polycarbonate conforming to IS: 14971 or polystyrene conforming to IS: 10142 or sterile glass bottles only. The transparency of a container shall not be less than 85 percent in light transmittance
- Petty Food Manufacturer" means any food manufacturer, who (a) manufactures or sells any article of food himself or a petty retailer, hawker, itinerant vendor or temporary stall holder; or distributes foods including in any religious or social gathering except a caterer; or (b) such other food businesses including small scale or cottage or such other industries relating to food business or tiny food businesses with an annual turnover not exceeding Rs 12 lakhs and/or whose
    1) Production capacity of food (other than milk and milk products and meat and meat products) does not exceed 100 kg/ltr per day or
    2) Procurement or handling and collection of milk is up to 500 litres of milk per day or
    3) Slaughtering capacity is 2 large animals or 10 small animals or 50 poultry birds per day or less
- "State Licensing Authority" means Designated Officers appointed under Section 36(1) of the Act by the Food Safety Commissioner of a State or UT
- A Registration or license granted under these Regulations shall be valid and subsisting, unless otherwise specified, for a period of 1 to 5 years as chosen by the Food Business Operator, from the date of issue of registration or license subject to remittance of fee applicable for the period and compliance with all conditions of license
- The Registration or License shall continue to be in force till such time that the orders are passed on the renewal application which in no case shall be beyond 30 days from the date of expiry of registration or license
- Any renewal application filed beyond the period mentioned under Regulation 2.1.7 (2) above but before the expiry date, shall be accompanied by a late fee of Rs 100 per day for each day of delay

- List of food business falling under the purview of Central Licensing Authority

1) Dairy units including milk chilling units equipped to handle or process more than 50,000 litres of liquid milk/day or 2500 MT of milk solid per annum.

2) Vegetable oil processing units and units producing vegetable oil by the process of solvent extraction and refineries including oil expeller unit having installed capacity more than 2 MT per day. III.

3) All slaughter houses equipped to slaughter more than 50 large animals or 150 or more small animals including sheep and goats or 1000 or more poultry birds per day.

4) Meat processing units equipped to handle or process more than 500 kg of meat per day or 150 MT per annum.

5) All food processing units other than mentioned under (I) to (IV) including relabellers and repackers having installed capacity more than 2 MT/day except grains, cereals and pulses milling units. VI. 100 % Export Oriented Units.

6) All Importers importing food items including food ingredients and additives for commercial use

7) All food business operators manufacturing any article of food containing ingredients or substances or using technologies or processes or combination thereof whose safety has not been established through these regulations or which do not have a history of safe use or food containing ingredients which are being introduced for the first time into the country.

8) Food Business Operator operating in two or more states

9) Food catering services in establishments and units under Central government Agencies like Railways, Air and airport, Seaport, Defence etc.

- "Food for special dietary use" shall have the meaning assigned to it in section 22 of the Act
- "Food with added probiotic ingredients" means food with live micro-organisms beneficial to human health, which when ingested in adequate numbers as a single strain or as a combination of cultures, confer one or more specified or demonstrated health benefits in human beings
- "Functional food" shall have the meaning assigned to it in section 22 of the act
- "Health supplements" shall have the meaning assigned to it in section 22 of the act
- "Non-food" means an ingredient or a substance which is not a 'food' as referred to in clause (j) of section 3 of the act
- "Novel food" shall have the meaning assigned to it in section 22 of the act; (k) "nutraceuticals" shall have the meaning assigned to it in section 22 of the Act

- The nutraceuticals shall contain any of the ingredients specified in Schedule I or Schedule II or Schedule IV or Schedule VI or Schedule VII or Schedule VIII
- The articles of food for special dietary use shall contain any of the ingredients specified in Schedules I or Schedule II or Schedule III or Schedule IV or Schedule VI or Schedule VII or Schedule VIII
- "Best before" means the date which signifies the end of the period under any stated storage conditions during which the food shall remain fully marketable and shall retain any specific qualities for which tacit or express claims have been made and beyond that date, the food may still be perfectly safe to consume, though its quality may have diminished. However the food shall not be sold if at any stage the product becomes unsafe
- "Date of manufacture" means the date on which the food becomes the product as described; 3. "Date of packaging" means the date on which the food is placed in the immediate container in which it will be ultimately sold
- "Infant" means a child not more than twelve months of age
- "Lot number" or "code number" or "batch number" means the number either in numericals or alphabets or in combination thereof, representing the lot number or code number or batch number, being preceded by the words "Lot No" or "Lot" or "code number" or "Code" or Batch No" or "Batch" or any distinguishing prefix by which the food can be traced in manufacture and identified in distribution
- "Multipiece package" means a package containing two or more individually packaged or labelled pieces of the same commodity of identical quantity, intended for retail either in individual pieces or packages as a whole
- "Non- Vegetarian Food" means an article of food which contains whole or part of any animal including birds, fresh water or marine animals or eggs or products of any animal origin, but excluding milk or milk products, as an ingredient
- "Prepackaged" or "Pre-packed food", means food, which is placed in a package of any nature, in such a manner that the contents cannot be changed without tampering it and which is ready for sale to the consumer
- "Principal Display Panel" means that part of the container/package which is intended or likely to be displayed or presented or shown or examined by the customer under normal and customary conditions of display, sale or purchase of the commodity contained therein
- "Use – by date" or "Recommended last consumption date" or "Expiry date" means the date which signifies the end of the estimated period under any stated storage conditions, after which the food probably will not have the quality and safety attributes normally expected by the consumers and the food shall not be sold

- Containers made of plastic materials should conform to the following Indian Standards Specification, used as appliances or receptacles for packing or storing whether partly or wholly, food articles namely
  1) IS:10146 (Specification for Polyethylene in contact with foodstuffs)
  2) IS:10142 (Specification for Styrene Polymers in contact with foodstuffs)
  3) IS:10151 (Specification for Polyvinyl Chloride (PVC), in contact with foodstuffs)
  4) IS:10910 (Specification for Polypropylene in contact with foodstuffs)
  5) IS:11434 (Specification for Ionomer Resins in contact with foodstuffs)
  6) IS:11704 Specification for Ethylene Acrylic Acid (EAA) copolymer
  7) IS:12252 - Specification for Poly alkylene terephathalates (PET)
  8) IS:12247 - Specification for Nylon 6 Polymer
  9) IS:13601 - Ethylene Vinyl Acetate (EVA)
  10) IS:13576 - Ethylene Metha Acrylic Acid (EMAA)
  11) Tin and plastic containers once used, shall not be re-used for packaging of edible oils and fats
- The package, label or the advertisement of edible oils and fats shall not use the expressions "Super Refined", "Extra-Refined", "Micro-Refined", "Double-Refined", Ultra-Refined", "Anti-Cholesterol", "Cholesterol Fighter", "Soothing to Heart", "Cholesterol Friendly", "Saturated Fat Free" or such other expressions which are an exaggeration of the quality of the Product
- Bio-safety Level I: These biological agents are not known to cause disease in healthy adult humans and pose only a minimal potential hazard for laboratory personnel and the environment. *Bacillus subtilis, Naegleria gruberi,* infectious canine hepatitis virus and non infectious E. coli are representative of those microorganisms meeting these criteria
- Bio-safety Level II: Practices and safety facilities must meet the perquisites to deal with a broad spectrum of indigenous moderate risk agents. These agents are known to cause diseases but immunization or antibiotic treatment is available. Examples are Hepatitis B virus, the *Salmonella, Toxoplasma spp.* and infectious *E. coli* strains.
- Bio-safety Level II+: The term 'Infectious Material' applies to blood, any other body fluid, and other potentially infectious material like biopsies. All body fluids shall be considered as infectious materials. Such work can only be performed in the Biohazard laboratory in the Ground Floor.
- Bio-safety Levels III and IV are not applicable to NCBS/InStem/CCAMP

- FSSAI notifies comprehensive regulatory standards for BASMATI rice for the first time in Jan 2023. As per these standards BASMATI rice shall possess the natural fragrance characteristics of BASMATI rice and free from artificial coloring. BASMATI rice is a premium variety of rice cultivated in the Himalayan foothills of the Indian SUB- CONTINENT
- GEAC (Genetic Engineering Appraisal Committee) has approved the environmental release of Dhara Mustard Hybrid – 11 (DMH -11), is a genetically engineered variant of mustard. ICAR suggest that DMH – 11 has 28% higher yields than its parent Varuna and was 37% better than zonal checks or local varieties
- Apis Karinjodian – New species of Bee discovered in India. A new species of endemic honeybee has been discovered in the Western Ghats
- Mumbai Central Railway station certified as country's first Eat right satation with a 4 –star rating awarded by FSSAI as a part of Eat Right India Movement launched in 2018. FSSAI is a autonomous body under Union Ministry of Health & Family Welfare
- Prayagraj bags 5 star "Eat Right Station" (2022) certification from FSSAI, for providing high quality, nutritious food to passengers, thereby becoming the first station in Uttar Pradesh to get this recognition
- As part of Eat Right India led by FSSAI, India targets to reduce industrially produced trans fatty acids on food supply to less than 2% by 2022
- The world Food Safety Day 2019 was observed on 7th June with the Theme – Food Safety, Everyone's Business. It was first ever World Food Safety Day
- The Himalayan Yak has been approved as a food animal by the FSSAI. The move is expected to help slow the decline of the high altitude bovine animal population by incorporating it into the conventional milk and meat industries
- The Cabinet Committee on Economic Affairs (CCEA) has approved Minimum Support Prices (MSPs) for copra for 2023 season. MSP for Fair average Quality of milling copra has been fixed at Rs. 1080 per quintal and for ball copra at Rs 11750 per quintal for 2023 season
- Centre has named the New Integrated Food Security Scheme as Pradhan Mantri Garb Kalyan Ann Yogana, PMGKAY. Cabinet had approved new integrated food security scheme for providing free food grains to Antodaya Ann Yogana and Primary Household Beneficiaries. Implementation of new scheme has started from Jan 1, 2023. It will benefit more than 80 crore poor and poorest of poor people
- A recent survey by the FSSAI has found that 15% of food items including protein powders and dietary supplements used by athletes and bodybuilders in India are unsafe for consumption or substandard. The survey, which was conducted during 2021- 22, found that 4,890out of 144,345 samples conducted were unsafe

- FSSAI has recently issued a draft notification on Indian Nutrition Labelling (INR) modeled on the health star – rating System.The draft notification issued by the FSSAI makes changes to the Safety and Standards (Labelling & Display) Regulations, 2020. It requires packaged food to display the prescribed format of INR by assigning a rating from ½ star (least healthy) to 5 stars (Healthiest)
- Draft Food Safety and Standards (Genetically modified or Engineered foods) Regulations, 2021 was issued by FSSAI on Nov 15, 2021. The draft regulation applicable to Genetically Modified Organisms (GMOs), Genetically Engineered Organisms (GEOs) and Living Modified Organisms (LMOs)
- Madya Pradesh Cabinet has approved the Penal Law (Madya Pradesh Amendment) Bill, 2021 on February 2, 2021. This bill was approved in order to give life imprisonment to food adulterers in states
- On October 5, 2020, Ministry of Housing and Urban Affairs Signed Memorandum of Understanding with Swiggy to take Street food vendors online. This was achieved under PM Svanidhi Scheme. This programme was launched in five cities such as Chennai, Ahmedabad, Indore, Delhi and Varanasi
- CSIR – CFTRI has made protein rich biscuits for COVID -19 patients. The biscuits have been sent to the COVID -19 patients in AIIMS. Usual biscuits contain 8% to 9% of protein. However, these enriched biscuits and rusks contain 14% of protein
- The United Nations General Assembly at its 75th session in March 2021 declared 2023 The international year of Millets

Part – 4

Additional Information

CHAPTER-1

Important Days Related to Food & Health

"Every failure is just another step closer to a win, Never stop trying"

-Robert M. Hensel

- January 30 - Anti Leprosy Day
- February 2 – World Wetland's Day
- February 4 – World Cancer Day
- February 10 – National Deworming Day
- March 3 – World wildlife Day
- March 8 – International women's Day
- 21st March to 4th April – Poshan Pakwada
- March 12 – World Kidney Day
- March 15 – World consumer right's Day
- March 22 –World water Day
- March 24 – World Tuberculosis Day
- April 7 – World Health Day
- April 11 – National Safe Motherhood Day
- April 11 – World Parkinson's Disease Day
- April 17 – World Haemophilia Day
- April 22 – World Earth Day
- April 25 – World Malaria Day
- April 30 – Ayushman Bharat Diwas
- May 5 – World Asthma Day
- May 8 – World Thalassemia Day
- May 9 – Mother's Day
- May 12- World Nurse's Day
- May 22 – International Day for Biological Diversity

- May 28- World Tobacco Day
- May – 28 – World Hunger Day
- June 1 – World Milk Day
- June 5 – World Environment Day
- June 7 – World Food Safety Day
- June 14 – Blood Donar Day
- June 21 – International Yoga Day
- July 1 – National Doctor's Day
- July 6 – World Zoonosis Day
- July 11 – World Population Day
- July 28 – World Hepatitis Day
- August 1 -7 – World Breastfeeding Week
- September 1 – 7 – National Nutrition Week
- September 29 – World Heart Day
- October 1 – International Coffee Day
- October 10 – World Mental Health Day
- October 12 – World Arthritis Day
- October 15- Global Hand Washing Day, National Women Farmer's Day (Rashtriya Mahila Kisan Diwas)
- October 16 – World Food Day
- October 20 – World Osteoporosis Day, World Statistics Day
- November 12 – World Pneumonia Day
- November 14 – World Diabetes Day
- November 16 – World COPD Day
- November 21 – World Fisheries Day
- November 26 – National Milk Day
- December 1 – World AIDS Day
- December 3 – World Disability Day
- December 4 – Women in Agriculture Day
- December 5 – World Soil Day
- December 15 – International Tea Day
- December 23 – Kisan Diwas (Farmer' Day)

CHAPTER-2

Institutions/Organization/Acts/ Law, establishment Date and their Headquarters

	Institutions	Establishment	HQ
BIS	Bureau of Indian Standards	1986	New Delhi
CFTRI	Central Food Technological Research Institute	1950	Mysore
DFRL	Defense Food Research Laboratory	1961	Mysore
FAO	Food and Agriculture Organization	1945	Rome
FPO	Fruit Products Order	1955	New Delhi
NDDB	National Dairy Development Board	1965	Anand
NDRI	National Dairy Research Institute	1923	Karnal
NIFTEM	National Institute of Food Technology Entrepreneurship and Management	2006	Sonepat
NIN	National Institute of Nutrition	1958	Hyderabad
PFA	Prevention of Food Adulteration	1954	New Delhi
FSSAI	Food Safety and Standard Authority of India	2011	New Delhi
ISO	International Organization for Standardization	1947	Geneva
WHO	World Health Organization	1948	Geneva
WTO	World Trade Organization	1995	Geneva

CHAPTER-3

National Policies and Action Plans

- 1974 - National Policy for Children
- 1983 - National Health Policy
- 1986 - National Policy on Education
- 1987 - National Policy on Child Labour
- 1993 - National Nutrition Policy
- 1996 - Communication Strategy for Child Development
- 1991–2000 - National Plan of Action for SAARC Decade of the Girl Child
- 1992 - National Plan of Action for Children
- 1995 - National Plan of Action on Nutrition
- 1954 – National Water Supply and Sanitation Programme
- 1972 – ARWSP (Accelerated Rural Water Supply Programme
- 1981 – International Drinking Water Supply and Sanitation Programme
- 2002 – Swajaldhara
- 2008 – National Urban Sanitation Policy

CHAPTER-4

Tests to Detect Adulteration

Test: 1

Test for Detection of Sesame Oil in Pure Ghee to determine whether the ghee is adulterated with hydrogenated fat/ vanaspati which contains sesame oil

Chemicals: 1 per cent sucrose solution Concentrated hydrochloric acid Procedure:

- Take 5 test tubes. In Test tube A pour approx 2 ml of sesame oil
- In Test tube B pour approx 2 ml of groundnut oil
- In Test tube C pour approx 2 ml of melted vanaspati
- In Test tube D pour approx 2 ml of melted branded ghee
- In Test tube E pour approx 2 ml of melted loose ghee
- To each test tube, add 1 ml of 1 per cent sucrose solution
- Then to each test tube, add 1ml of concentrated hydrochloric acid
- Shake each test tube well. Observation: Note if a pink colour develops
- Development of pink colour indicates presence of sesame oil

Interpretation: Are the ghee samples pure or adulterated

Test: 2

For presence of excessive amount of stalks in tea leaves

- Weigh 5 gm of tea leaves into a conical flask or a beaker. Label the container
- To this add 500 ml of water and boil the flask/beaker for 15 minutes
- Filter out the water
- Transfer the tea sample to a flat white plate and with a forceps, pick out the stalks and place them in a preweighed petridish or crucible
- Dry the stalks at 100 degrees until all the moisture has evaporated
- Weigh the stalks
- Calculate the percentage of stalks in the tea

Interpretation: The proportion of stalks in the tea should be less than 25 per cent

Test -3

For detecting Light berries in Black Pepper Chemicals

Chemicals - Alcohol water mixture (sp.gr 0.8 to 0.82)

- Take about 10g of the pepper sample in a 250 ml beaker
- Add approximately 150–200 ml of the alcohol water mixture.
- Pick out the berries which rise to the top and float.
- Dry the berries and weigh them.
- Calculate the percentage of dried berries
- **Interpretation**: The higher percentage of light berries, suggests that the berries have been extracted from the black berries

Test - 4

For the presence of metanil yellow in turmeric Chemicals

Chemicals - Hydrochloric acid concentrated

- Take about 2 g of turmeric sample in a test tube
- Add 5ml of distilled water
- Mix well
- Add concentrated hydrochloric acid (about 5 ml to 10 ml) slowly into the tube
- Observation: Observe the test-tube for development of pink to magenta colour.

Interpretation: Development of pink to magenta colour denotes the presence of metanil yellow which is a toxic adulterant

Test - 5

For the presence of starch in milk and ice cream

Chemicals: Iodine solution

- In a test tube, add approximately 10 ml of milk or melted ice cream
- Add iodine solution, drop by drop
- Mix the contents of the test tube
- Observation: Observe for appearance of blue colour

Interpretation: Development of blue colour indicates the presence of starch in the sample

Test -6

For the presence of colophenial resins in asafetida (hing)

- Chemicals: 0.5 per cent copper acetate solution in water Petroleum ether
- Take about 1-2 g of asafetida sample in a test tube

- Add approximately 10 ml of petroleum ether
- 2. Shake the test tube well. 3. Filter the contents of the tube
- 4. To 5 ml of the filterate add 5 ml of copper acetate solution
- . 5. Shake and allow the layers to separate
- Observation: Note whether a blue or green colour develops in the ether layer.

Interpretation: Development of blue or green colour denotes the presence of colophenial resins that are not permitted

Part – 5

Computer Literacy & Information Technology

Computer Literacy & Information Technology

"Life is but an endless series of experiments"

-Mahatma Gandhi

Computer

- An electronic device that receives data, process it and gives meaningful informations
- Word Computer is originated from Latin words 'Computus' and 'Computare'
- Father of computer – Charles Babbage
- Collection of facts and figures are called Data
- Processed data is called information
- The way that computers manipulate data into informations is called Processing

Characteristics of computer

- Accuracy
- Speed
- Versatility
- Storage capacity
- Automaton
- Diligence
- Reliability

Functional Units of computer

- Input Unit
- Central Processing Unit
- Output Unit

Input Unit

Devices which receives data for processing called Input devices. Major Input devices are

- Keyboard
- Mouse
- Light pen
- Joystick
- Scanner
- Track ball
- Microphone
- Digital Camera
- Touch Screen
- Barcode reader
- Optical mark reader (OMR) – interprets pencil marks on paper
- Magnetic Ink Character Recognition (MICR) – used by banking industry to facilitate processing of cheques

Central Processing Unit

- Controls overall functioning of the computer.
- All the data processing is done. CPU is known as the brain of the computer
- CPU executes multiple programmes at a time - MultiTasking

Parts of CPU

- Arithmetic and Logic Unit (ALU)
- Control Unit
- Memory Unit

Output Unit

- User get the results of processed data through output devices. Major output devices are
- Monitor
- Printer
- Projector
- Speaker
- Sound Card
- Video card
- Plotter
- Head phone

- ✓ The Primary Input Device – Keyboard
- ✓ The Primary Output Device – Monitor

Keys on keyboard

- Alphanumeric keys – Letters and Numbers
- Punctuation keys – Comma, Period, Semicolon, etc
- Special Keys – Function keys, Arrow keys, Caps Lock key, Num Lock key, etc
- Number of function key on keyboard – 12
- Largest key – Space Bar
- Key placed on the top left corner – Escape Key (Esc)

Mouse

- Pointing device used in computer
- Unit which is represent the speed of a mouse – Micky
- First Mouse was marketed by - APPLE
- Most commonly, working of wireless mouse is based on Infra red rays

Monitor

- Cathode Ray Tube (CRT) is used in older monitors
- Modern monitors are typically a Thin Film transistor Liquid Crystal Display (TFT – LCD) panel
- Resolution of monitor is associated with the number of pixels on monitor

Printer

- Fastest printer – Laser Printer
- Divided into two categories – Impact Printer and Non Impact Printer
- The output resolution of a printer is measured in DPI (Dots per inch)
- Printed copy of a document is known as Hard copy
- Non printed copy of a document is known as Soft copy

Memory

- Used for the storage of the data
- Classified into primary and Secondary

Primary Memory

- Also known as main memory

- Primary Memory is classified into RAM and ROM
- RAM is a volatile memory. Because it loses its data when computer is turned off. Located on Mother board
- ROM is a non volatile memory, Because it doesn't lose it's data even after the computer is turned off. We can't change the data stored in ROM

Secondary Memory

- Also known as external Memory
- Stores Data Permanently
- Examples- Magnetic Tape, Magnetic Discs (Hard Disk, Floppy Disk), Optical Discs (CD, DVD, Blue Ray Disc), Flash Drives

Magnetic Tape

- A recording medium consisting of a thin tape with coating of fine magnetic material used for recording data

Hard Disk

- Hard Disk divided into Tracks and Sectors
- Normal size of a Hard Drive Sector is 512 Bytes
- Speed of a Hard Disc is measured in Revolutions Per Minute (RPM)

Floppy Disk

- Size of a common Floppy Disk – 3.5 inches
- Storage capacity – 1.44 MB

Optical Disks

- Examples of Optical Discs are CD, DVD and Blue Ray Disc
- Data on optical Disks is stored in the form of Light and Dark pits
- Storage capacity of a Standard Compact Disk (CD) is 650 – 750 MB (70 minutes of audio)
- Diameter of a standard CD – 12 cm
- Technology used in CD is LASER (Light Amplification by Stimulated Emission of Radiation) Technology
- DVD – Digital Versatile Disk
- Storage capacity of a DVD is 4.7 GB
- Optical Disk having high storage capacity – Blue Ray Disc
- Storage capacity of a Single Layer Blue Ray Disc is 25 GB

Flash Drives

- Is a non volatile computer storage chip made up of EEPROM
- Examples of Flash Memory Storage Devices are USB Flash Drive, Memory Cards

Measurement of Memory

- Smallest unit of memory – Bit
- Bit is shortest form of Binary Digit
- Memory of a computer is usually measured in Bytes
- Storage capacity of a hard disk is measured in Megabytes, Gigabytes and Terabytes
- 1 Bit is 1 or 0
- ½ Byte is known as Nibble
- 1Nibble – 4 Bits
- 1 Byte – 8 Bits
- 1 KB – 1024 Bytes
- 1MB – 1024 KB
- 1 GB – 1024 MB
- 1 TB – 1024 GB

Cache memory

- A small high speed memory which is used to store a portion of data temporarily from the main memory
- Cache memory is used to increase the processing speed
- Cache memory acts between CPU and RAM

Register

- Serially interconnected group of high speed memory cells inside the CPU is called Register
- Register is the fastest memory as compared to Cache memory

Buffer

- Storage area in RAM where data is stored for a short amount of time

Hardware and Software

- **Hardware** - Is a physical equipments and components of a computer that can be seen and touched. Eg: Motherboard or Printed Circuit Board, Keyboard, Mouse and Printer

- **Software** - Is a set of instructions given to computer, written in particular language (C, C++, Java, etc) to control and coordinate computer hardwares. Software cannot be sensed by touch.

Types of Softwares

1. **System Software** - Coordinates the operations of various hardware components. Examples are Operating system, Utility Software, Device drives
2. **Application software** – Designed to help the user to perform specific tasks. Examples are MS office, Tally, Media Players

Firmware

- Firmware is a combination of Hardware and Software
- Software which is available on hardware called Firmware
- Computer chips that have programmes recorded on them are known as firmware
- Common firmware containing devices are Mobile phones, Digital cameras, Computers
- Examples of Firmware are ROM, EPROM, Flash memory

Operating System

- Operating system is a Collection of programmes which control overall operations of the computer
- It works as an interface between computer hardware and user
- Process of Loading the operating system in the memory when computer is switched ON is called Booting
- Important operating system are Linux, DOS, Windows, Mac OS, Unix, Ubuntu etc
- Windows operating was developed by Microsoft
- Android operating system for mobile phone was developed by Google
- Mac OS (Macintosh Operating system) was developed by Apple
- LINUX operating system was developed by Linus Benedict Torvalds
- Warm boot or Soft boot is one method of resetting a computer system that is already powered ON
- The process of turning ON the computer after it has been powered OFF is known as Cold boot or hard boot
- Software package known as "India's own PC operating system" – BOSS (Bharat Operating Systems Solution)

- BOSS is a free software which supports 18 languages
- BOSS was developed by C-DAC(Chennai)

Super Computer

- Father of super computer- Seymour Cray
- Father of Indian super computer – Dr.Vijay P Bhatkar
- Super computers are used for very complex calculation. Used for the application in Aerospace, Geology, oil explorations, molecular dynamics etc..
- First super computer CDC 6600
- India's first super computer Param 8000
- PARAM is a series of super computers developed by C-DAC in Pune under the leadership of Dr.Vijay P Bhatkar
- C-DAC was setup in 1998
- First director of C-DAC - Dr.Vijay P Bhatkar
- Super computers developed by India are EKA, PARAM, KABRU, BLUEGENE
- The super computer Param Kanchenjunga was launched in Sikkim

Programming Language

- Language that can be used to create programmes is known as programming language
- A programming language is a primary interface of a programmer with a computer

Low level Languages - Two types of low level languages are Machine languages and Assembly Languages

Machine Languages

- Binary language is used as machine language
- Computer performs all the arithmetical and logical operation in binary form (o's and 1's)
- Only one language understood by the computer is machine language

Assembly Language

- Assembly language is a second generation low level language
- Assembly language uses symbolic codes to represent corresponding machine codes
- Assembly languages are faster than high level languages

High level language

- High level language uses English words and familiar mathematical symbols
- Programs written in high level language has to be converted to machine language before execution
- Examples for high level languages are BASIC, FORTRAN, ALGOL, COBOL, LISP, PROLOG, C, C++, Java, Visual Basic, Python etc
- Programming language used for business data processing – COBOL (Common Business Oriented Language)
- Languages used the creation of web pages HTML, PHP, Java script etc
- HTML was developed by Tim Berners Lee

Bug and Debug

- Error in software or programs is known as bug
- Process of eliminating errors in programs- Debugging
- Y2K bug is also known as Millennium Bug

Translators

- Translators are programmes used to convert a program written to other languages to machine language. Eg. Assembler, Compiler, Interpreter

Computer networks

- In a computer network computers are connected to each other for communication
- Data transmission rate of a communication channel is usually measured in- Bits per second
- Three types of basic computer networks are LAN, MAN and WAN

LAN (Local Area Network)

- Is the network that is usually used inside an office building or classroom
- Most common technologies currently used to build LAN – Ethernet and WiFi

MAN (Metropolitan Area Network)

- Network that spread over a city
- Network that is used in cable TV connection is MAN

WAN (Wide Area Network)

- WAN spans a relatively large geographical area

- WAN interconnects countries
- Biggest wide area network is Internet

PAN (Personal Area Network)

- Is a communication network connecting personal devices

INTERNET

- Father of Internet – Vinton Cerf
- Several thousands of individual computer networks are interconnected to form Internet
- Internet protocol suit is commonly is known as TCP/IP (Transmission Control Protocol/Internet Protocol)
- The network which is considered as the ancient form of Internet- ARPANET (American Defense Department)
- Internet in India was started by VSNL (Videsh Sanchar Nigam Limited)

IP Address

- IP Address is a unique numerical value assigned to each device participating in a conputer network

E-mail

- E-mail was introduced by Ray Tomlinson
- Unwanted or non requested E-mails received in a folder is known as spam

World Wide Web

- WWW is a system of interlinked documents assessed through internet
- Headquarters of WWW is Geneva
- Pages consist of information on WWW is known as web page
- Web browsers retrieve webpages from web servers
- URL is a web address which indicates web page
- Cookies are created when user's browswe loads particular websites

Protocol

HTTP

- Hypertext Transfer Protocol (HTTP). HTTP Protocol defines how messages are formatted and transmitted and what actions web servers and browsers should take

- URL begins with http://

HTTPS

- Hypertext Transfer Protocol Secure (HTTPS). It is a secure form of HTTP.
- It means all communication between browser and website is encrypted
- URL begins with https://

FTP

- File Transfer Protocol (FTP)
- It is used in a computer network to copy large files from remote computer to requester's computer

WAP

- Wireless Application Protocol WAP)
- Used in wireless devices like mobile phones to use Internet

ARP

- Address Resolution Protocol (ARP)
- Used for mapping the IP address to a hardware address

SMTP

- Simple Mail Transfer Protocol (SMTP)
- Protocol that helps to send e – mails

POP3

- Post Office Protocol (POP 3)
- Protocol which is used to receive e - mail

Search engine

- A software that is designed to search for information the world wide web
- First search engine – Archie (1990)
- Important search engines are Google, Yahoo, Bing, Ask.com

Web Browser

- It is a software application to retrieve and view information over World Wide Web
- Important web browsers are Google chrome, Mozilla firefox, Internet Explorer, Safari, Opera, Epic

- First Web Browser is Nexus (1990)
- Fastest web browser – Safari (Developed by APPLE)
- First web browser developed in India is Epic (Developed by Hidden Reflux, Bengaluru)

Social Networking

- Social networking service is a web based platform to build social network among people having same interest, activities and backgrounds
- Popular networking sites are Facebook, Whatsapp, Twitter, Linkedin, My space, Skype, Google plus

Cyber crimes

- **Snooping** – Is an unauthorized access to another person's or company's data
- **Defamation** – Act of any intentional false communication that harms the reputation of an individual, business, product, government or nation. Defamation is also known as calumny, Traducement or Vilification
- **Data diddling** – Unauthorized changing of data before or during their input to a computer system
- **Forgery** – Forgery includes counterfeit currency notes, postage and revenue stamps, mark sheets, etc can be forged using sophisticated devices, printers and scanners
- **Phishing** – Practice of sending fake emails in the name of reputed companies to retrieve personal information such as passwords and credit card details
- **E-mail bombing** – Repeatedly sending an e-mail message to a particular address for abuse
- **E-mail spamming** – Use of E- mails for sending unsolicited bulk e-mails and commercial messages over the internet
- **E-mail spoofing** –Creation of E-mail messages with fake sendor address to mislead the recipient
- **Pornography** – The portrayal of sexual acts for the purpose of sexual excitement
- **Software cracking** – Modification of software to remove or disable features which are undesirable by a person
- **Software piracy** – Unauthorized copying, reproduction, use or manufacture of product is called software piracy
- **Password sniffer** – A small program that monitor and retrieve the user name or password of network users during their login

- **Web Jacking** – Hacking of websites by password cracking and alteration of contents for fulfilling political objectives or money
- **Cyber Stalking (Cyber bullying)**- Practice of using Internet to harass or threaten someone
- **Hacking** – Process of unauthorized access of information system is known as hacking. Hacking comes under section 66 of IT act 2000
- **Identity theft** – Requirement of identifying information without permission and using fraudulently to obtain goods and services
- **Intellectual Property right (IPR)** – Intellectual Property refers to creations of mind: inventions, literary and artistic works etc. IPR is a general term for assignment of property rights through patents, copyrights and trademarks
- **Denial of service (DOS)** – An attack meant to shutdown a machine or network, making it inaccessible to its intended users

Computer virus

- A virus is a computer program that can damage the operations of a computer system
- General full form of VIRUS – Vital Information Resource Under Siege
- Examples for computer viruses – TEXAS Virus, Nimda, Blaster, I Love You, Guppy, Melissa, Slammer
- First computer virus – Brain

Antivirus

- A computer software which is used to prevent, detect and delete the presence of VIRUS in a computer
- Examples are Avast, McAfee, AVG Antivirus, Kaspersky, Norton, Avira

Malwares

- Malware is a general term used to refer malicious softwares that can harm the computer
- Examples are Computer Viruses, Worms, Trojan horses, Spyware, Copycat etc.

Ransomware

- Ransomeware make the user unable to access the system displaying some kind of screen demanding some form of payment to have the computer unlocked
- Examples are Wanna Cry, Petya, Golden Eye, Crysis, Locky, Cryptolocker, Powerware, Cryptowall, Cerber, Hydra Crypt

File Extentions

- .txt – Text file
- .pdf – Portable document format file
- .gif – Image file
- .jpg – JPEG image file
- .mpg – Animation /movie file
- .mp3 – Audio file
- .mov – Video file
- .html – Web page file
- .docx – MS Word
- .pptx – MS Powerpoint
- .xlsx – MS Excel
- .accdb – MS Access

General Keyboard Shortcuts

- CTRL+C - Copy
- CTRL+X - Cut
- CTRL+V - Paste
- CTRL+S - Save
- CTRL+P - Print
- CTRL+Y - Redo
- CTRL+Z - Undo
- CTRL+A - Select all
- CTRL+H - Replace
- CTRL+F - Find
- CTRL+G - Go to
- CTRL+D - To open font dialog box in MS Word
- F5 - Refresh
- Alt+F4 - Exit
- Alt+Tab - Switch between minimized applications

ABBREVIATIONS

- AI – Artificial Intelligence
- CD – Compact Disk
- COBOL – Common Business Oriented Language

- CAPTCHA – Completely Automated Public Turing test to tell Computers and Humans Apart
- DTP – Desk Top Publishing
- E Com – Electronic Commerce
- FM – Frequency Modulation
- GPRS – General Packet Radio Service
- GPS – Global Positioning System
- GUI – Graphical User Interface
- IMEI – International Mobile Equipment Identity
- ISP – Internet Service Provider
- JPEG – Joint Photographic Expert Group
- MODEM – Modulator Demodulator
- OCR – Optical Character Reader
- OMR – Optical Mark Reader
- PDF – Portable Document Format
- SIM – Subscriber Identity Module
- SMS – Short Message Service
- URL – Uniform Resource Locator
- USB – Universal Serial Bus
- WiFi – Wireless Fidelity

Artificial Intelligence

Artificial Intelligence, or AI, is when machines and computers are built to do things that usually need human intelligence. That means AI can learn, think, solve problems, and even talk or write – just like people.

How Did AI Come Into Our Lives?

A Quick Trip Down AI Memory Lane

- 1950: Alan Turing asks, "Can machines think?" (He gave us the Turing Test!)
- 1956: The term "Artificial Intelligence" was first used at Dartmouth College.
- 1966: The first chatbot, called ELIZA, was made to talk like a human.
- 1997: A robot named Deep Blue beat the world chess champion!
- 2011: Watson, an AI system, won the quiz show Jeopardy!
- 2016 and after: AI started helping with driving cars, translating language, solving medical problems, and much more!

Top 100 AI Tools

The definitive ranking of the 100 most-used AI tools right now, based on real traffic signals across 20K+ tools in the directory. Rankings are calculated from a popularity score (0–10) derived from traffic signals across the directory.

1. ChatGPT

10.0/10

ChatGPT is an advanced language model developed by OpenAI, based on the GPT-4 architecture."GPT" stands for "Generative Pre-trained Transformer," designed for natural language processing. ChatGPT offers a general-purpose AI chatbot assistant that can help with a variety of tasks in different areas. You can use ChatGPT for free, but it also offers a premium model based on subscription that can provide you with access to more advanced models and extra features like DALL-E, Custom GPTs, memory, File chat, and more.

2. Microsoft Copilot

9.9/10

Copilot offers a research assistant, personal planner, and creative partner at your side whenever you search the web. With this set of AI-powered features, you can use it for a variety of tasks to help you with daily workflows. Ask your actual question. When you ask complex questions, Bing gives you detailed replies. Get an actual answer. Copilot looks at search results across the web to offer you a summarized answer and links to its sources. Be creative. When you need inspiration, Copilot can help you write poems, stories, or even create you a brand new image. With the Copilot experience, you can also ask follow-up questions such as, "can you explain that in simpler terms," or, "give me more options" to get different and even more detailed answers in your search. However, in Copilot, each conversation will have a limited number of interactions, to keep the interactions grounded in search.

3. Bing Image Creator

9.6/10

Bing's Image Creator is an AI-powered tool that allows users to generate images from text descriptions. Users can create unique visuals by simply entering descriptive prompts, and the tool uses advanced AI to bring those ideas to life. The service is integrated into Bing, with options for enhancing image generation speed through the use of Microsoft Rewards points. Points can be earned by engaging in activities like searching on Bing. The platform currently supports sign-ins through personal or work/school accounts, and it is gradually expanding to more regions. Image Creator can generate diverse imagery, including scenes like spring carnivals, underwater cities, rainbow waterfalls, and northern lights vistas. The tool is subject to occasional usage delays or regional restrictions, and users are encouraged to check back if they experience issues.

4. Canva AI

9.4/10

Canva's AI Image Generators is a suite of tools that empowers users to turn text into visuals, offering a range of art styles and customization options. With Magic Media, users can generate images from text prompts, while Create an Image, powered by Dream Lab, allows uploading a reference image to apply new aesthetics or textures. This tool supports multiple user groups, including content creators, entrepreneurs, and budding artists, providing a cost-efficient way to generate captivating branding materials and push the limits of creative possibilities. AI Image Generators are available for use with limited free options, and users can choose from various styles, ratios, and editing tools to customize their images. The tool ensures safe and responsible use through automated reviews and user reporting. Additionally, users can access a library of free images, icons, and graphics, and enjoy features like photo editing, background removal, and text-to-photo functions.

5. Google Gemini

9.3/10

Gemini is an AI chatbot and assistant provided by Google. It provides direct access to Google's advanced artificial intelligence capabilities. It utilizes large language models that have learned from an extensive database of trillions of words and understand the intricate patterns in human communication. This enables Gemini to respond to prompts in a natural conversational manner. As it interacts with users, Gemini continuously improves through feedback, but should be viewed as a tool with limitations, not possessing its own thoughts or feelings. Gemini's primary features include its direct connection to Google's advanced AI systems and the use of large language models. This combination allows for exceptional understanding, processing, and generation of human-like responses to various prompts. Users can explore a wide range of applications for Gemini, from explaining complex concepts to brainstorming ideas. However, it is crucial to remember that while Gemini can assist with tasks such as writing or answering questions, it cannot replace personal relationships or make significant life decisions. It should be treated as an aid rather than a substitute for real-life connections and personal responsibility. "Gemini" caters to individuals from diverse backgrounds and age groups who seek assistance with writing, learning, planning, and general information gathering. Its human-like responses in everyday language patterns make it an excellent resource for educational purposes or when seeking inspiration for creative projects. Students, writers, and professionals alike can benefit from Gemini as it expands their knowledge and generates ideas.

6. Character AI

8.9/10

Character.ai lets users create and interact with personalized AI characters. Using advanced natural language processing, it enables real-time, dynamic conversations with customizable characters. These can be tailored for various use cases, including entertainment, education, and customer support, offering a highly engaging and adaptable AI experience.

7. Deepseek

8.7/10

DeepSeek represents a major advancement in AI technology, offering leading performance open source LLM combined with enhanced speed for its users. It has achieved a significant breakthrough in inference speed compared to earlier models, positioning itself at the forefront of open-source capabilities while rivaling even the most sophisticated closed-source models worldwide. DeepSeek-V3.2 is now fully available and provides free access, inviting users to experience this intelligent model firsthand through its API. This powerful tool not only promises an improved user experience but also redefines possibilities for developers who wish to build with it. By offering both English and Chinese language support, DeepSeek-V3 aims to cater to a global audience, emphasizing inclusivity in technological innovation.

8. DALL-E 2

8.6/10

Dall·2 is an AI system that is capable of creating realistic images and art through natural language descriptions.It combines different concepts, attributes, and styles to generate original and photorealistic images. The tool also allows users to edit existing images with natural language captions, add or remove elements, and create different variations from the original. Safety measures have been implemented to prevent the generation of harmful content and to mitigate potential risks.

9. Grok AI

8.6/10

GrokisaconversationalAIchatbotdevelopedbyxAI,Grokisdesignedtoenhance user interaction by providing answers to a wide range of questions, including those that might be considered "spicy" or controversial, which other AI systems typically avoid. Grokutilizesalargelanguagemodel(LLM)toengageusersindialogue,makingitcapableof understandingandgeneratinghuman-likeresponses.Itcanaccessreal-timedatathroughthe socialmediaplatformX(formerlyTwitter),allowingittoprovideup-to-dateinformation. The latest version, Grok-1.5V, is multimodal, meaning it can process both text and visual inputs, such as documents and images.

10. Claude AI

8.5/10

Claude is a next generation AI assistant built by Anthropic and trained to be safe, accurate, and secure to help you do your best work. It is designed to be skillful, flexible, and customizable to suit the needs of each user. With a natural conversation style, it can provide relevant and accurate answers to user questions. Claud is always available and can handle rote office work, freeing up time for more complex challenges. It is trained to be trustworthy and can integrate with existing product toolchains with minimal effort. Claude is specially known for it's code generation ability, advanced reasoning and safety.

11. Perplexity AI

8.5/10

Perplexity AI chat tool aimed at acting as an extremely powerful search engine . The tool uses large language models to answer questions posed by users. It is an answer engine that aims to deliver accurate answers to questions using AI . They also have a flagship product called Perplexity which is a superpower for curiosity that lets users ask questions or get instant summaries while browsing the internet

12. Notion AI

8.4/10

Notion AI is an integrated AI assistant designed to enhance productivity within the Notion workspace. It offers a range of features, including a powerful Q&A function, writing assistance, and table autofill capabilities. Users can ask questions to quickly retrieve information from their wikis, projects, and docs, aiding in efficient knowledge management. The writing assistant helps with brainstorming, drafting, and editing text directly within Notion, while the table autofill feature transforms large datasets into actionable insights. Notion AI also supports language translation and technical jargon simplification. Security is prioritized with features like encryption, advanced permissions, and compliance with GDPR and CCPA. Enterprise users benefit from additional security tools, single sign-on, and user provisioning. Notion AI is versatile, catering to various team functions and personal use cases, making it a comprehensive tool for improving workflow and collaboration.

13. QuillBot AI

8.4/10

QuillBot is a writing and editing tool that offers various features to assist users in rewriting text, checking grammar and plagiarism, generating citations, and creating content. Its paraphrasing tool allows users to rewrite text in a unique, yet contextually accurate manner. QuillBot also features an AI chat function for brainstorming and writing assistance, a summarizer for condensing long texts, and a translator for instant translation. Additionally, users can generate high-quality content with the help of QuillBot's creative modes and citation generator. The tool is available as a Chrome extension, making it easily accessible across multiple platforms.QuillBot's features are designed to help professionals, students, and content creators produce polished and professional writing. Overall, QuillBot aims to simplify the writing process and save users time and effort.

14. Google AI Studio

8.4/10

Google AI Studio provides a unified platform for accessing and testing Gemini multimodal models across text, image, audio, and video. Developers can use Gemini models, Imagen for image generation, Veo for video generation, and Gemini TTS for controllable single- and multi-speaker audio via API and SDK. The integrated playground supports prompt testing and rapid iteration for tasks such as code generation, reasoning, and content creation. Deployment features include one-click deployment, API key and project management, and centralized monitoring of usage, rate limits, and logs. Comprehensive documentation, quickstart guides, and code samples for Python, Node.js, and REST streamline API integration and app development. Centralized dashboards and monitoring tools help teams track usage, manage resources, and troubleshoot models in production.

15. DeepL Translate

8.3/10

DeepL Translate is renowned for its accuracy and nuanced translations, outpacing major competitors like Google, Microsoft, and Facebook. It supports translation for 32 languages, including popular pairs like Spanish to English and French to English. The tool offers multiple translation modes, including text and document translation for formats such as PDF, DOCX, and PPTX.DeepL Write enhances writing by correcting grammar and punctuation, rephrasing sentences, and refining tone. It features automatic language detection and provides more fluent translations compared to other services.DeepL's robust AI capabilities ensure high-quality translations that capture the meaning and context of the original text, making it a preferred choice for millions of users globally.

16. Nano Banana 2

8.1/10

Nano Banana 2, the latest evolution of Google's image generation model, is designed to deliver lightning-fast creativity alongside advanced intelligence. Building on the success of Nano Banana Pro, Nano Banana 2 combines Gemini Flash's speed with enhanced world knowledge, allowing users to create stunning, photorealistic visuals at incredible speeds. Offering precise instruction following, subject consistency (maintaining character fidelity up to 14 objects), production-ready specs for any resolution from 512px to 4K, and integrated web search grounding for accurate depictions. This powerful tool is now available across Google products – including Gemini app, Search, AI Studio, Google Cloud, and Flow – making it ideal for marketing mockups, data visualizations, storyboarding, and generating high-quality assets for social media and beyond.

17. Doubao

8.1/10

18. Shutterstock Image generator

8.0/10

19. Remove.bg

8.0/10

20. Grok Imagine 2.0

8.0/10

21. Quark

8.0/10

22. Suno

8.0/10

23. CapCut

7.9/10

24. Grammarly

7.9/10

Grammarly is an AI-powered writing assistant designed to enhance the quality of your writing.It offers a range of tools including grammar checking, plagiarism detection, and paraphrasing, helping users craft professional, clear, and convincing text effortlessly. Grammarly provides personalized suggestions based on context and audience, ensuring the right tone and style.It integrates seamlessly with various applications like Slack, Outlook, and Notion, eliminating the need for context switching. With a strong emphasis on security, Grammarly ensures user data is never sold or used for advertising.It is trusted by over 70,000 teams and 30 million individuals, significantly improving productivity and writing quality across different sectors.

25. Sora2

7.9/10

Sora is an AI model designed by OpenAI to convert text instructions into vivid, lifelike video scenes.

26. Veo3

7.9/10

Veo3 is an advanced video generation model that creates high-quality 4K visuals with realistic motion.

27. Flow - Google

7.9/10

28. Picsart

7.9/10

29. Qwen Chat

7.8/10

30. Github Copilot

7.8/10

31. Fotor AI avatar generator

7.7/10

32. Gamma

7.7/10

33. Le Chat - Mistral

7.7/10

34. Miro AI

7.7/10

35. ZeroGPT

7.6/10

36. Zoom AI Companion

7.6/10

Create, embed, and share personalized AI chat apps without coding using Dialogly.

37. TurboScribe

7.6/10

TurboScribe is an AI-powered transcription tool offering ultra-fast conversion of audio and video files to text.

38. SlidesGo

7.6/10

Slidesgo's AI Presentation Maker is a free tool that generates presentations with customizable slides and design styles

39. Namecheap Logo Maker

7.5/10

40. ElevenLabs

7.5/10

41. Beacons AI

7.5/10

42. Tableau

7.5/10

43. Loveable.dev

7.5/10

44. InVideo

7.4/10

Invideo AI transforms text into high-quality, cinematic videos with AI-generated visuals, voiceovers, and subtitles.

45. VSCO

7.4/10

46. Photoroom

7.4/10

47. GPT Zero

7.4/10

48. Wave.Video

7.4/10

49. OpenClaw AI

7.4/10

50. Civitai

7.4/10

51. Midjourney

7.4/10

52. Gauth AI

7.4/10

53. Simplified

7.3/10

54. Manus AI

7.3/10

55. QuickTools by Picsart

7.3/10

56. Thomson Reuters

7.3/10

57. Fotor

7.3/10

58. Hostinger

7.3/10

59. Epidemic Soun

7.3/10

60. Cutout Pro

7.3/10

61. Kling AI

7.3/10

62. Spotify DJ

7.3/10

Spotify Web Player offers a browser interface to stream a vast music and podcast catalog.

63. Scribbr

7.3/10

64. Poe.com

7.3/10

Poe.com is a web tool for chatting with multiple AI models from one interface.

65. AntiGravity - Google

7.3/10

66. HeyGen

7.2/10

67. Mistral AI

7.2/10

68. Pixlr

7.2/10

69. HiggsField AI

7.2/10

70. DeepAI

7.2/10

71. Bitbucket

7.2/10

Bitbucket is a Git platform integrated with Jira, designed for development teams.

72. VEED

7.2/10

73. Mailchimp

7.2/10

74. Movavi Picverse

7.2/10

75. MiriCanvas

7.2/10

76. Genspark.ai

7.2/10

77. Base44

7.2/10

78. Replit

7.2/10

79. Portaly

7.2/10

80. Intercom

7.2/10

81. Upscale.media

7.2/10

82. Hint

7.2/10

83. Leonardo.ai

7.2/10

84. Reimagine

7.2/10

85. ClipDrop Replace Background

7.2/10

86. Uncrop

7.2/10

87. AI Face Swap

7.2/10

AI Face Swap lets you swap faces in photos, GIFs, and videos without signup.

88. AI Writer by Picsart

7.1/10

89. Blackbox AI

7.1/10

90. n8n.io

7.1/10

91. OpenArt Photo Booth

7.1/10

The AI Workspace is a tool that generates imaginary images using AI.

92. Stock Image Transformer

7.1/10

Upload a stock photo and use AI to generate multiple variations that match desired style, composition, and color.

93. Venice.ai

7.1/10

94. Remaker Face Swap

7.1/10

Face vary is a user-friendly online face changer tool powered by AI.

95. Apeture (by Lexica)

7.1/10

Lexica Aperture is a V5 texttoimage AI that generates up to 960×1440pixel images from naturallanguage prompts.

96. Bubble

7.1/10

Bubble is a nocode platform that lets users build web, mobile, and SaaS apps quickly.

97. Adobe Speech Enhancer

7.1/10

98. RF AI Images

7.1/10

99. Chatsonic

7.1/10

100. GrokiPedia

7.1/10

Grokipedia is an AI-driven knowledge base featuring over 885,279 articles and a user-friendly search function.

Part- 6
Topic wise Practice MCQs

CHAPTER-1

INDIAN AND INTERNATIONAL FOOD LAWS

(AN OVERVIEW)

"Find purpose. The means will follow" -Mahatma Gandhi

1. A Sample for testing to Accredited laboratory is send by
   a) Food Safety officer b) Designated officer
   c) Food Business Operator d) None of these
2. When a sample has been taken by food safety officer, he will send to food analyst on
   a) On same day itself b) Next 2 days
   c) Next day d) **Succeeding working day**
3. The food analyst issue the report in
   a) Form V A b) Form VI
   c) Form VI A d) **Form VII A**
4. In case of imported food articles the food analyst shall send the report within period of
   a) 2 days b) 7 days
   c) **5 days** d) 14 days
5. Any person aggrieved by any decision or order of the tribunal may file appeal to high court within period of
   a) 15 days b) **60 days**
   c) 30 days d) 45 days
6. All proceeding before Adjudicating officer are deemed to be
   a) Non Judicial proceedings b) Quasi Judicial Proceedings
   c) **Judicial Proceedings** d) None of these
7. The appeal by Food Business Operator to designated officer against the report of food analyst to be made within
   a) **30 days** b) 15 days
   c) 7 days d) 14 days
8. Any food articles delivered to consumer by E - commerce FBO, shall have shelf life of ___ Before expiry at the time of delivery to consumer
   a) 30% or 15 days b) **30% or 45 days**
   c) 40% or 30 days d) 45% or 30 days

9. A raw milk is bought to a dairy plant by a producer or farmer within____ of milking

a) 5 hours b) **4 hours**

c) 3 hours d) 2 hours

10. The requirement of list of ingredients, Lot no, Nutritional information may not be on package label

a) **Less than 100 sq. cm** b) More than 100 sq. cm

c) More than 150 sq. Cm d) All of the above

11. Printing Inks for use on food packages shall confirm to

a) IS : 12247 b) **IS : 15495**

c) IS : 13576 d) IS : 13601

12. The wax used for coating paper or board for packaging of food shall be

a) White bees wax b) **Paraffin wax**

c) Yellow bees wax d) Carnauba wax

13. Maximum permitted amount of Non- volatile substances released from material or article into food stimulant is

a) Specific Migration Limit b) **Over –All Migration Limit**

c) Compounded Migration Limit d) None of these

14. Every manufacturer and packer of fortified food shall give undertaking on quality assurance

a) Monthly b) **Twice in a year**

c) Quarterly d) Once in a year

15. ___ are not defined under section 22 of FSSA act 2006

a) Functional food b) **Staple food**

c) Novel food d) Organic food

16. Health supplements shall use additives mentioned under

a) Schedule – V A b) Schedule – V E

c) Schedule – V F d) **All of these**

17. The International food standard body is

a) Indian Council of Medical Research b) Codex Alimentarius

c) **Codex Alimentarius Commission** d) FAO of United Nations

18. The tagline on package of fortified food is

a) Swasth Poshan Sampoorna Jeevan

b) **Sampoorna Poshan Swasth Jeevan**

c) Swasth Poshan Swasth Jeevan d) None of these

19. The time limit for chemical testing of samples by referral laboratories fixed by FSSAI is

a) **Within 5 working days** b) Within 7 working days

c) Within 10 working days d) Within 15 working days

20. For the purpose of import license from Central Licensing Authority the food importer has to

a) Obtain License from State authority

b) **Register with Director of Foreign Trade**

c) Registration under FSSA d) None of these

21. An up – to date food recall plan is required for FBO'S engaged in

a) Manufacture b) Import

b) Wholesale d) **All of the above**

22. License granted under __ of FSSA

a) **Section 31** b) Section 32

c) Section 33 d) Section 45

23. The procedure for launching prosecution in

a) **Section 42** b) Section 38

c) Section 55 d) Section 44

24. The minimum qualification for appointment of presiding officer of Food Appellate Tribunal is

a) Judicial Magistrate First class b) **District Judge**

c) Additional District Magistrate

d) Retired Food Safety Commissioner

25. In case where special court are established, the offences punishable with imprisonment of __ years tried

a) 3 years b) 5 years

c) **More than 3 years** d) More than 5 years

26. Food additive means

a) Added substance for improving nutritional qualities

b) Normally consumed as a food

c) **Added for technological or Organoleptic properties**

d) None of the above

27. Chief Executive Officer of food authority is appointed by

a) **Central Government** b) Chairman of food authority

c) Selection committee of food authority d) All of the above

28. Scientific panels are established by

a) Chairman of food authority b) **Food authority**

c) CEO of food authority

d) Selection committee of food authority

29. Food article if injurious to health can be

a) **Only unsafe food** b) Only substandard
c) Only misbranded d) None of the above

30. The food Safety Supervisor course and certification is undertaken by

a) ITGFSAN b) FoSCoRIS
c) **FosTaC** d) All of these

31. Legal metrology Act came into force in

a) 1986 b) **2009**
c) 1975 d) 1940

32. Chapter ___ of LM act is related to offences and penalties

a) IV b) **V**
c) II d) VI

33. Quality council of India was setup in the year of

a) 1998 b) 1996
c) **1997** d) 1990

34. Total urea content in the milk shall not be more than

a) **700 ppm** b) 500 ppm
c) 200 ppm d) 100 ppm

35. TSS of Tomato puree Not less than

a) **9.0 percent** b) 5.0 percent
c) 4.0 percent d) 1.0 percent

36. TSS of Tomato Paste Not less than

a) **25 percent** b) 50 percent
c) 10 percent d) 33 percent

37. Refined sugar contains sucrose Not less than

a) **99.5 per cent by weight** b) 97 per cent by weight
c) 95 per cent by weight d) 90 per cent by weight

38. PLANTATION WHITE SUGAR (commonly known as sugar contain sucrose Not less than

a) **98 per cent by weight** b) 90 per cent by weight
c) 80 per cent by weight d) 88 per cent by weight

39. Silver leaf food grade-shall be in the form of sheets, free from creases and folds and shall contain not less than

a) **99.9 per cent of silver** b) 95.9 per cent of silver
c) 94.9 per cent of silver d) 97.9 per cent of silver

40. Ponceau 4R, Carmoisine and Erythrosine imparts

a) **Red colour**
b) Green colour
c) Blue colour
d) Black colour

41. Tartrazine and Sunset Yellow FCF imparts

a) **Yellow colour**
b) Blue colour
c) Red colour
d) Black colour

42. Indigo Carmine and Indigo Brilliant Blue FCF imparts

a) **Blue**
b) Red
c) Black
d) Green

43. Fast Green FCF imparts

a) **Green**
b) Yellow
c) Black
d) Blue

44. The maximum limit of colour content in final beverage for consumption shall not exceed ___and that of aluminium content shall not exceed____ of the final beverage for consumption

a) **8.3 ppm, 4.4 ppm**
b) 5 ppm, 4 ppm
c) 7 ppm, 2 ppm
d) 8 ppm, 1 ppm

45. Maximum limit of Artificial Sweetener Saccharin Sodium in Carbonated Water

a) **100 ppm**
b) 200 ppm
c) 600 ppm
d) 500 ppm

46. Class I preservative shall be

a) Common salt.
b) Sugar.
c) Dextrose.
d) **All of the above**

47. Emulsifying and stabilizing agents may be added to Fruit Products are

a) Pectin
b) Sodium alginate
c) Calcium alginate
d) **All of the above**

48. Flour treatment agents are

a) Ammonium chloride
b) L- cystein mono hydrochloride
c) Ammonium phosphate
d) Benzoyl peroxide
e) **All of the above**

49. The quantity of sample of food to be sent to the Food Analyst of Infant Food/ Weaning Food

a) **500 gms**
b) 100 gms
c) 400 gms
d) 800 gms

50. Iodized salt (when fortified with Iodine) - The total matter insoluble in water where an anticaking agent has been added shall not exceed

a) **2.2 per cent**
b) 4 per cent
c) 5 per cent
d) 6 per cent

51. Joint FAO/WHO Expert Committee on food additives (JECFA) active since

a) **1956** b) 1985
c) 1966 d) 1999

52. Joint FAO/WHO Expert Meetings on Pesticide Residues (JMPR) active since

a) 1977 b) 1955
c) 1965 d) **1963**

53. Joint FAO/WHO Expert Meetings on Microbiological Risk Assessment (JEMRA) active since

a) **2000** b) 1985
c) 2003 d) 2005

54. Joint FAO/WHO Expert Meetings on Pesticide Specification (JMPS) active since

a) **2002** b) 2005
c) 2006 d) 2009

55. JEMNU Stands for

a) **Joint FAO/WHO Expert Meeting on Nutrition**
b) Joint FAO/WHO Expert Monitoring on Nutrition
c) Joint FAO/WHO Expert Machinery on Nutrition
d) Joint FAO/WHO Export Meeting on Nutrition

56. TBT (Technical Barriers to Trade) Agreement covers

a) Technical regulations (mandatory) b) Standards (Voluntary)
c) Conformity assessment Procedures d) **All of the above**

57. SPS (Sanitary and Phytosanitory measures) Agreement protects

a) Codex Alimentarius - Human health
b) OIE – World Organization for Animal Health
c) IPPC – International Plant Protection Convention, FAO
d) **All of the above**

58. BIS has their own laboratory for checking quality of product at

a) Delhi b) Mysore
c) **Patna** d) Kochi

59. According to FSSA, Penalty for misleading advertisement may be extended to

a) 2 lakh rupees b) 5 lakh rupees
c) 7 lakh rupees d) **10 lakh rupee**

60. Which agency provides advice and support on levels of radionuclide contamination in foods and on food irradiation

a) **IAEA** b) IPPC
c) ISO d) BIS

61. Class Title of Cocoa bean, Coco nib, Coco mass, Cocoa press cakes, Cocoa powder (Fine/Dust) is

a) **Cocoa solids** b) Milk solids

c) Cocoa d) Cocoa powder

62. Area of principal display panel up to 100 cms^2 the minimum size of diameters is

a) 1 mm b) 7mm

c) **3mm** d) 4mm

63. Maximum permitted level of additives such as BHA and BHT is

a) 2% b) 1.5%

c) **0.5%** d) 0.10%

64. Polydextrose, Soybean oligosaccharides, Isomalto- oligosaccharides & Fructo oligosaccharides are

a) **Prebiotic compounds** b) Probiotic compounds

c) Preservatives` d) None of these

65. Packaging material in direct contact with food products called

a) **Primary food packaging** b) Secondary food packaging

c) Teritary food packaging d) Packaging

66. Packaging material which encloses primary food packaging and does not come in direct contact with food products termed as

a) **Secondary Food packaging** b) Primary Food packaging

c) Teritary Food Packaging

67. Recall alert means any alert issued to the public by the

a) Food safety officer b) Food analyst

c) Designated officer d) **Chief Executive Officer**

68. "Unsafe food" means food as defined under

a) clause (zo) of sub- section (1) of section 5 of the Act

b) clause (zy) of sub- section (1) of section 4 of the Act

c) **clause (zz) of sub- section (1) of section 3 of the Act**

69. Objectives of the food recall procedure

a) Ensure removal of food under recall from all stages of food chain in accordance with section 28 of the Act

b) Ensure dissemination of information to concerned consumers and customers

c) Ensure retrieval, destruction or reprocessing of food under recall

d) **All of the above**

70. The person carrying the imported articles of food for personal consumption shall submit the declaration in

a) FORM- 5 b) **FORM- 7**

c) FORM- 8 d) FORM- 9

71. The importer shall submit the declaration in ____for clearance of imported food consignment

a) FORM – 12 b) FORM – 18

c) **FORM – 11** d) FORM - 16

72. Aflatoxin contaminant in all articles of food the limit is

a) 40 μg/kg b) **30 μg/kg**

c) 10 μg/kg d) 20 μg/kg

73. Aflatoxin M1 contaminant limit in milk is

a) **0.5μg/kg** b) 0.75μg/kg

c) 1.05μg/kg d) 1.5μg/kg

74. All pasteurized milk of different classes shall be cooled immediately to a temperature of

a) **10° C** b) 15° C

c) 20° C d) 18° C

75. Chhana or Paneer shall not contain more than____ moisture and the milk fat content not less than___ of dry matter

a) **70%, 50%** b) 30%, 70%

c) 25%, 50% d) 45%, 65%

76. If the sample container received by the FA is found broken condition or unfit for analysis, within how many days should the analyst request the DO to send second part of sample for analysis - **7 days**

77. WTO Head Quarters

a) Dublin, Ireland b) Berlin, Germany

c) **Geneva, Switzerland** d) Ottawa, Canada

78. The solvent extraction oil, De oiled meal & edible flour order

a) **1967** b) 1962

c) 1973 d) 1975

79. Central License: For Turnover above

a) **20 Crore** b) 20 Lakhs

c) 10 Crore d) 5 Crore

80. Dry wine is a wine that contains up to ___ Sugar

a) **0.9 %** b) 2 %

c) 2.3 % d) 1.75 %

81. Sweet wine is a wine that contains more than___ sugar

a) **4.5 %** b) 10 %

c) 7 % d) 9 %

82. Perry is a wine prepared from

a) **Pear juice**
b) Apple juice
c) Grape juice
d) Cashew apple

83. Lager beer is prepared by using___ and matured at low temperature

a) Top fermenting yeast
b) Bacteria
c) **Bottom fermenting yeast**
d) *Rhizopus*

84. Ale beer is prepared by using___ and is usually lighter in colour

a) Bottom fermenting yeast
b) *Rhizopus*
c) *Aspergillus*
d) **Top fermenting yeast**

85. If the wine contains more than____ So_2/l the label must declare "Contains sulfur dioxide or Contains sulfite"

a) 20 mg
b) 15 mg
c) 18 mg
d) **10 mg**

86. "Rectified spirit" means spirit purified by distillation to achieve strength of not less than __ alcohol by volume

a) 65 %
b) **95 %**
c) 75 %
d) 50 %

87. Yeast means a unicellular micro-organism responsible for fermentation of sugars to produce

a) Propanol and carbon dioxide
b) Methanol and carbon dioxide
c) **Ethanol and carbon dioxide**
d) Diethyl and carbon dioxide

88. Alcoholic beverage containing more than 0.5 % abv but not more than 8.0 % abv may be called as

a) Medium alcoholic beverage
b) High alcoholic beverage
c) **Low alcoholic beverage**
d) None of these

89. Brandy is an alcoholic beverage made by distillation of

a) **Wine**
b) Beer
c) Mead
d) Honey

90. Fortified wine is a wine with high alcohol content by addition of alcohol provided a minimum____ from fermentation of grapes, grape must fruits

7 %

91. Protein efficiency ratio (PER) be minimum ____if the product other than infant milk substitute claimed to have higher quality protein

a) 7.5
b) 1.5
c) **2.2**
d) 3.5

92. _____is required for normal nerve and heart function

a) **Thiamine** b) Riboflavin

c) Pantothenic acid d) Cholecalciferol

93. _____is necessary to release the energy from food

a) Riboflavin b) Niacin

c) Pyridoxine d) **All of the above**

94.___ supports a healthy immune system

a) **Zinc** b) Folic acid

c) Niacin d) Calcium

95. _____is important for maintaining normal functioning of Nervous system and blood formation

a) **Vitamin B12** b) Vitamin K

c) Vitamin D d) Vitamin A

96. ______is important for foetal development and prevention of birth defects

a) Riboflavin b) Retinol

c) Niacin d) **Folate & Folic acid**

97. In case alcoholic beverages one shall maintain records for a period of____ from date or month of supply from the manufacturer

2 years

98. Cottage Cheese and Creamed Cottage Cheese are ____

a) Semi hard cheese b) **Soft un ripened cheese**

c) Soft ripened cheese d) Hard cheese

99. ____means the systematic measures applied and steps taken by manufacturers and packers of fortified food throughout the manufacturing or packing process to ensure finished food complies with the provisions of Act and regulations

Quality assurance

100. ____means articles of food intended for mass consumption on a daily basis, include rice, wheat, wheat flour, Atta, Maida, Oil, Salt, Milk

a) Necessary foods b) Neutral foods

c) **Staple foods** d) Available foods

CHAPTER-2

Planning Organization and Setting up of Food Analysis Laboratory Including NABL/ ISO/ IEC – 17025: 2017 and Laboratory Safety

1. ILAC International Laboratory Accreditation Cooperation was formed in
   a) October 1950 in Copenhagen
   b) **October 1977 in Copenhagen**
   c) October 1940 in Copenhagen
   d) October 1920 in Copenhagen
2. International arrangements are managed by ILAC in the fields of
   a) Calibration, Testing   b) Medical testing, Inspection
   c) Proficiency testing providers
   d) Reference material producers accreditation
   e) **All of the above**
3. ILAC works closely with the regional co-operation bodies involved in accreditation notably EA in
   a) Asia   b) **Europe**
   c) America   d) Russia
4. ILAC works closely with the regional co-operation bodies involved in accreditation notably APAC in
   a) India   b) Europe
   c) **Asia – Pacific**   d) Russia
5. ILAC works closely with the regional co-operation bodies involved in accreditation notably AFRAC in
   a) **Africa**   b) Europe
   c) America   d) India
6. ILAC works closely with the regional co-operation bodies involved in accreditation notably IAAC in
   a) Norway   b) **America**
   c) Russia   d) Switzerland

7. ILAC works closely with the regional co-operation bodies involved in accreditation notably SADCA in

a) Canada
b) Ireland
c) **Southern Africa**
d) Iceland

8. ILAC works closely with the regional co-operation bodies involved in accreditation notably ARAC in

a) Norway
b) **Arab region**
c) Germany
d) London

9. NABL grants accreditation as per ISO/IEC 17025 for

a) Calibration Laboratories
b) Testing Laboratories
c) **Both A and B**
d) None of these

10. NABL grants accreditation as per ISO/IEC 15189 for

a) Calibration
b) **Medical Testing Laboratories**
c) Proficiency

11. NABL grants accreditation as per ISO/IEC 17043 for

a) Quality control
b) **Proficiency Testing Providers**
c) Hospital
d) Accreditation

12. NABL grants accreditation as per ISO 17034 for

a) Research
b) **Reference Material Producers**
c) Hospital
d) Environment

13. NABL grants accreditation as per ISO/IEC 17020 for

a) Industrial
b) **Inspection Bodies**
c) Environmen
d) Research

14. Expand (MLA)

a) **Multilateral Recognition Arrangements**
b) Multilateral Record Arrangements
c) Multitude Recognition Arrangements
d) Multilateral Recognition Ascent

15. APAC (Asia Pacific Accreditation Cooperation) was established on

a) 1 Jan 2018
b) 1Jan 2017
c) 1 Jan 2013
d) **1 Jan 2019**

16. APAC is the amalgamation of

a) APLAC | b) PAC
c) **Both A and B** | d) None of these

17. APAC's primary role

a) **To manage and expand a mutual recognition bodies in the Asia Pacific region**

b) To manage recognition bodies in the Canada

c) To manage and expand in the Switzerland

d) To manage and expand in the Cuba

18. World Accreditation Day, a global initiative established by IAF and ILAC to promote the value of accreditation on

a) 7 June | b) 2 June
c) 1 June | d) **9 June**

19. Theme of Accreditation for 2022 is

a) **Accreditation: Sustainability in Economic Growth and the Environment**

b) Economic Growth and the Environment

c) Environment Sustainability

d) Accreditation: Third Party recognition

20. Expand MRA

a) Multilateral Recognition Arrangement

b) Mutual Records Arrangement

c) Mutual Recognition Assessment

d) **Mutual Recognition Arrangement**

21. Expand CAB

a) Collateral Accreditation Bodies

b) **Conformity Accreditation Bodies**

c) Collected Accreditation Bodies

d) Controlled Accreditation Bodies

22. Accreditation is the __ party attestation related to a conformity assessment body

a) First | b) **Third**
c) Second | d) None of these

23. Expand CRM

a) Certified Registered Materials | b) Certified Record Materials
c) **Certified Reference Materials** | d) Centered Record Materials

24. In India reference cultures obtained from American Type Culture Collection (ATCC) is located in

a) **Rockville, Maryland** b) Russia

c) Canada d) Africa

25. In India reference cultures obtained from IMTECH located in

a) Delhi b) **Chandigarh (MTCC)**

c) Andhra Pradesh d) Tamil Nadu

26. In India reference cultures obtained from National Collection of Industrial Micro-organisms (NCIM) National Chemical Laboratory (NCL) located in

a) Punjab b) Pondicherry

c) Kerala d) **Pune**

27. In India reference cultures obtained from Christian Medical College (CMC) located in

a) Punjab b) **Vellore**

c) Gujarat d) Assam

28. In India reference cultures obtained from National Institute of Communicable Diseases (NICD) is found in

a) **Delhi** b) Manipur

c) Assam d) West Bengal

29. In India reference cultures obtained from Central Research Institute located in

a) Uttarkhand b) **Kasouli, Himachal Pradesh**

c) Nepal d) Orissa

30. APHA section of 9020B is

a) **Intra laboratory Quality Control Guidelines**

b) Intra laboratory Environmental Guidelines

c) Intra laboratory Industrial Guidelines

d) Intra laboratory Products Guidelines

31. ISO 5725-6 : 1994 represents

a) Sampling

b) Replication

c) **Accuracy (trueness and precision) of measurement method and results**

d) Randomness

32. Expand AOAC

a) Association of Official Agricultural Centre

b) **Association of Official Agricultural Chemists**

c) Association of Agricultural Chemists

d) Association of Official Chemists

33. Expand APHA·

a) American Public Healing Association

b) American Private Health Association

c) Asian Public Health Association

d) American Public Health Association

34. Expand GMO

a) **Genetically Modified Organism**

b) Genetically Monthly Organism

c) Genetically Modified Oil

d) Genetically Modified Organization

35. Applied to qualitative microbiological tests- the lowest number of micro-organisms that can be detected, but in numbers that cannot be estimated accurately called

a) **Limit of Detection** b) Random sample

c) Variablitiy d) Variance

36. As applied to quantitative microbiological tests - The lowest number of micro-organisms within a defined variability that may be determined under the experimental conditions of the method under evaluation termed as

a) Line of Determinated b) Limit of Detour

c) **Limit of Determination**

37. Occurs when the alternative method gives a negative result without confirmation when the reference method gives a positive result. This deviation becomes a false negative result when the true result can be proved as being positive called

a) **Negative Deviation** b) Positive

c) Neutral

38. Occurs when the alternative method gives a positive result without confirmation when the reference method gives a negative result. This deviation becomes a false positive result when the true result can be proved as being negative known as

a) Negative b) **Positive Deviation** -

c) Static

39. Determination of laboratory testing performance by means of inter-laboratory comparisons (ISO Guide 43: 1996) denotes

a) Multitude b) **Proficiency Testing**

c) Accreditation d) Lateral

40. Collective term for reference strain, reference stocks and working cultures called

a) **Reference Cultures** **b)** Observable

c) Stocks d) Numbers

41. Thoroughly investigated method, clearly and exactly describing the necessary conditions and procedures, for the measurement of one or more property values to have accuracy and precision called

a) Mathematical b) **Reference Method**

c) Practical d) Observable

42. A set of separate identical cultures obtained by a single sub-culture from the reference strain (ISO 11133-1:2000) called

a) Conformity b) **Reference Stocks**

c) Lengthy d) Accurate

43. Micro-organisms defined at least to the genus and species level, catalogued and described according to its characteristics and preferably stating its origin (ISO 11133-1:2000). Normally obtained from a recognized national or international collection termed as

a) Samples b) **Reference Strains**

c) Species d) Genus

44. As applied to microbiological tests - The fraction of the total number of positive cultures or colonies correctly assigned in the presumptive inspection (ISO 13843:2000) known as

a) Reliability b) Projection

c) **Sensitivity** **d)** Results

45. Applied to microbiological tests - The fraction of the total number of negative cultures or colonies correctly assigned in the presumptive inspection (ISO 13843:2000) called

a) Reliability b) **Specificity**

c) Graphical d) Testing

46. A primary sub-culture from a reference stock (ISO 11133-1:2000) termed

a) Testing culture b) Presumptive

c) **Working Culture** **d)** None of these

47. Expand (IFGC)

a) **International Fuel Gas Code**

b) International Fuel Gas Campaign

c) International Fuel Gas Captivity d) Indian Fuel Gas Code

48. Expand (LEV)
a) Local external ventilation
b) Local extra ventilation
c) Local exhaust venter
d) **Local exhaust ventilation**

49. Expand (ACH)
a) Aerated Change Rate
b) Air Center Rate
c) **Air Change Rate**
d) Air Change Range

50. Expand (FHES)
a) Funnel Hood Exhaust System
b) Fume Hood Exchange System
c) **Fume Hood Exhaust System**
d) Fume Heavy Exhaust System

51. Bin used for Biohazard – Laboratory waste is
a) **Red Bin**
b) Blue Bin
c) Green Bin
d) Orange Bin

52. Which color bin is used for Ethidium bromide gel, gloves, tubes and tips which contaminated with EtBr
a) Red Bin
b) Blue Bin
c) Yellow Bin
d) **Large grey Bin**

53. Attestation by third party assessment body termed as
a) Recognition
b) **Accreditation**
c) Acceptance
d) Certification

54. Issue of a statement based on a decision following review that fulfillment of specified requirements have been demonstrated called
a) **Attestation**
b) Letter issue
c) Conformity
d) Certification

55. Activity of establishing, with regard to actual or potential problems, provisions for common and repeated use, aimed at the achievement of the optimum degree of order in a given context called
a) **Standardization**
b) Optimization
c) Acceptance
d) None of these

56. *Bacillus subtilis* comes under
a) **Biosafety Level I**
b) Biosafety Level II
c) Biosafety Level III
d) Biosafety Level IV

57. Expand NABCB
a) National Accreditation Bench for Certification Bodies
b) National Association Board for Certification Bodies
c) **National Accreditation Board for Certification Bodies**
d) National Ascent Board for Certification Bodies

58. Expand NRBPT

a) National Record Board for Personnel and Training

b) National Registration Board for Pursue and Training

c) National Registration Board for Personnel and Testing

d) **National Registration Board for Personnel and Training**

59. Expand NABH

a) National Attendance Board for Hospitals and Healthcare

b) National Accreditation Board for Hospitals

c) **National Accreditation Board for Hospitals and Healthcare**

d) National Arrangement Board for Hospitals and Healthcare

60. Expand NABL

a) National Accreditation Board for Testing Laboratories

b) **National Accreditation Board for Testing and Calibration Laboratories**

c) National Board for Testing and Calibration Laboratories

d) National Accreditation Board for Laboratories

61. Expand NBQP

a) **National Board for Quality Promotion**

b) National Board for Quality Products

c) National Board for Quality Processing

d) National Board for Quality Process

62. Expand QIES

a) Quality Infer and Enquiry Services

b) Quality Information and Excise Services

c) **Quality Information and Enquiry Services**

d) Quality Intro and Enquiry Services

63. Crude fat is calculated by formula

% crude fat = (Weight of ether soluble material/Weight of sample) × 100

64. Protein content of food samples is usually determined by

a) **Kjeldahl method** b) Solvent method

c) Liquid extraction method d) Solution content

65. Pectin is Estimated by

a) Soxhlet method b) **Calcium Pectate Method**

c) Solvent method d) None of these

66. Tannins can be estimated by

a) Volumetric
b) Colorimetric method
c) **Both A and B**
d) None of these

67. Polyphenols play important role in protecting __ in some fruits

a) **Ascorbic acid**
b) Tartaric acid
c) Benzoic acid
d) Sulphuric acid

68. Tannins are responsible for undesirable astringency of

a) **Cashew apple**
b) Coconut
c) Banana
d) Apple

69. Tannins are responsible desirable astringency of

a) Apple
b) Apple juice
c) Amla
d) **All of the above**

70. Coliform counts tests includes

a) Presumptive test
b) Confirmed test
c) Completed test
d) **All of the above**

71. Assessment of surface sanitation by

a) **Swab Rinse Method**
b) Disinfection
c) Rubbing
d) Sterlization

72. Microbiological spoilage of canned fruits and vegetables is due to either under processing or post processing contamination by

a) Insects
b) Moisture
c) **Leakage**
d) None of these

73. The pH of most canned fruits ranges from

a) **3.7 to 4.5**
b) 8.4 to 9.0
c) 7.2 to 9.0
d) 1.2 to 6.0

74. *Bacillus stearothermophilus* Causes

a) Sulphide spoilage
b) **Flat sour spoilage**
c) Spoilage
d) None of these

75. *Clostridium thermosaccharolyticum* Causes

a) Soft swell
b) **Hard swell**
c) Swell
d) None of these

76. *Clostridium nigrificans* Causes

a) **Sulphur stinkers**
b) Flat sour
c) Corrosion
d) None of these

77. Mesophilic spore formers Cause

a) Liquefaction
b) **Putrefaction**
c) Gelatinization
d) All of the above

78. Nutritional and biochemical composition are

a) Quality sampling
b) **Proximate Analysis**
c) Quantity sampling
d) Techniques

79. Analysis of specific compounds and elements called

a) **Ultimate Analysis**
b) Analytical
c) Accuracy
d) Precision

80. Lipids and fat-soluble components are

a) **Crude Fat**
b) Protein
c) Fiber
d) Salts

81. Flavonoids and cinnamic acid derivatives are

a) **Tannins**
b) Acids
c) Alcohols
d) Ethanol

82. Tentative or unconfirmed test called

a) Confirmatory test
b) **Presumptive Test**
c) Analytics
d) None of these

83. Spoilage in cans with acid formation without Bulging

a) **Flat Sour Spoilage**
b) Swelling
c) Destruction
d) Crack liners

84. Can spoilage with hydrogen swell and heavy corrosion called

a) **Hard Swell**
b) Soft swell
c) Spoilage
d) None of these

85. Color code for Oxygen gas cylinder is

a) **Black**
b) Red
c) Blue
d) Green

86. Volumetric equipment generally in use in a biological/microbiological testing laboratory are

a) Glass Pipettes
b) Disposable Pipettes
c) Automatic Pipettes
d) Automatic Dispensers

All of the above

87. ___used for routine use should be primary sub-cultures from the reference stock

a) **Working Cultures**
b) Top culture
c) Standard
d) Stock

88. _____ used by the laboratory immediately prior to testing is considered as part of the test procedure

a) Sampling
c) **Sub-sampling**
c) Lot
d) All of the above

89. Expand (BSC)

a) Biological Surface Cabinets
c) Billing Safety Cabinets
c) Best Safety Cabinets
d) **Biological Safety Cabinets**

90. Radiation Producing Machines

a) X-ray radiographic and/or irradiation facilities
b) Accelerator facilities
c) Analytical x-ray machines (e.g., x-ray diffraction, electron microscopes)
d) Cabinet radiography units
e) Accelerators used for radioisotope production
f) **All of the above**

91. Devices Containing Radioactive Materials

a) Sealed sources
b) Irradiators
c) Moisture/density gauges
d) High activity non-sealed sources
e) **All of the above**

92. Non-ionizing radiation sources

a) Lasers
b) Ultraviolet lights
c) Large magnets
d) **All of the above**

93. Expand (LGAC)

a) Laser-Generated Air Container
b) Laser-General Air Contaminants
c) **Laser-Generated Air Contaminants**
d) Low-Generated Air Contaminants

94. Radio Frequency and Microwave Devices ranges to

a) (30 kHz to 50 GHz)
b) (30 kHz to 100 GHz)
c) **(30 kHz to 300 GHz)**
d) (20 kHz to 500 GHz)

95. *Salmonella*, *Toxoplama sp*, *Hepatitis* B virus, *E. coli* comes under

a) Bio – safety level I
b) **Bio – safety level II-**
c) Bio – safety level II+
d) Bio – safety level III

96. Cylinder colour of flammable gases is

a) Blue
b) Brown
c) **Red**
d) Green

97. (MAQ)

a) Maximum Allowable Quality
b) **Maximum Allowable Quantity**
c) Maximum Allowed Quantity
d) Minimum Allowable Quantity

98. (LIMS)

a) Laboratory Information Management
b) **Laboratory Information Management System**
c) Laboratory Informed Management System
d) Laboratory Information Merit System

99. Mixing of flammable solvents and corrosive chemicals is a

a) Physical hazard
b) **Chemical hazard**
c) Biological hazard
d) None of these

100. Nutritional parameters are

a) Total fat
b) Total protein
c) Amino acids
d) **All of the above**

CHAPTER-3

Principles of Food Preservation, Processing and Packaging

1. Naturally occurring pigments Quinones in
   a) Roots b) Bark
   c) **Both A and B** d) Stem
2. Naturally occurring pigments Cochineal found in
   a) Fruits b) **Cochineala Insect (*Dactylopius coccus*)**
   c) Vegetables d) None of these
3. Naturally occurring pigments Polyphenols present in
   a) Carrot b) **Tea leaf**
   c) Beetroot d) Radish
4. Quality Assurance was developed during the 1980s, based on the principles of
   a) **Good Manufacturing Practice** b) Good Laboratory Practices
   c) Good Agricultural Practices d) None of these
5. ____is used throughout each stage of a process, and includes raw materials, processing, storage and distribution
   a) GAP b) **HACCP**
   c) GLP d) GMP
6. Expand (PLCs)
   a) **Programmable logic controllers** b) Project logic controllers
   c) Programmable length controllers d) Programmable logic capacitors
7. _____is the unit operation in which contaminating materials are removed from the food and separated to leave the surface of the food in a suitable condition for further processing
   a) Sorting b) **Cleaning**
   c) Washing d) Rinsing
8. Examples of wet-cleaning equipment
   a) Spray washers b) Brush washers
   c) Drum or rod washers d) **All of the above**
9. Equipment used for dry cleaning
   a) Air classifiers b) Magnetic separators
   c) Separators based on screening of foods d) **All of the above**

10. ____is the separation of foods into categories on the basis of a measurable physical property

a) **Sorting** b) Cleaning

c) Arranging d) None of these

11. Size sorting also called as___

a) Sieving b) Screening

c) **Both A and B** d) Arranging

12. _____means the assessment of overall quality of a food using a number of attribute

a) **Grading** b) Packaging

c) Processing d) Certification

13. ____ is used in the processing of fruits and vegetables to remove unwanted or inedible material, and to improve the appearance of the final product.

a) Cleaning b) **Peeling**

c) Washing d) All of the above

14. Eggs are visually inspected over____ lights termed candling

a) Mercury light b) **Tungsten lights**

c) Neon Light d) UV

15. _____method is suitable for citrus fruits where skin is easily removed and little damage or loss of fruit

a) **Knife peeling** b) Lye peeling

c) Flash peeling d) None of these

16. Flame peeling developed for

a) Carrot b) Cabbage

c) Radish d) **Onions**

17. _____is the unit operation in which the average size of solid pieces of food is reduced by the application of grinding, compression or impact forces

a) Size reduction b) Comminution

c) **Both A and B** d) Milling

18. Size reduction of liquids to droplets by

a) **Atomization** b) Spraying

c) Homogenization d) Pasteurization

19. In size reduction, force used to reduce the size of foods are

a) Compression forces b) Impact forces

c) Shearing (or attrition) forces d) **All of the above**

20. ___ used for Food colors as size reduction equipment

a) **Ball mill** b) Roll mill

c) Gear mill d) None of these

21. ____are widely used to mill wheat

a) Miller | b) Compressor mill
c) **Roller mills** | d) All of the above

22. liquid–liquid emulsion of oil in water (o/w) is

a) **Milk** | b) Margarine
c) Juice | d) All of the above

23. liquid–liquid emulsion of water in oil (w/o)

a) Milk | b) **Margarine**
c) Honey | d) Crush

24. Polar groups bind to water and therefore produce

a) **o/w emulsions** | b) w/o emulsions
c) Both a and b | d) None of these

25. Non-polar agents are adsorbed to oils to produce

a) **w/o emulsions** | b) o/w emulsions
c) Emulsions | d) Dispension

26. Agents with low HLB values____ are lipophilic and used for w/o emulsions

a) Below 5 | b) Below 4
c) Below 1 | d) **Below 9**

27. HLB values between ____ are intermediate and used as wetting agents

a) 3 & 4 | b) **8 & 11**
c) 4 & 7 | d) 2 & 4

28. High values ____are hydrophilic and are used for o/w emulsions, detergents and solubilizers

a) **(11 to 20)** | b) (11 to 30)
c) (11 to 40) | d) (11 to 22)

29. Main types of homogenizer are

a) High-speed mixers | b) Pressure homogenizers
c) Colloid mills | d) **All of the above**

30. Ultrasonic homogenizers use high-frequency sound waves ____to cause alternate cycles of compression and tension in low-viscosity liquids and cavitation of air bubbles

a) **(18–30 kHz)** | b) (18–40 kHz)
c) (18–50 kHz) | d) (18–60 kHz)

31. Low-fat spreads are

a) o/w emulsions | b) **w/o emulsions**
c) Emulsion | d) Mixing

32. Cake batters are____

a) **o/w emulsions** b) w/o emulsion

c) Sticky d) Fluidity

33. ____is the removal of insoluble solids from a suspension

a) Centrifugation b) Ultrasonication

c) Cavitation d) **Filtration**

34. Solvents used to extract Decaffeinated coffee

a) Supercritical carbon dioxide b) Water

c) Methylene chloride d) **All of the above**

35. Solvents used to extract Fish livers, meat byproducts

a) Acetone b) Ethyl ether

c) **Both a and b** d) None of these

36. Solvents used to extract Hop extract

a) Oxygen b) Nitrogen

c) Argon d) **Supercritical carbon dioxide**

37. Solvents used to extract Instant coffee and Instant tea

a) Ether b) Methanol

c) Ethanol d) **Water**

38. Reverse osmosis (RO) otherwise called

a) Osmosis b) Filtration

c) Centrifugation d) **Hyperfiltration**

39. Nanofiltration (NF) otherwise termed as

a) To filter b) To test

c) Filter d) **Loose reverse osmosis**

40. An extension of UF, in which water is added back to the extract during the concentration process is known as

a) Filtration b) **Diafiltration**

c) Extraction d) Sorting

41. ____is used to separate electrolytes from non-electrolytes and to exchange ions between solutions

a) Dialysis b) **Electrodialysis (ED)**

c) Filtration d) Sedimentation

42. Fermented sausages____ are produced from a mixture of finely chopped meats, spice mixtures, curing salts (sodium nitrite/nitrate), salt and sugar

a) Salami b) Pepperoni

c) Medwurst d) Bologna

e) **All of the above**

43. Palm sap is fermented by naturally occurring_____ to produce palm wine

a) *Bacillus sp*
b) *E. coli*
c) *Streptococcus*
d) ***Zymomonas spp***

44. Citric acid is produced by

a) *Rhizopus*
b) *Mucor*
c) *Aeromonas*
d) ***Aspergillus niger***

45. _____Enzymes of largest volume (35%) used in detergent manufacture

a) Cellulase
b) Lipase
c) Zymogen
d) **Proteases**

46. _____is used for the production of high-fructose corn syrup (HFCS) sweeteners from glucose

a) **Glucose isomerase**
b) Amylase
c) Cellulase
d) Lipase

47. Products are widely used as an alternative to sucrose in the bakery and confectionery industries

a) HFCS-42
b) HFCS-55
c) **Both A and B**
d) None of these

48. The degree of hydrolysis of starch is measured by the

a) Sucrose
b) Fructose
c) Mannose
d) **Dextrose equivalent (DE)**

49. ______are produced from starch using the enzyme cyclodextrin glycosyl transferase

a) **Cyclodextrin**
b) Glucan
c) Mannan
d) Fructan

50. Bromelain is a mixture of proteases which hydrolyze plant and animal proteins to

a) Amino acids
b) Peptides
c) **Both a and b**
d) None of these

51. _____converts the flavour compound diacetyl to flavourless acetoin to improve the flavour in beer

a) **Diacetyl reductase**
b) Hops
c) Ether
d) Ethanol

52. Fungal _____can be used to make 5 -nucleotide flavour enhancers which accentuate 'meaty' flavours in soups, sauces and gravies

a) Lipase
b) Catalase
c) Peroxidase
d) **Phosphodiesterases**

53. _____ hydrolyses the bitter component 'limonin' in orange juice

a) Eugenol
b) Citrinin
c) **Limoninase**
d) None of these

54. ____breaks down Naringin in grapefruit juice

a) Phenolase
b) **Nariniginase**
c) Aspartate
d) Ether

55. ___ converts pentosans to D-xylose and L-arabinose to reduce bread staling, to reduce dough viscosity, to lighten the crumb of rye bread and to prevent it from separating from the crust during baking

a) Diester
b) **Pentosanase**
c) Hexose
d) Ribose

56. ___converts β-glucans to β-D-glucose to facilitate filtration of barley wort in brewing

a) Cellulase
b) Xylase
c) **β-glucanases**
d) All of these

57. ____converts stachyose and rafinnose to monosaccharides to reduce flatulence produced by leguminous foods

a) Xylose
b) Ribitol
c) **Stachyase**
d) None of these

58. Protease trypsin retards the development of oxidised flavours in

a) **Milk**
b) Fruits
c) Vegetables
d) Squash

59. Collagenase & elastase soften and tenderise connective tissues

a) Milk
b) **Meat**
c) Fruits
d) None of these

60. Expand (JECFI)

a) **Joint FAO/IAEA/WHO Expert Committee on the Wholesomeness of Irradiated Food**
b) Joint Expert Committee on the Wholesomeness of Food
c) Joint Expert Committee Weather of Irradiated Food
d) Joint Expert Committee on the Wholesomeness of Irregular Food

61. Maximum average dose of____ 'presents no toxicological hazard and no special nutritional or microbiological problems in foods'

a) 5 kGy
b) 7 kGy
c) **10 kGy**
d) 15 kGy

62. γ -radiation from__ or ___is used in most commercial plants

a) **Cobalt-60 (60Co), caesium-137 (137Cs)**
b) Carbon dioxide, UV
c) Nitrogen, Monoxide
d) None of these

63. Insects and parasites such as tape worms or *Trichinella* require lower doses of

a) 0.15 kGy
b) 0.17 kGy
c) 0.20 kGy
d) **0.25 kGy**

64. Sterilization also termed as

a) **Radappertisation**
b) Pasteurization
c) Radurization
d) All of the above

65. A dose of 48 kGy is needed for a 12D reduction of

a) *Rhizopus*
b) *Staphylococcus*
c) *Streptococcus*
d) ***Clostridium botulinum***

66. Fresh poultry carcasses irradiated with a dose of ____are virtually free of *Salmonella spp*

a) **2.5 kGy**
b) 3.5 kGy
c) 4.5 kGy
d) 8.5 kGy

67. Higher doses, up to___ can be applied to frozen poultry or shellfish

a) 5 kGy
b) **10 kGy**
c) 12 kGy
d) 15 kGy

68. ___ is essential ingredient for flavour modification

a) **Salt**
b) Sugar
c) Fat
d) Protein

69. A two-fold increase in shelf life of mushrooms and inhibition of cap opening can be achieved by doses of____

a) 0- 1 kGy
b) **2–3 kGy**
c) 4- 5 kGy
d) 7-9 kGy

70. Low doses, below____ are effective for disinfestation and also extend the shelf life by delaying ripening

a) **1 kGy**
b) 4 kGy
c) 6 kGy
d) 8 kGy

71. ____detects radicals produced by irradiation, which are stable in solid or dry components of foods

a) Raman spectroscopy
b) **Electron Spin Resonance (ESR) spectroscopy**
c) Chromatography
d) Spectrum

72. ____process produced only thermal destruction of micro-organisms because only low electricity voltages were used

a) Magnetic field
b) **Pulsed electric field processing**
c) Resonance
d) Microwave

73.____ has no 'heating' or 'cooling' periods, and there are rapid pressurization/ de-pressurization cycles, thus reducing processing times compared to thermal processing

a) Refrigeration b) Freezing Drying

c) **High pressure processing** d) None of these

74. ___ is responsible for cloud destabilisation in juices, gelation of fruit concentrates and loss of consistency in tomato products

a) **Pectinesterase** b) Cellulase

c) Protease d) Lipase

75. Shearing and compression effects of_____ cause denaturation of proteins that result in reduced enzyme activity

a) Cryogenic b) **Ultrasound**

c) Crystallization d) Sedimentation

76. Combined heat and ultrasound treatment under pressure, termed

a) Sonication

b) **'Mano-Thermo-Sonication' (MTS)**

c) Ultrasound d) Distillation

77. ____ is to destroy enzymic activity in vegetables and some fruits, prior to further processing

a) Heating b) Cooling

c) Drying d) **Blanching**

78. ____ is added to blancher water to form insoluble calcium pectate complexes and thus to maintain firmness in the tissues

a) **Calcium chloride (1–2%)** b) Calcium chloride (5- 8 %)

c) Calcium chloride (11- 15 %) d) Calcium chloride (20 – 25 %)

79. In fruit juices the main cause of colour deterioration is enzymic browning by

a) **Polyphenoloxidase** b) Oxidase

c) Catalase d) Methanol

80. In low-acid foods (pH 4.5), the heat resistant, spore forming micro-organism___ is the most dangerous pathogen

a) *Salmonella* b) *Streptococcus*

c) *E. coli* d) ***Clostridium botulinum***

81. ___ means probability of survival spores must be reduce to one can in a billion ie, 10^{12}

a) Disinfection b) **12 D Concept**

c) Sterlization d) None of these

82. Before filled containers are processed, it is necessary to remove air by an operation termed

a) Filling
b) **Exhausting**
c) Cooling
d) Heating

83. Cold filling the food and then heating the container and contents to 80–95^{0}C with the lid partially sealed called

a) Boiling
b) **Clinching**
c) Cooling
d) None of these

84. ____in food processing is mostly confined to the production of alcoholic spirits and separation of volatile flavour and aroma compounds

a) Evaporation
b) Condensation
c) **Distillation**
d) All of the above

85. ____is a process which combines several unit operations including mixing, cooking, kneading, shearing, shaping and forming

a) **Extrusion**
b) Sealing
c) Packaging
d) Processing

86. Sugar-based products extruded foods

a) Chewing gum
b) Liquorice Toffee
c) Caramel
d) **All of the above**

87. Expand (TVP)

a) **Texturised vegetable protein**
b) Texturised vapour protein
c) Texturised vegetable pectin
d) Texturised vent protein

88. Production of characteristic____ is one of the main features of extrusion technology

a) **Textures**
b) Taste
c) Flavour
d) Smell

89. ____ is defined as 'the application of heat under controlled conditions to remove the majority of the water normally present in a food by evaporation'

a) Cooling
b) **Dehydration (or drying)**
c) Freezing
d) Chilling

90. In ____Layers of food are dried on trays, which are stacked on trucks programmed to move semicontinuously through an insulated tunnel, having one or more types of air flow

a) **Tunnel driers**
b) Exhausting
c) Kiln drying
d) None of these

91. In ___Food is dried on a mesh belt in beds 5–15 cm deep

a) Kiln drying
b) Bin drying
c) **Conveyor driers (belt driers)**
d) None of these

92. ___is a unit operation which is mainly used to alter the eating quality of a food

a) **Frying** b) Dehydration

c) Chilling d) Freezing

93. ____ method is most suited to foods which have a large surface-area-to-volume ratio (for example bacon slices, eggs, burgers and other types of pattie)

a) Deep frying b) **Shallow (or contact) frying**

c) Both a and b d) None of these

94. Expand (NVDP)

a) **Non-volatile decomposition products**

b) Non-volatile desalination products

c) Non-volatile decomposition processing

d) Non-volatile decomposition profit

95. Dielectric and ohmic heating are____ methods in which heat is generated within the product

a) Indirect b) **Direct**

c) Both a and b d) None of these

96. Infrared heating is an___ method that relies on heat that is generated externally being applied to the surface of the food mostly by radiation

a) Direct b) **Indirect**

c) Collateral d) Locative

97. Chilling is the unit operation in which the temperature of a food is reduced to between

a) **1°C and 8°C** b) 5°C and 9°C

c) 4°C and 6°C d) 7°C and 8°C

98. Expandable polystyrene has applications in

a) Disposable packaging b) Drinking cups

c) **Both A and B** d) None of these

99. ____used for household wraps and excellent barrier properties

a) **Polyvinylidene chloride** b) Polyethylene

c) Ether d) Benzoyl

100. ___ are used as inside layer of retort pouches or tubs

a) **Polypropylene** b) Ethylene

c) Chloroform d) Styrene

CHAPTER-4

Principles and Basics of Human Nutrition

1. Carbohydrate is a chemical compound made up of
   - a) **Carbon, hydrogen and oxygen**
   - b) Carbon and oxygen
   - c) Carbon and hydrogen
   - d) None of these
2. The basic unit of a carbohydrate is a
   - a) **Monosaccharide**
   - b) Disaccharide
   - c) Oligosaccharide
   - d) Fructans
3. Simple sugars which contain a single unit called
   - a) Oligosaccharides
   - b) **Monosaccharides**
   - c) Raffinose
   - d) All of the above
4. Double sugars which contain two monosaccharide units called
   - a) Monosaccharides
   - b) **Disaccharides**
   - c) Oligosaccharides
   - d) Ribose
5. Complex compounds which contain many monosaccharide units termed
   - a) **Polysaccharides**
   - b) Monosaccharides
   - c) Disaccharides
   - d) None of these
6. Sucrose is a combination of
   - a) (1 raffinose, 1 fructose)
   - b) (1 galactose , 1 fructose)
   - c) (1 glucose , 1 Mannose)
   - d) **(1 glucose , 1 fructose)**
7. Lactose is a combination of
   - a) (1 fructan , 1 glucose)
   - b) (1 galactose , 1 mannose)
   - c) (1 glucose , 1 glucose)
   - d) **(1 galactose , 1 glucose)**
8. Maltose is a combination of
   - a) (2 stachyose) molecules
   - b) (2 raffinose) molecules
   - c) **(2 glucose) molecules**
   - d) (2 fructans) molecules
9. Glucose (dextrose) , Fructose (levulose) and Galactose are examples of
   - a) Oligosaccharides
   - b) **Monosaccharides**
   - c) Disaccharides
   - d) None of these

10. Sucrose, Lactose and Maltose are examples of

a) **Disaccharides** b) Oligosaccharides

c) Ribose d) Xylulose

11. ___ is the storage form of carbohydrates in plants

a) Glycogen b) Pectin

c) Chitin d) **Starch**

12. ____includes all the starch that escapes digestion in the small intestines

a) Soluble starch b) **Resistant starch**

c) None of these

13. ___ is an animal starch stored in all animals

a) Starch b) Maltose

c) Chitin d) **Glycogen**

14. ___ which are also indigestible carbohydrates, are found in fruits

a) Chitin b) **Pectins**

c) Glycogen d) None of these

15. ___and ___are abundantly found in nature in seed coats, skins of fruits and as a structural part of all plants

a) Cellulose, Lignin b) Cellulose, Mylin

c) **Cellulose, Hemicellulose** d) Cellulose, chitin

16. Fat is a complex molecule constituting a mixture of____ and____ and generally glycerol

a) **Fatty acids, alcohol** b) Cellulose, fiber

c) Sugar, fiber d) None of these

17. ___ contain a glycerol base with three fatty acids

a) Fat b) **Triglycerides**

c) Fiber d) Cellulose

18. ____ is a common cooking medium of hydrogenated fat

a) Ghee b) **Vanaspathi**

c) Milk d) Yogurt

19. Vanaspathi is fortified with Vitamin A and D of

a) 200 IU and 50 IU b) 300 IU and 50 IU

c) **700 IU and 50 IU** d) 800 IU and 50 IU

20. The predominance of saturated fatty acids in a fat makes it____ at room temperature

a) **Liquid** b) Gel

c) Semisolid d) Solid

21. Saturated fatty acids, found in animal product

a) Palmitic b) Stearic

c) **Both A and B** d) None of these

22. ____are those which cannot be synthesized by the body and need to be supplied through diet

a) **Essential fatty acids** b) Non essential fatty acids

c) Fatty acids d) None of these

23. Linolenic acid, linoleic acid and arachidonic acid are

a) Non essential fatty acids b) **Essential fatty acids**

c) Amino acids d) All of the above

24. _____are those which can be synthesized by the body and need not be supplied through diet

a) **Non-essential fatty acids** b) Essential fatty acids

c) Vitamins d) Minerals

25. Palmitic acid, oleic acid and butyric acid are examples of

a) **Non-essential fatty acids** b) Fatty acids

c) Steroids d) None of these

26. The normal blood level of cholesterol is _____(100 ml) of blood

a) 150 to 200 mg/dl b) 150 to 500 mg/dl

c) 150 to 600 mg/dl d) **150 to 300 mg/dl**

27. The body normally synthesizes____ about of cholesterol daily

a) **2 g** b) 5 g

c) 9 g d) 10 g

28. Cholesterol is a precursor of the

a) Fats b) Vitamins

c) Carbohydrates d) **Bile salts**

29. Omega-3 fatty acids are

a) Alpha Linolenic Acid (ALA) b) Eicosapentaenoic Acid (EPA)

c) Docosahexaenoic Acid (DHA) d) **All of the above**

30. Omega-6 fatty acids are

a) Linoleic Acid (LA) b) Arachidonic Acid

c) **Both A and B** d) None of these

31. Expand ADHD

a) **Attention Deficit Hyperactivity Disorder**

b) Additive Deficit Hyperactivity Disorder

c) Attention Destroy Hyperactivity Disorder

d) Attention Deficit Hyperactivity Disease

32. Omega-3 fatty acids have also shown neuro-protective action in

a) Parkinson's disease b) Alzheimer's disease

c) **Both A and B** d) None of these

33. EPA and DHA are present in

a) Oily fish b) Walnut

c) **Both A and B** d) None of these

34. Omega-6 (n-6) fatty acids occur in

a) Fat b) Oil sources

c) **Both A and B** d) None of these

35. ____ is a process which hardens liquid fat by converting unsaturated fatty acid components to their saturated form

a) Crystallization b) **Hydrogenation**

c) Sublimation d) Distillation

36. Examples of hydrogenated fats sold in the market are

a) Vanaspathi b) Margarine

c) **Both A and B** d) Ghee

37. Unsaturated vegetable oils _____ are treated with hydrogen to produce a plastic fat for cooking purposes or to resemble table fat like butter and ghee

a) Cottonseed b) Corn

c) Soyabean d) **All of the above**

38. Pickles, salad dressings, all oils, vanaspati, margarine, butter are

a) **Visible fats** b) Invisible fats

c) Glycerol d) None of these

39. Egg-yolk, baked goods, whole milk, all sweetmeats, cream, cheese, ice-cream, nuts, oilseeds are

a) **Invisible fats** b) Visible fats

c) Fibres d) None of these

40. One gram of fat gives about___ calories

a) **9** b) 8

c) 7 d) 5

41. Fat is the carrier of the fat-soluble vitamins

a) A b) D

c) E d) K

e) **All of the above**

42. Prevention of hunger is called___ of fats

a) Hidden hunger
b) **Satiety value**
c) Malnutrition
d) Disorder

43. A skin condition known as "Phrynoderma" (toad skin) is observed in due to the deficiency of

a) **Essential fatty acids**
b) Non essential fatty acids
c) Lack of vitamins
d) None of these

44. Partially hydrogenated vegetable oils are the major contributors of___ in foods

a) Vitamins
b) **TFA**
c) Minerals
d) All of the above

45. TFA in the diet comes from

a) Deep fried fast foods
b) Bakery products
c) Packaged snack foods
d) **All of the above**

46. Major TFA present in ruminant fat is

a) **Vaccinic acid**
b) Linolenic
c) Linoleic
d) Acetic

47. ___is the major trans isomer (80–90%)

a) **Elaidic acid**
b) Ethanol
c) Glycerol
d) Lipids

48. ____contains a carboxyl (COOH) or acidic group and an amino (NH_2) group

a) **Amino acid**
b) Fiber
c) Fat
d) None of these

49. Methionine, Threonine and Isoleucine are examples of

a) **Essential amino acids**
b) Non essential amino acids
c) Fatty acids
d) All of the above

50. Cystine, Glycine and Aspartic acid are examples of

a) **Non-essential Amino Acids**
b) Essential amino acids
c) Vitamins
d) Fibre

51. A chain containing more than three amino acids is called ____which ultimately forms protein

a) **Polypeptide**
b) Chains
c) Peptide
d) Branched

52. Complete Proteins examples

a) Milk
b) Meat
c) Poultry
d) Fish
e) **All of the above**

53. All plant sources of proteins are

a) **Incomplete proteins** b) Complete proteins

c) Amino acids d) Fat

54. ____is the only animal protein which is an incomplete protein

a) Myosin b) **Gelatin**

c) Actin d) Myoglobin

55. Antibiotics such as___ inhibit the absorption of amino acids by blocking the synthesis of transport protein in the intestinal mucosal cell

a) Pyromycin b) Actinomycin-D

c) **Both A and B** d) None of these

56. Hormones such as adrenocorticotrophic hormone (ACTH) and insulin, are____ in nature

a) Fats b) **Protein**

c) Fibre d) Minerals

57. Actin and myosin are responsible for the action of

a) **Muscles** b) Pigments

c) Colorants d) None of these

58. ___is a precursor of niacin and serotonin

a) **Tryptophan** b) Serine

c) Valine d) leucine

59. Proteins yield approximately

a) 3.0 cal/g b) **4.0 cal/g**

c) 5.0 cal/g d) 9.0 cal/g

60. Protein malnutrition called

a) **Kwashiorkor** b) Anemia

c) Pellegra d) Beri Beri

61. ____ is one of the most effective foods for treatment and prevention of such protein malnutrition in children

a) **Dry skimmed milk** b) Juice

c) Squash d) cordial

62. Kwashiorkor meaning

a) **Red boy** b) Green boy

c) Strength d) All of the above

63. Basic formula for Biological Value is

BV= (Nitrogen retained/Nitrogen absorbed) × 100

64. Eggs have a BV of

a) 57–77
b) **87–97**
c) 47–87
d) 37–87

65. Whey has a BV between

a) 10–15
b) 16–19
c) **106–159**
d) 107–259

66. Cow's milk has a BV of

a) 55–60
b) **85–90**
c) 75–80
d) 45–70

67. Rice and Tofu (Soya-curds) have a BV of

a) 15
b) 55
c) **75**
d) 85

68. No animal protein has a BV

a) <32
b) <42
c) <52
d) **<72**

69. No plant protein has a BV

a) >25
b) >45
c) **>75**
d) >95

70. A combination of cereal and pulse in the ratio of ____has been found to give an optimum combination

a) 2:1
b) **5:1**
c) 7:1
d) 9:1

71. Net Protein Utilization (NPU) can be calculated by

NPU = BV × Digestability

72. Protein Efficiency Ratio (PER) can be calculated

PER = Weight gain in grams/Dietary protein in grams

73. Whole egg has a PER of

a) 2.8
b) **3.8**
c) 6.8
d) 9.8

74. Gelatin has PER of

a) 4
b) **0**
c) 8
d) 9

75. Expand PDCAAS

a) Pectin Digestibility Corrected Amino Acid Score
b) Protein Directed Corrected Amino Acid Score

c) **Protein Digestibility Corrected Amino Acid Score**

d) Protein Digestibility Corrected All Acid Score

76. ___ is official assay for evaluating protein

a) **PDCAAS** b) Acid analysis

c) Volumetric analysis d) Analytical

77. (PDCAAS) for Soybean, Milk and Egg is

a) 0.5 b) **1.0**

c) 2.0 d) 7.0

78. _____is a chemical score based on chemical analysis of the protein and not on a biological test

a) **Amino Acid Score** b) Hedonic score

c) Variability score d) Difference score

79. Amino acid score is determined by

Amino acid score = (mg of amino acid per gram of test protein/ mg of amino acid per gram of reference protein) × 100

80. In wheat the limiting amino acid is

a) **Lysine** b) Histidine

c) Alanine d) Valine

81. _____ diet consists of plant foods, along with eggs, milk and milk products

a) Non veg b) Veg

c) **Ovolactovegetarians** d) None of these

82. ___ diet is of plant origin, supplemented with milk and milk products

a) Non veg b) Veg

c) **Lactovegetarians** d) All of the above

83. ____eat all foods of plant origin

a) Non veg b) **Pure vegetarians or Vegans**

c) Mixed food d) None of these

84. Skim milk is a richer source of ___ than whole milk

a) **Protein** b) Fat

c) Fiber d) Glucose

85. Egg is a good source of

a) B7 b) B1

c) B9 d) **B12**

86. Grains are a good source of

a) Fat b) **Zinc**

c) Magnesium d) Potassium

87. ___are major sources are meats, milk and dairy products

a) **Riboflavin** b) Folate

c) Cobalamin d) None of these

88. The nutraceuticals shall contain any of the ingredients specified in

Schedule I, Schedule II , Schedule IV, Schedule VI, Schedule VII and Schedule VIII

89. ____present in foods like wheat germ, soybean, peanuts and skimmed milk may prevent the formation of a fatty liver

a) Acids b) **Choline**

c) Alcohols d) Ether

90. Food allergen Labelling and Consumer Protection Act of

a) **2004** b) 2008

c) 2010

91. Eight foods as major food allergens

(Milk, Eggs, Fish , Crustacean shellfish, Treenuts , Peanuts, Wheat and Soybeans)

92. Our body contains about____ water

a) 55 percent b) **65 percent**

c) 85 percent d) 95 percent

93. An infant's body contains___ water than that of an adult

a) **More** b) Low

c) Moderate d) None of these

94. Blood contains___ % water

a) **85–90** b) 55–70

c) 45–80 d) 25–60

95. ___water is found per g of protein

a) 3.4 g b) 4.1 g

c) **0.4 g** d) 5.4 g

96. ___water is found per gram of fat

a) 4.2 g b) **0.2 g**

c) 7.2 g d) 9.2 g

97. Fruits and vegetables contain___ water

a) 40–60 percent b) 20–50 percent

c) 10–50 percent d) **80–90 percent**

98. Milk contains____ percent water

a) **80–88** b) 10–28

c) 30–58 d) 60–78

99. ____ is a method of treating dehydration by making the patient drink readily available preparations, such as Electral, Electrose, Peditral, etc. dissolved in water

a) **ORT - Oral Rehydration Therapy** b) Therapy

c) Triangle method d) All of the above

100. ____results due to excess intake of water

a) **Water intoxication** b) Food intoxication

c) Disorder d) None of these

CHAPTER-5

FOOD CHEMISTRY

1. Cellulose, lignin and some portions of hemicellulose are examples of

   a) SDF (Soluble Dietary Fibre) b) **IDF (Insoluble Dietary Fibre)**

   c) Both a and b d) None of these

2. Pectins, gums, Beta-glucans, mucilages and major portions of hemi cellulose are examples of

   a) **SDF (Soluble Dietary Fibre)** b) IDF (Insoluble Dietary Fibre)

   c) Proteins d) Minerals

3. Amylose, Amylopectin, Fructans Galactomannans are

   a) Fat b) Fiber

   c) **Storage polysaccharides** d) None of these

4. Structural components of the plant cell walls are

   a) Pectins b) Hemicellulose

   c) Cellulose d) **All of the above**

5. Isolated polysaccharides naturally occurring are

   a) Gums b) Mucilages

   c) Pectin d) **All of the above**

6. Vitamins A, D, E and K are

   a) Water soluble vitamins b) **Fat-soluble vitamins**

   c) Minerals d) Proteins

7. B and C vitamins are

   a) **Water-soluble** b) Fat soluble

   c) Proteins d) fiber

8. Dehydrocholesterol and Ergosterol are precursors of

   a) **Vitamin D** b) Vitamin A

   c) Vitamin C d) Vitamin B

9. Vitamin was coined by____ who discovered a water-soluble substance in rice polishings which prevented beri-beri

   a) William b) Harvey

   c) Richard d) **Casimir Funk**

10. Bitot's spots on conjunctiva of eye are the deficiency of

a) **Vitamin A** b) Vitamin B

c) Vitamin C d) Vitamin D

11. Osteomalacia (in adults) are the deficiency of

a) Vitamin B b) Vitamin A

c) **Vitamin D** d) Vitamin C

12. Increased haemolysis of RBC, Creatinuria are due to the deficiency of

a) Vitamin A b) **Vitamin E**

c) Vitamin D d) Vitamin K

13. Delay in clotting of blood is due to the deficiency of

a) **Vitamin K** b) Vitamin E

c) Vitamin A d) Vitamin C

14. ___ found in beans interfere with the replication of cell DNA, thereby, preventing the multiplication of cancer cells

a) Tannins b) **Saponins**

c) Polyphenols d) Lutein

15. Cyanogenic glycosides of cassava can be leached out with

a) Alcohol b) **Water**

c) Spirit d) Ethanol

16. Capsaicin, found in hot peppers protects DNA from

a) Heart attack b) Osteoporosis

c) Dermatitis d) **Carcinogens**

17. ___ are substances added to food to preserve flavor or enhance its taste, appearance, or other qualities

a) **Food additives** b) Adulterants

c) Branded food d) None of these

18. A green dye made from

a) *E. Coli* b) *Streptococcus*

c) *Bacillus* d) **Chlorella algae**

19. ___coloring, made from caramelized sugar, used in cola products and also in cosmetics

a) Tannin b) **Caramel**

c) Phenolase d) lectin

20. Toxic amino acid___ from khesari dal can be removed by using a process similar to that of parboiling paddy

a) **BOAA** b) Linolenic acid

c) Linoleic acid d) Arachidonic acid

21. ___are condensed polyphenolic compounds widely distributed in plants

a) **Tannins**
b) Colorants
c) Preservatives
d) None of these

22. Dyes dissolve in water, but are not soluble in

a) **Oil**
b) Water
c) Alcohol
d) Ethanol

23. Lakes are the combination of

a) **Dyes and insoluble material**
b) Dyes and soluble material
c) Both a and b
d) None of these

24. ____is defined as a substance gives another substance flavor, altering characteristics of the solute, causing it to become sweet, sour and tangy

a) **Flavorant or essence**
b) Toxins
c) Colorants
d) All of the above

25. Common natural sweeteners are

a) Sugar
b) Corn syrup
c) Honey
d) **All of the above**

26. ___is a hygroscopic substance to keep moisture and retains moisture in the air by drawing water vapor into or beneath organism's or object's surface

a) Anticaking agent
b) Sweetners
c) Colorants
d) **Humectant**

27. Propylene glycol, hexylene glycol, and butylene glycol are examples of

a) Antioxidants
b) Colorants
c) Sweetners
d) **Artificial humectant**

28. Natural humectants are

a) Aloe vera gel
b) Egg yolk
c) Egg white
d) **All of the above**

29. ____ is used to lighten or whiten a substrate through chemical reaction

a) Anticaking agents
b) Preservatives
c) **Bleaching agent**
d) All of the above

30. Bleaching agents are

a) Benzoyl peroxide
b) Calcium peroxide
c) Nitrogen dioxide
d) **All of the above**

31. ____is a substance which can increase viscosity of a liquid without substantially changing its other properties

a) Salt
b) Sugar
c) Dyes
d) **Thickeners**

32. Polysaccharides as a thickener food includes

a) Starches b) Vegetable gums

c) Pectin d) **All of the above**

33. ____ is an additive placed in powdered or granulated materials of table salt or confectionaries to prevent formation of lumps (caking)

a) **Anticaking agent** b) Artificial sweetner

c) Humectants d) None of these

34. Examples for anticaking agent are

a) Sodium aluminosilicate b) Sodium ferrocyanide

c) Potassium ferrocyanide d) **All of the above**

35. __ forms chelate complexes with polyvalent metal ions, especially copper, iron and nickel to prevent oxidation of fats in the food

a) Antioxidants b) **Sequestrant**

c) Dyes d) All of the above

36. Common sequestrants are

a) Calcium chloride (E509)

b) Calcium disodium ethylene diamine tetra-acetate (E385)

c) Glucono delta-lactone (E575) d) **All of the above**

37. Artificial sweetner Aspartame is

a) 50 times sweeter than sugar b) 100 times sweeter than sugar

c) **180 times sweeter than sugar** d) 200 times sweeter than sugar

38. Artificial sweetner Acesulfame K is

a) 100 times sweeter than sugar b) **200 times sweeter than sugar**

c) 300 times sweeter than sugar d) 500 times sweeter than sugar

39. Artificial sweetner Saccharin is

a) 50 times sweeter than sugar b) 80 times sweeter than sugar

c) 100 times sweeter than sugar d) **300 times sweeter than sugar**

40. Artificial sweetner Sucralose is

a) **600 times sweeter than sugar** b) 800 times sweeter than sugar

c) 900 times sweeter than sugar d) 100 times sweeter than sugar

41. Nutraceuticals assigned to it in section__ of the Act

a) **22** b) 25

c) 28 d) 29

42. Functional food assigned to it in section ___ of the Act

a) **22** b) 24

c) 33 d) 35

43."Nutritional ingredients" means the ingredients specified in Schedules other than food additives specified in

a) Schedule I A to Schedule II F
b) Schedule IIA to Schedule III F
c) **Schedule V A to Schedule V F**
d) Schedule VI A to Schedule VI F

44. "Nutrient ingredients" means vitamins, minerals, and amino acids as specified in

a) Schedule II and Schedule III
b) **Schedule I and Schedule II**
c) Schedule III and Schedule IV
d) Schedule IV and Schedule V

45. No food business operator shall use additives in probiotic preparations except those specified in

a) Schedule VIA to Schedule VI F
b) Schedule VIIA to Schedule VIII F
c) **Schedule VA to Schedule VF**
d) Schedule IA to Schedule I F

46. A food business operator shall use only plant or botanical ingredients specified in___ for the preparation of specialty food containing plant or botanical ingredien

a) **Schedule IV**
b) Schedule II
c) Schedule III
d) Schedule V

47. Richest source of phytates in

a) **Unrefined cereals and millets**
b) Refined cereals and millets
c) Sugars
d) Salt

48. Inhibitors present in soya, lima, kidney beans and duck egg white has

a) **Trypsin Inhibitors**
b) Phenols
c) Tannins
d) None of these

49. Phytates bind with Iron, Zinc, Calcium and Magnesium

50. Tannins bind with___ forming compounds which are not absorbed in the gut

a) **Iron**
b) Calcium
c) Magnesium
d) None of these

51. Phytochemicals such as Geraniol ˜and Limonene are

a) **Onoterpenes**
b) Flavonoids
c) Tannins
d) None of these

52. Phytochemicals such as Beta-Carotene ,˜ Lutein and Lycopene are

a) Tannins
b) **Carotenoids**
c) Lipids
d) Proteins

53. Phytochemicals such as Daidzein and Genistein are

a) **Isoflavones**
b) Flavonoids
c) Terpenes
d) All of the above

54. Heat increment of feeding which was earlier termed as

a) Basic Metabolic Rate
b) **Specific dynamic action**
c) RDA
d) Specific action

55. 1 g of fat yields

a) 2.0 cal or 38 J
b) 3.0 cal or 38 J
c) 5.0 cal or 38 J
d) **9.0 cal or 38 J**

56. 1 g of protein yields

a) 1.0 cal or 17 J
b) 2.0 cal or 17 J
c) 3.0 cal or 17 J
d) **4.0 cal or 17 J**

57. Carrier of genetic information

a) **DNA**
b) RNA
c) tRNA
d) mRNA

58. An intermediate in the expression of genetic information and other diverse roles

a) **RNA**
b) DNA
c) Lysosome
d) Golgi appartus

59. Central Dogma of life

DNA → mRNA → Protein

60. Nucleotides are made up of

a) Sugar
b) Heterocyclic base
c) Phosphate
d) **All of the above**

61. The chemical linkage between monomer units in nucleic acids is a

a) Hydrogen bond
b) **Phosphodiester**
c) Covalent bond
d) Van der waals force

62. Avery, MacLeod & McCarty showed strong evidence that DNA is genetic material in

a) 1940
b) 1942
c) 1943
d) **1944**

63. Chargaff' Rule states that

a) **A=T and C=G**
b) A=A and C=T
c) A=G and C=C
d) T=T and A=G

64. Watson & Crick - structure of DNA

a) 1951
b) **1953**
c) 1955
d) 1958

65. DNA-histone assembly is called a

a) **Nucleosome**
b) Reticulum
c) Golgi bodies
d) Endoplasm

66. Histones are rich in

a) Isoleucine and arginine residues
b) Arginine and valine residues
c) Leucine and aspargine residues
d) **Lysine and arginine residues**

67. Process by which DNA is copied with very high fidelity called

a) **Replication** b) Fission

c) Transcription d) None of these

68. Process by which the DNA genetic code is read and transferred to messenger RNA (mRNA)

a) **Transcription** b) Translation

c) Replication d) All of the above

69. The process by which the genetic code is converted to a protein, the end product of gene expression

a) Transcription b) **Translation**

c) Amino acid d) All of the above

70. Golden rice is a variety of rice produce precursors for ____in the edible parts of rice

a) **Beta carotene (Pro Vitamin A)** b) Vitamin D

c) Vitamin E d) Vitamin C

71. Protein that unwinds the DNA double helix

a) Amylase b) **Helicase**

c) Lipase d) Invertase

72. Enzyme that replicates DNA using each strand as a template for the newly synthesized strand

a) Ligase b) **DNA polymerase**

c) Catalase d) None of these

73. Enzyme that catalyzes the formation of the phosphodiester bond between pieces of DNA

a) Peroxidase b) Lipase

c) Helicase d) **DNA ligase**

74. DNA replication is

a) **Semi-conservative** b) conservative

c) Spiral d) Not found

75. Replication of the leading strand occurs continuously in ____ direction of new strand.

a) 4' → 7' b) **5' → 3'**

c) 3' → 5' d) 1' → 3'

76. Replication of the lagging strand occurs

a) **Discontinuously** b) Continuously

c) Both a and b d) None of the above

77. RNA contains ___rather than 2-deoxyribose and ___rather than thymine

a) **Ribose, uracil**
b) Xylulose, hexose
c) Guanine, cytosine
d) Adenine, thymine

78. Major kinds of RNA

a) Messenger RNA
b) Ribosomal RNA
c) Transfer RNA
d) **All of the above**

79. DNA is found in the

a) **Cell nucleus and mitochondria**
b) Lysosome
c) Golgi complex
d) None of these

80. GM of *Pseudomonas* was able to disintegrate

a) **Trichlorophenoxyacetic acid**
b) Ethanol
c) Acetic acid
d) Butyric acid

81. mRNAs are transported from the nucleus to

a) **Cytoplasm**
b) Ribosome
c) Lysosome
d) Golgi complex

82. Name the bacterial enzymes that cleave DNA at specific sequences

a) Amylase
b) Protease
c) Lipase
d) **Restriction endonucleases**

83. Most commonly used methods of radioactivity

a) Ionisation of gases
b) Excitation of solids and liquids
c) Ability to expose photographic emulsions i.e, autoradiograph
d) **All of the above**

84. The electric pulse produced is measured by

a) **Amperometer**
b) Potometer
c) Pycnometer
d) Voltmeter

85. In 1983 American company Eli Lilly produced first genetically engineered human insulin termed as

a) **Humuline**
b) Choline
c) Hops
d) All of the above

86. Proportional Counters or gas amplification causes

a) Secondary
b) Tertiary ionization
c) **Both A and B**
d) Primary

87. In____ Counters all the isotopes including beta emitters induce complete ionization

a) Coulter
b) **Geiger-Mueller**
c) Both a and b
d) None of these

88. ______is the time taken by the ion pairs to reach their respective electrodes with usually 100-200μS

a) **Dead time**
b) Lag
c) Log
d) Stationary

89. Radioactive isotopes can excite a compound called ___

a) **Fluor**
b) Radiation
c) Excite
d) Light

90. In photomultiplier tube, the electric pulse that results from the conversion of light energy to

a) Chemical energy
b) Shift energy
c) **Electrical energy**
d) All of the above

91. In ____ the fluorescing substance is held in a light tight aluminium chamber

a) **Solid scintillation counting**
b) Liquid scintillation counting
c) Semisolid scintillation counting

92. Crystal used for alpha isotopes

a) Aluminium
b) Magnesium
c) Iron
d) **Zinc sulfide**

93. Crystal used for beta isotopes

a) **Anthracene**
b) Zinc
c) Aluminium
d) Potassium

94. Crystal used for gamma isotopes

a) Silver iodide
b) Potassium iodide
c) **Sodium iodide**
d) Calcium

95. In____ counting the sample is mixed with a scintillation cock tail containing solvent and one or more fluors

a) Semisolid scintillation
b) Solid scintillation
c) **Liquid scintillation**
d) All of the above

96. In ____Ionising radiations acts upon photographic emulsions to produce a latent image

a) Distillation
b) **Autoradiography**
c) Crystallization
d) Sedimentation

97. _____ can be used to track the distribution of a substance within a natural system such as a cell or tissue

a) **Radioactive tracer**
b) Medicine
c) X – Ray
d) None of these

98. The urea breath test commonly used as dose of ^{14}C labeled urea to detect____ infection

a) *E. coli*
b) *Streptococcus*
c) *Staphylococcus*
d) ***H. pylori***

99. Expand SPECT

a) Single photodiode emission compete tomography
b) Single emission computed tomography
c) Single photon emission computed topography
d) **Single photon emission computed tomography**

100. Minimize exposure by placing absorbing shield between worker and source called

a) **Shielding**
b) Barrier
c) Coat
d) Cover

CHAPTER-6

FOOD MICROBIOLOGY AND FOOD HYGIENE

1. *Acetobacter* causes definite spoilage problem in
   a) Fish b) Egg
   c) **Alcoholic beverages** d) Milk
2. *Alcaligenes viscolactis* causes ropiness in
   a) Bread b) **Milk**
   c) Water d) Juice
3. *Alcaligenes metalcaligenes* gives limy growth on
   a) Cordial b) Squash
   c) Nectar d) **Cottage cheese**
4. *Bacillus linens* produces orange red pigmentation and helps ripening in
   a) **Brick or Limburger Cheese** b) Egg
   c) Fruits d) Vegetables
5. ___ is the primary source of *Clostridium spp*
   a) Sewage b) Water
   c) Fruits d) **Soil**
6. ____ is an example of saccharolytic obligate thermophile
   a) *Bacillus*
   b) ***Clostridium thermosaccharolyticum***
   c) *E. coli* d) *Streptococcus*
7. *Erwinia carotovora* associated with market disease called
   a) Water lesion b) **Bacterial soft rot**
   c) Ropiness d) None of these
8. *Gluconobacter* can oxidize ethanol to
   a) **Acetic acid** b) Butyric acid
   c) Linolenic acid d) Linoleic acid
9. *Klebsiella pneumoniae* is the causative organism for a bacterial_____ in humans
   a) Tuberculosis b) Sepsis
   c) Leprosy d) **Pneumoniae**

10. ____ has been known to cause phosphorescence of meats and fish

a) *Staphylococcus* b) ***Photobacterium phosphoreum***

c) *Klebsiella* d) *Listeria*

11. ____ ferment the lactates to produce gas that form holes or eyes

a) *Clostridium* b) *Bacillus*

c) ***Propionibacterium freudenreichii*** d) *Listeria*

12. ___ are beta- hemolytic, coagulase positive strains produce enterotoxin

a) *Chlorobium* b) *Aspergillus*

c) *Rhizopus* d) ***Staphylococcus***

13. Molds examples for rhizoids or holdfasts mycelial structures

a) *Rhizopus* b) *Absidia*

c) **Both A and B** d) None of these

14. Molds examples for foot cell mycelial structures

a) ***Aspergillus*** b) *Rhizopus*

c) *Mucor* d) *Bacillus*

15. Molds examples for rhizoids or holdfasts mycelial structures

a) *Rhizopus* b) *Absidia*

c) **Both A and B** d) *Geotrichum*

16. Molds examples for dichotomous or Y shaped, branching mycelial structures

a) *Pencillium* b) *Aspergillus*

c) ***Geotrichum*** d) *Mucor*

17. ___ are cutoff or bud from special fertile hyphae called conidiospores and open, not enclosed in any container

a) **Conidia** b) Blastospore

c) Rhizoids d) Budding

18. Sporangiospores are in _____ at the tip of fertile hypha

a) Ascospore b) **Sporangium**

c) Mycelium d) Rhizoids

19. _____are formed by fragmentation of a hypha

a) Hypha b) **Arthrospores**

c) Rhizoids d) All of the above

20. How many spores found per ascus

a) **Eight spores** b) Six spores

c) Five spores d) Two spores

21. Mushrooms, plant rusts, smuts are classified under

a) Ascomycetes b) **Basidiomycetes**

c) Deutromycetes d) Zygomycetes

22. Example for Osmophilic or saccharophilic bacteria

a) *Deinococcus* b) ***Leuconostoc***

c) *Rhizobium* d) *Azospirillum*

23. *Pencillium expansum*, blue green spored mold causes ____of fruits

a) Ropiness b) cloudiness

c) Rigid d) **Soft rot**

24. *Trichothecium roseum* is a

a) Green mold b) **Pink mold**

c) Blue mold d) Black mold

25. *Geotrichum candidum* is a

a) Bacteria b) Fungi

c) **Dairy mold** d) None of these

26. *Neurospora sitophila* is a

a) **Red bread mold** b) Green mold

c) Virus d) Bacteria

27. White spot in meat is caused by

a) ***Sporotrichum carnis*** b) *Streptococcus*

c) *Clostridium* d) *Listeria*

28. Lemon shaped conidia are in chains found in

a) *Aspergillus* b) ***Sclerotinia***

c) *Clostridium* d) *E.coli*

29. _____ yeasts are very active fermenters and grows rapidly at 20^{0}C

a) Bottom yeasts b) **Top yeasts**

c) Both a and b d) None of these

30. ___ yeasts do not clump, grow more slowly and are best fermentors at lower temperatures (10 – 15^{0}C)

a) **Bottom yeasts** b) Top yeasts

c) None of these

31. Cryopreservation in liquid nitrogen at ___ helps survival of pure cultures for long storage times

a) **-196^{0}C** b) -296^{0}C

c) -396^{0}C d) -96^{0}C

32. In Lyophilization or freeze drying culture is rapidly frozen at a very low temperature____ and then dehydrated by vacuum

a) **70⁰C** b) 60⁰C

c) 50⁰C d) 40⁰C

33. Methods of pure culture isolation are

a) Streak plate method b) Pour plate method

c) Spread plate method d) **All of the above**

34. Floppy baby syndrome is caused by

a) Hyperthyroidism b) **Infant botulism**

c) Marasmus d) Kwashiorkar

35. Diptheria toxin are produced by

a) *Bacillus* b) ***Corynebacterium diptheriae***

c) *Clostridium* d) *Staphylococcus*

36. Streptolysin O and Streptolysin S is produced by

a) ***Streptococcus pyogenes*** b) *Staphylococcus*

c) *Rhizopus* d) *Aspergillus*

37. ___ are soluble proteins found in cell extracts or in the growth medium found in gram negative bacteria

a) Exotoxin b) **Endotoxin**

c) Enterotoxin d) None of these

38. ___ are soluble proteins secreted outside the bacteria through their cell wall and these substances are heat labile, being inactivated by boiling

a) Endotoxins b) **Exotoxins**

c) Both a and b

39. GMP is also sometimes referred to as

a) **cGMP** b) mGMP

c) iGMP d) nGMP

40. _____ is found in sea water causes soft tissue and ear infections in humans

a) ***Vibrio alginolyticus*** b) *Clostridium*

c) *Bacillus* d) *E.coli*

41. *Clostridium perfringens* causes

a) **Gas gangrene** b) Pneumoniae

c) Leprosy d) Tuberculosis

42. *E.coli* is used as an indicator for

a) **Fecal contamination** b) Food contamination

c) Health d) None of these

43. Emetic syndrome is also called as ____ because its association with starchy products like rice and dishes

a) **Chinese restaurant syndrome** b) Turner syndrome

c) Down syndrome d) Klinefelter syndrome

44. Widal test is used to detect the

a) *Staphylococcus* b) *Streptococcus*

c) *Yersinia pestis* d) ***Salmonella***

45. Kauffman white serotyping scheme was proved the most useful technique for differentiating with the genus

a) *Clostridium* b) *Rhizobium*

c) *Aspergillus* d) *Salmonella*

46. Eggs should be cooked at __ for 15 seconds

a) >15^{0}F b) **>145^{0}F (67^{0}C)**

c) >45^{0}F d) >16^{0}F

47. Raw eggs should be stored at ___

a) < 15^{0}F b) < 35^{0}F

c) **< 45^{0}F (7.2^{0}C)** d) < 55^{0}F

48. As per GHP water used in food processing units should meet the

a) Non portability test b) Cleaning test

c) Drinkability test d) **Portability test**

49. *Yersinia pestis* causes

a) Botulism b) Typhoid

c) Malaria d) **Plague**

50. Mycotoxins are produced as ___metabolites of fungi

a) **Secondary** b) Primary

c) Teritary d) All of the above

51. Those parameters of plant and animal tissues that are an inherent part of the tissues are referred to as

a) Extrinsic parameters b) **Intrinsic parameters**

c) Factors d) All of the above

52. Moisture content, pH, Oxidation reduction potential, Nutrient content, Antimicrobial constituents and Biological structures comes under

a) **Intrinsic parameters** b) Extrinsic parameters

c) Parameters d) Factors

53. Most spoilage bacteria do not grow below

a) 0.1 a_w b) 0.41 a_w

c) 0.51 a_w d) **0.91 a_w**

54. Many of the food items and plant juices tend to have Eh values from

a) - 300 to -400 b) **+ 300 to +400**

c) 0 d) ∞

55. The Primary 'N' source utilized by microorganisms are

a) Fats b) Fibre

c) **Amino acids** d) All of the above

56. Parameters of foods those properties of the storage environment that affect both the foods and their microorganisms called

a) **Extrinsic** b) Intrinsic

c) Considerations d) Properties

57. Temperature of storage, Relative humidity of the environment, Presence and concentration of gases in the environment are comes under

a) Intrinsic parameters b) **Extrinsic parameters**

c) Objects d) None of these

58. CO_2 is known to retard

a) **Fungal spoilage** b) Algal spoilage

c) Parasite spoilage d) None of these

59. The storage of food in atmospheres containing increased amounts of CO_2 up to about 10% is referred to as

a) **Controlled atmosphere storage** b) Modified atmosphere storage

c) Cold storage d) Freezer storage

60. Beer is spoiled by the yeast

a) ***Hansenula*** b) *Rhizopus*

c) Mucor d) **Debaromyces**

61. Cheese is spoiled by the yeast

a) Mucor b) ***Debaromyces***

c) *Hansenula* d) *Rhizopus*

62. Potatoes, certain varieties of apples are examples of

a) **Semi perishable foods** b) Perishable foods

c) Non perishable foods d) All of the above

63. Meat, fish, poultry, most fruits, vegetables, milk comes under the group

a) **Perishables food** b) Non perishable

c) Semi perishable d) None of these

64. Bacteria producing H_2O_2 may cause a green pigmentation through the oxidation of nitrosohaemochrome to

a) Myoglobin b) Haemoglobin

c) **Choleomyoglobin** d) Myosin

65. Bacterial production of H_2S converts muscle pigment to green

a) Actin b) **Sulphmyoglobin**

c) Myosn d) Myoglobin

66. The nutrient content of the yolk material and its pH in fresh eggs ___ make it an excellent source of growth for most microorganisms

a) 4.8 b) 5.8

c) **6.8** d) 7.8

67. Lysozyme is present in

a) **Egg white** b) Egg yolk

c) Egg shell d) Egg chalazae

68. Lysozyme enzyme is effective against

a) **Gram +ve bacteria** b) Gram -ve bacteria

c) Protozoa d) Fungi

69. Custard rot caused by

a) ***Proteus vulgaris*** b) *Pseudomonas*

c) *E. Coli* d) *Staphylococcus*

70. Fungi, *Penicillium* and *Cladosporium sp* cause spoilage of eggs known as

a) Rots b) **Pinspots**

c) Cloudiness d) Turbidness

71. *Proteus sp* and *Pseudomans graveolens* also cause a condition in eggs known as

a) **Mustiness** b) Rot

c) Tangy d) Spoilage

72. Expand NIST

a) National Institute of Specification and Technology

b) National Institute of Standards and Technology

c) **National Institute of Survey and Technology**

d) National Institute of Survey and Technology

73. The average water content of vegetables is about

a) 68% b) 78%

c) **88%** d) 98%

74. Black rot of cabbage and cauliflower is caused by

a) ***Xanthomonas campestris***
b) *Streptococcus*
c) *Mycobacterium*
d) *Bordetella*

75. Sugar, flour and dry beans are examples of*Candida*

a) Eatables
b) **Stable or non-perishable foods**
c) Semi perishable
d) Perishable

76. Anthracnose caused by

a) ***Colletotrichum***
b) *Clostridium*
c) *Bacillus*
d) *Arthrobacter*

77. Average water content of fruits is about

a) 55%
b) **85%**
c) 75%
d) 95%

78. ___ is a tool to assess hazards and establish control systems that focus on prevention rather than relying mainly on end-product testing

a) **HACCP**
b) GMP
c) GHP
d) GAP

79. Establish the corrective action to be taken when monitoring indicates that a particular CCP is not under control comes under ___ principle of HACCP

a) **Principle 5**
b) Principle 4
c) Principle 2
d) Principle 1

80. Establish documentation concerning all procedures and records appropriate to these principles and their application comes under ___ principle of HACCP

a) Principle 3
b) **Principle 7**
c) Principle 4
d) Principle 5

81. ___infection is an intestinal illness that often occurs in outbreaks

a) *Listeria*
b) **Norwalk virus**
c) *Vibrio*
d) *Bacillus*

82. Aflatoxin B1 is the most potent natural

a) **Carcinogen**
b) Toxic
c) Poison
d) None of these

83. ___ is the time required to kill a given number of organisms at a specified temperature

a) **Thermal death time**
b) F value
c) D value
d) All of the above

84. ____ is the time in minutes required at specified temperature to kill 90% of microorganisms thereby reducing the count by 1 log units

a) F value b) **D value**

c) Z value d) T value

85. ___ value refers to degrees of F required for the thermal destruction curve to drop by one log cycle

a) **Z value** b) F value

c) D value d) All of the above

86. ___ value is the time in minutes required to kill all spores/ vegetative cells at 250^{0}F

a) **F value** b) Z value

c) D value d) None of these

87. 12D concept is used mainly in

a) **Low acid canned foods (pH >4.6)**

b) High acid foods

c) Acid foods d) All of the above

88. _____method is usually based on inoculating replicate tubes of an appropriate liquid medium (usually 3, 4 or 5) with three different sample sizes or dilutions

a) **Most Probable Number Counts** b) Serial dilutions

c) Plating methods d) Microscopic methods

89. _____ method amplify specific fragments of DNA, usually less than 3kb in length, and allow detection of a single copy of target sequence

a) **Polymerase chain reaction (PCR)**

b) Thin Layer chromatography

c) Paper chromatography

d) Column chromatography

90. _____ improves the sensitivity of the reaction by first amplifying a larger sequence using a pair of outer primers followed by amplification of a shorter sequence within the amplicon using a second set of inner primers

a) **Nested PCR** b) RT PCR

c) Chromatography d) Analytes

91. ____uses conventional PCR to amplify an RNA template after it has been transcribed into DNA

a) Nested PCR b) Electrophoresis

c) **Reverse transcriptase PCR** d) None of these

92. _____uses an alternating electric field to tease apart the large DNA molecules

a) **Pulsed field gel electrophoresis (PFGE)** b) Spectroscopy

c) Chromatography d) All of the above

93. In restriction fragment length polymorphism (RFLP), _____is used to cut DNA into a number of fragments depending on the number and location of restriction sites present

a) Polymerase enzyme
b) Lipase enzyme
c) Ligase enzyme
d) **Restriction enzyme**

94. According to the World Health Organization (WHO) _____refers to conditions and practices that help to maintain health and prevent the spread of diseases

a) **Hygiene**
b) Sanitation
c) Health
d) None of these

95. ___ diagram depicts how germs spread and how that can be prevented

a) **F diagram**
b) T diagram
c) L diagram
d) All of the above

96. On 2nd October 2014, the Prime Minister, Shri Narendra Modi, launched the

a) Agriculure Program
b) **Swachh Bharat Mission (SBM)**
c) Space Research Program
d) All of the above

97. Waste water generated in the kitchen, bathroom and laundry is called

a) Black Water
b) **Grey water**
c) Both a and b
d) None of these

98. Central Rural Sanitation Programme (CRSP) in

a) 1956
b) **1986**
c) 1946
d) 1996

99. Total Sanitation Campaign (TSC) in

a) **1999**
b) 1993
c) 1994
d) 1992

100. Nirmal Bharat Abhiyan in

a) 2015
b) 2017
c) 2018
d) **2012**

CHAPTER-7

PHYSICAL, CHEMICAL AND INSTRUMENTAL ANALYSIS

1. Nutrition Labeling and Education Act of

    a) **1990** b) 1994

    c) 1998 d) 2000

2. The Dietary Supplement Health and Education Act of

    a) 1990 b) 1992

    c) 1993 d) **1994**

3. Food Additives Amendment enacted in

    a) 1950 b) **1958**

    c) 1960 d) 1965

4. Color Additives Amendment of

    a) **1960** b) 1990

    c) 2000 d) 2001

5. Reference Daily Intakes (RDI) for Vitamin A

    a) **5000 IU** b) 6000 IU

    c) 8000 IU d) 9000 IU

6. Reference Daily Intakes (RDIs) for Vitamin C

    a) 50 mg b) 55 mg

    c) **60 mg** d) 80 mg

7. Reference Daily Intakes (RDI) for Iron

    a) **18 mg** b) 25 mg

    c) 50 mg d) 80 mg

8. Reference Daily Intakes (RDIs) for Vitamin D

    a) 200 IU b) **400 IU**

    c) 800 IU d) None of these

9. Reference Daily Intakes (RDIs) for iodine

    a) **150 μg** b) 200 μg

    c) 500 μg d) 800 μg

10. The term RDI is used for

a) Essential vitamins
b) Minerals
c) Both A and B -A
d) None of these

11. The term DRV is used for food components of Total fat, Saturated fat, Cholesterol, Total carbohydrate, Dietary fiber, Sodium, Potassium and Protein

12. ____ is the standard for measurement of the energy value of substances and to express the body's energy requirement

a) **Calorie**
b) Energy
c) Strength
d) All of the above

13. 1 calorie =

a) 3.184 joules
b) **4.184 joules**
c) 5.184 joules
d) 8.184 joules

14. The unit used in nutritional work "kilo-calorie" (kcal), which equals

a) **1000 calories**
b) 2000 calories
c) 5000 calories
d) All of the above

15. ____is the midpoint or middle number in a list of numbers ordered from lowest to highest

a) Mean
b) Mode
c) Variance
d) **Median**

16. ____ is the total of all the values, divided by the number of values

a) **Mean**
b) Median
c) SD
d) Variability

17. ____ is a measure of how close the data are to the true value

a) **Accuracy**
b) Precision
c) Right
d) Variance

18. ____is a measure of the reproducibility of the data

a) Accuracy
b) Calculative
c) Subjective
d) **Precision**

19. ___ measures the spread of experimental values and gives a good indication of how close the values are each other

a) Mode
b) **Standard de viation**
c) Mean
d) Experimental error

20. _____ is the difference between largest and smallest observation

a) Mean
b) Mode
c) Acceptibility
d) **Range**

21. Coefficient of variation (CV) also known as

a) Dispersion
b) Normal distribution
c) **Relative standard deviation**
d) All of the above

22. ____ is the number of standard deviations a sore or a value away from the mean

a) **Z score**
b) L score
c) R score
d) None of these

23. ____is the sample size minus one (n − 1), and the desired level of confidence

a) Acceptability
b) **Degrees of freedom**
c) Precision
d) Poisson distribution

24. _____ is simply the difference between experimental value and the true value

a) Replicative error
b) **Absolute error**
c) Subjective error
d) All of the above

25. ____of a particular analytical method means it detects only component of interest

a) Standard
b) **Specificity**
c) Acceptibility
d) None of these

26. ____relates to magnitude of change of a measuring device (instrument) with changes in compound concentration

a) Analysis
b) Significant
c) **Sensitivity**
d) Type error

27. ___errors are always present in any analytical measurement

a) **Random or indeterminate**
b) Non random
c) Site specific
d) Product specific

28. ___ is the lowest possible increment that can detect with some degree of confidence (or statistical significance)

a) Variability
b) Specificity
c) **Limit of detection (LOD)**
d) Precision

29. ____ or calibration curve is used to determine unknown concentrations

a) Dump bell curve
b) Variance curve
c) **Standard curve**
d) All of them

30. ___is a generic term used to describe the relationship and evaluation between two variables

a) Non fitting
b) **Curve fitting**
c) Peak highness
d) Radiance

31. ____ data are called the independent variable and are assumed to be essentially free of error

a) **X - axis** b) Y - axis

c) Z - axis d) None of these

32. ___data (the dependent variable) may have error associated with them

a) X - axis b) **Y - axis**

c) Z - axis d) R - axis

33. ____ is calculated based on values of samples within the assay matrix and thus is considered a more rigorous performance test

a) LOD b) **MDL**

c) LOQ d) All of them

34. ____is used often because, it gives a better perception of the straight line even though it does not indicate the direction of the correlation

a) Variability b) **Coefficient of determination (r^2)**

c) Curve d) None of these

35. ____ is the lowest analyte concentration that can be quantitatively detected with a stated accuracy and precision

a) **Limit of Quantification (LOQ)** b) LOD

c) MDL d) All of the above

36. ____is used rather loosely to describe some judgment of the number of reportable digits in a result

a) Curve fitting b) Angle

c) mage d) **Significant figure**

37. ___ is a statistical formula used to compare variances across the means (or average) of different groups

a) Distribution b) **Analysis Of Variance (ANOVA)**

c) Reference value d) Precision

38. The small portions taken for analysis are referred to as

a) Collections b) Objects

c) **Samples** d) None of these

39. Entire lot or entire production for a certain period of time, in case of continuous processes is called

a) **Population** b) Samples

c) Lot d) All of the above

40. The process of taking samples from a population is called

a) **Sampling**
b) Weighting
c) Analyzing
d) Calculating

41. Variance is an estimate of the

a) Certainty
b) **Uncertainty**
c) Population
d) Means

42. The most efficient way to improve accuracy is to improve the

a) **Reliability**
b) True value
c) False value
d) Analyzing

43. A predetermined procedure for the selection, withdrawal, preservation, transportation, and preparation of the portions to be removed from a lot as samples

a) Procedure
b) **Sampling plan**
c) Steps
d) Precaution

44. In___ sampling, it is performed to decide on the acceptability of a population based on whether the sample possesses a certain characteristic or not

a) **Attribute**
b) Variable
c) Acceptable
d) All of the above

45. In ____sampling it is performed to estimate quantitatively the amount of a substance

a) Attribute
b) Random
c) **Variable sampling**
d) None of these

46. ____ can be performed by the food processor before receiving a lot of materials from a supplier, or by a buyer who is evaluating the processor's output

a) **Acceptance sampling**
b) Variable
c) Attribute
d) None of these

47.____ risk describes the probability of accepting a poor quality population

a) **Consumer's risk**
b) Producer risk
c) Both a and b
d) All of the above

48. ____ risk is the probability of rejecting an acceptable product

a) **Producer risk**
b) Consumer risk
c) Risk analysis
d) Identification

49. ____prescribe the selection of a sample from a population based on chance

a) Non Probability sampling plan
b) **Probability sampling plans**
c) Risk analysis
d) Precaution

50. ____sampling requires the number of units in the population be known and each unit is assigned an identification number

a) Stratified sampling

b) **Simple random sampling**

c) Both a and b

d) None of these

Part -7
Evaluate Yourself

CHAPTER-1

Fill in the Blanks

"Our greatest ability as humans is not to change the world, but to change ourselves" -Mahatma Gandhi

1. ___ is the science of measuring specific gravity or density
2. Measuring specific gravity is based on__
3. The dinitrosalicylic acid method will measure____ naturally occurring in foods or released by enzymes
4. The refractive index (RI) detector is commonly employed for__
5. For GC, sugars must be converted into
6. ____can be defined as the study of the interaction between electromagnetic radiation and matter
7. Absorption spectroscopy is based on the Beer Lambert law
8. ____law says that, for a homogeneous and non scattering liquid sample, the concentration of an absorber is proportional to the sample absorbance
9. ____spectroscopy provides chemical and structural information
10. ___ scattering occurs as a result of the interactions of the incident photons with the polarizability or shape of the electron distribution in a molecule as it vibrates
11. The difference between the frequency of the laser and scattered photon is known as the
12. ____Concept is transfer of total headspace of a sample to a sensor array that detects the presence of volatile compounds
13. ___is a device made of sensors responding to some taste (soluble) of foods through the transduction of a signal or a pattern of signals
14. ___are instruments that separate ionized atoms or molecules according to their difference in mass to charge ratio (m/z)
15. ____Analyzers use an electric field to accelerate the ions through the same potential
16. _____involves multiple stages of mass spectrometry, with fragmentation occurring between the stages

17. GC detectors of_____ is the "classical" method for the determination of fatty acid composition
18. ____ is a physico-chemical method for separation of compound mixtures, based on the distribution of components between stationary (sorbent), and mobile flowing through a layer of the stationary phase
19. ___ analysis is a technique through which amount of analyte can be determined through the measurement of mass
20. LC separates mixtures of molecular weights from___to several millions (simple molecules, macromolecules, ions, and even viruses)
21. _____chromatography is the most specific chromatographic method based on selective noncovalent interaction between an analyte and specific molecules
22. Measurement of the volume of a unknown solution (the analyte) with a known concentration of a reagent called
23. ____chromatography is used for the separation of mixtures of anions (anion-exchange chromatography) or cations (cation-exchange chromatography)
24. ____chromatography is applied for separation of mixture of optical isomers (enantiomers) with the use of chiral stationary phase
25. ____chromatography is applied for separation of macromolecules (proteins, polysaccharides, etc.) by molecular weights
26. Ultra-high-pressure chromatography (UHPLC) uses columns with particle size less than__
27. Countercurrent chromatography or partition chromatography separates___
28. The time between sample injection and an analyte peak reaching a detector at the end of the column is termed the____
29. GC Detectors of Thermal conductivity detector (TCD) Responds___
30. GC Detectors of Flame ionization detector (FID) detects___
31. GC Detectors of Electron-capture (ECD) detects_____
32. GC Detectors of Nitrogen phosphorus detector (NPD) or thermionic detector detects
33. GC Detectors of Flame photometric detector (FPD) detects___
34. GC Detectors of Photoionization detector (PID) detects___
35. GC Detectors of Atomic emission detector (AED) detects__
36. ____ is the movement of charged particles under the influence of an applied electric field, and used in separation technique for biological molecules
37. Denaturation or melting of DNA is carried out at___
38. Annealing involves hydrogen bond formation between primers and their complementary sequences present on single-stranded DNA template at____

39. Primer Extension at temperature___
40. Taq polymerase, isolated from the hot springs bacterium__
41. Pfu polymerase, having isolated from__
42. Vent polymerase, isolated from___
43. ____ (using agarose or polyacrylamide) involves separation of (DNA), (RNA), or protein molecules using an electric field
44. ____ is the temperature at which the double-stranded DNA target will dissociate to become single-stranded and will allow annealing of primer sequence
45. A simple formula for calculation of the (Tm) Eq is__
46. ____are oligonucleotide probes that can report the presence of specific nucleic acids in homogenous solutions
47. ____ is the method developed for separation of large DNA molecules
48. _____spectroscopy is a rapid and nondestructive technique allowing the screening of a large number of samples
49. ____is a thermo analytical technique in which the difference in the amount of heat required to increase the temperature of a sample and reference is measured as a function of temperature
50. Southern blotting involves the isolation of ____from animals, digestion of DNA with restriction enzymes, electrophoresis on agarose gels to separate DNA by size, denaturation of the DNA, and transfer of the DNA to a membrane
51. The process of milling which reduces the number of microorganisms is a__
52. Actinomycetes are the normal flora of____
53. Boston brown bread is a_____
54. The percentage of ammonia used to reduce mold growth in high-moisture corn is ___
55. The organic acid used to combat rope in bakery products is____
56. The major factors involved in the spoilage of stored grains by molds include ____
57. Bleaching of white wheat flour is done by using oxidizing agents like a__
58. In bread *Bacillus subtilis* causes___
59. Swelling of moist macaroni is caused due to the presence of a __
60. Endomycopsis causes __
61. *V. parahaemolyticus* has an incubation period of____
62. Soft drinks are tested for chemicals when they are contained in a __
63. The toxic substance of the 'Chinese restaurant' syndrome is ___

64. *Corynebacterium* is detected by the analysis of___
65. Samples of suspected perishable foods must be kept cold ___
66. Cultures from nose, throat or skin lesions are used to test for__
67. Mucoid diarrhea is the predominant symptom in the detection of__
68. Neurological symptoms caused by puffer-fish poisoning is because of__
69. The predominant symptoms in the lower gastro-intestinal tract infection is__
70. Cyanosis occurs due to ___
71. A system to control the safety of a manufactured product is determined by__
72. HACCP is designed to ___
73. National academy of sciences is an authority on ___
74. The Codex guidelines for HACCP has ___
75. CIP refers to __
76. During transportation, perishable foods should be kept at __
77. An example of a wetting agent is __
78. CCP aims at preventing or reducing __
79. Validation ensures that the industry ___
80. The simplest record-keeping system to ensure effectiveness is by ___

Answers			
1.	Hydrometry	41.	*Pyrococcus furiosus*
2.	Archimedes' principle	42.	*Thermococcus litoralis*
3.	Reducing sugars	43.	Gel electrophoresis
4.	Carbohydrate analysis	44.	Melting temperature (Tm)
5.	Volatile derivatives	45.	$T_m = 4\,(G+C) + 2\,(A+T)^0C$
6.	Spectroscopy	46.	Molecular Beacons (mbs)
7.	Beer Lambert law	47.	Pulse Field Gel Electrophoresis (PFGE)
8.	Beer Lambert law	48.	Fluorescence spectroscopy
9.	Raman spectroscopy	49.	Differential scanning calorimetry (DSC)
10.	Raman scattering	50.	DNA
11.	Raman shift	51.	Bleaching
12.	E-nose concept	52.	Raw cereal grains
13.	An electronic tongue	53.	Canned
14.	Mass spectrometers	54.	2%
15.	Time-of-flight (TOF) analyzers	55.	Acetic acid

16.	Tandem mass spectrometry	56.	Microbial content, moisture level above 12%, physical damage
17.	FID (flame ionization detection)	57.	Benzoyl peroxide
18.	Chromatography	58.	Ropiness
19.	Gravimetric analysis	59.	*Enterobacter cloacae*
20.	50	60.	Chalky brea
21.	Affinity chromatography	61.	15-24 hours
22.	Titration	62.	Metal container
23.	Ion-exchange chromatography (IEC)	63.	MSG
24.	Chiral chromatography	64.	Throat swab
25.	Size-exclusion chromatography	65.	During transit to laboratory
26.	2 mm	66.	*Staphylococcus*
27.	Liquid - liquid mixtures	67.	*Giardia lamblia*
28.	Retention time	68.	Tetradon toxin
29.	If thermal conductivity is different from carrier gas (Universal)	69.	Abdominal cramps and diarrhea
30.	Organic compounds	70.	Nitrite poisoning
31.	Electron-capturing compounds such as halogens	71.	HACCP
32.	N- and P-containing compounds	72.	Prevent problems before they occur, Correct deviations as soon as detected
33.	P- and S-containing compounds	73.	Food safety
34.	Aromatics	74.	Seven principles
35.	Element selective	75.	Clean in place systems
36.	Electrophoresis	76.	3.3 - 6.6^{0}C
37.	90 - 94^0 C	77.	Polyether alcohol
38.	50 - 65^{0}C	78.	Physical hazards, chemical hazards and biological hazards
39.	72^0 C	79.	Complies with the required plan
40.	*Thermus aquaticus*	80.	Establishing documentation

CHAPTER-2

Mock Test 1

1. Dole process is related to
   a) Aseptic canning
   b) Blanching
   c) Comminution
   d) Ohmic heating
2. Zein is principal protein of which crop
   a) Wheat
   b) Mustard
   c) Corn
   d) Sesame
3. Who is considered as 'father of canning'
   a) Robert Hooke
   b) Louis Pasteur
   c) Nicholas Appert
4. Compound responsible for antimicrobial activity of clove is
   a) Eugenol
   b) Cinnamldehyde
   c) Camphene
   d) Terpineol
5. Cider is prepared from
   a) Wheat
   b) Barley
   c) Apple
   d) Grapes
6. Common adulterant in black pepper is
   a) Brick sand
   b) Papaya seed
   c) Urea
   d) Pomegranate seeds
7. Fat standards for double toned milk is
   a) 0.5%
   b) 1.5%
   c) 3.0%
   d) 6.0%
8. What is the maximum amount of time perishable food should be left out
   a) 2 hours
   b) 3 hours
   c) 4 hours
   d) 5 hours
9. Saffron is obtained from which portion of the plant
   a) Seed
   b) Stigma
   c) Sepal
   d) Petal

10. Consumer protection act came in year

a) 1973
b) 1986
c) 1993
d) 2006

11. Base material used for rum making is

a) Wheat
b) Rice
c) Barley
d) Sugarcane

12. Veal is the meat of

a) Pig
b) Calf
c) Goat
d) Buffalo

13. Barges is

a) A cocoa variety
b) Processing method of cocoa beans
c) Cocoa based drinks
d) Cocoa shipment method

14. Total plate count is expressed as

a) Cfu/ml
b) Cells/ml
c) Viable cells/ml
d) None

15. HACCP stands for

a) Hazard Analysis Central Critical Parameters
b) Hazard Analysis Critical Control Point
c) Hazard Analysis Combined Critical Point
d) Health Analysis Critical Control Point

16. The scientific name of the liquerice plant is

a) *Glycyrrhiza glabra*
b) *Cinnamomum tamala*
c) *Ocimum basilicum*
d) *Syzygium aromaticum*

17. Which of the following is regarded as king of spices

a) Chilly
b) Pepper
c) Turmeric
d) Aniseed

18. Central Agmark Laboratory is situated at

a) Chennai
b) Delhi
c) Nagpur
d) Kolkata

19. Compound responsible for butter flavor is

a) Diacetyl
b) Vanillin
c) Both a &b
d) Diethyl

20. Anti-nutritional factor present in egg

a) Avidin
b) Phytic acid
c) Saponin
d) Tannin

21. Red color of tomatoes is due to

a) Anthocyanin
b) Carotene
c) Riboflavin
d) Lycopene

22. Food sterilization via irradiation is also known as

a) Gas sterilization
b) Cold sterilization
c) Neutral sterilization
d) All

23. Which of the following is not a part of risk analysis

a) Risk assessment
b) Risk managment
c) Risk communication
d) Risk prevention

24. Which of the following compound is characterized by the presence of NH2 and carboxyl-COOH group

a) Carboxylic acid
b) Amino acid
c) Ascorbic acid
d) Retinol

25. The full form of MRA is

a) Microbiological Risk assessment
b) Marine Risk Assessment
c) Micro Risk Assessment
d) Major Risk Assessment

26. Pascal is the unit of measurement of

a) Temperature
b) Pressure
c) Heat
d) None

27. Hedonic scale is used for

a) Sensory analysis
b) Protein analysis
c) Fat analysis
d) None

28. Disease which arises due to insufficient glucose metabolism is

a) Diabetes mellitis
b) Bronchial asthma
c) Celiac disease
d) Goiter

29. Endomycopsis causes

a) Chalky bread
b) Blue bread
c) Red bread
d) None of the above

30. The Food Authority comprises of 22 members of which women shall make up to

a) Three fourth
b) One-third
c) Two-third
d) Half

31. Health is defined as a state of complete physical, mental and social well-being and not merely the absence of disease and infirmity by

a) WHO
b) UNESCO
c) FSSAI
d) FAO

32. The director of APEDA is appointed by

a) Central government
b) State government
c) Food Authority
d) APEDA

33. "Consumer" is defined as

a) Persons and families purchasing and receiving food in order to meet their personal needs

b) A single family that consumers food

c) Persons receiving food to sell or to meet their personal needs

d) A person who purchases food

34. Enforcement of the act comes under chapter

a) Chapter 2
b) Chapter 4
c) Chapter 7
d) Chapter6

35. Establishment of tribunal comes under section

a) Section 85
b) Section 70
c) Section 45
d) Section 71

36. Fermentation of glycerol in wine results in

a) Pousse
b) Amertume
c) Mousy flavour
d) Tourne

37. 1 Gray (Gy) =

a) 10 rads
b) 100 rads
c) 1 rad
d) 1000 rads

38. Which dietary component helps to maintain a constant body temperature in our body

a) Roughage
b) Vitamins
c) Water
d) Energy giving food

39. This nutrient helps insulate our body and cushion our organs

a) Water
b) Calcium
c) Potassium
d) Fat

40. Listeriosis is generally caused by

a) Hepatitis A virus
b) *L. monocytogenes*
c) Norovirus
d) *E. coli*

41. The mineral found in haemoglobin is called as

a) Sodium
b) Protein
c) Iron
d) Calcium

42. Benzoic acid is mostly used to preserve colored products because

a) Of its bleaching action
b) It may darken the product
c) Of its characteristic aroma
d) It may lighten product

43. The head office of FSSAI is situated in

a) Mumbai
b) Bangalore
c) Delhi
d) Chennai

44. Wort is a

a) Dense solution
b) Clear solution
c) Suspended particles
d) None of these

45. Most important organism in production of amylase is

a) *Bacillus subtilis*
b) *Saccharomyces*
c) *E. Coli*
d) *Geotrichum*

46. Codex standards are used to

a) Increase the revenue collection
b) Standardize the products by the manufacturers
c) Protect the interest of the food manufacturers
d) Protect the health of the consumers and ensure fair practices in the food trade.

47. 1 gm of alcohol gives how many calories

a) 8
b) 7
c) 10
d) 11

48. Vitamin B9 is commonly known as

a) Thiamine
b) Riboflavin
c) Folic acid
d) Ascorbic acid

49. Fiber is important to facilitate which function in the body

a) Provide energy
b) Absorb nutrients
c) Bowel movements
d) None of the above

50. Term used for addition of nutrients to food that were not originally present

a) Food Enrichment
b) Food Fortification
c) Food Diversifiaction
d) None of these

51. Full form of GMO

a) Gene mutated organism
b) Genome modified organism
c) Genetically modified organism
d) None of these

52. Milk is fortified with

a) Vitamin A
b) Vitamin C
c) Vitamin D
d) Both A and C

53. Carotenoids serve as precursors to which vitamin

a) Vitamin A　　b) Vitamin B

c) Vitamin C　　d) Vitamin D

54. Thiamine deficiency leads to which disease

a) Rickets　　b) Jaundice

c) Beriberi　　d) Scurvy

55. Term used for live bacteria found in yogurt

a) Antibiotics　　b) Adjuvants

c) Prebiotics　　d) Probiotics

56. Chemical name for Vitamin B5

a) Ascorbic acid　　b) Pantothenic acid

c) Acetic acid　　d) Hydrocholric acid

57. Which Vitamin is called as Phylloquinone

a) Vitamin A　　b) Vitamin K

c) Vitamin C　　d) Vitamin D

58. 1 gm of carbohydrate gives how much calories?

a) 4　　b) 5

c) 6　　d) 7

59. What is known as the sunshine vitamin

a) Vitamin D　　b) Vitamin A

c) Vitamin K　　d) Vitamin C

60. Wheat flour is fortified with which nutrient:

a) Vitamin A and Vitamin D

b) Iron, Folic Acid and Vitamin B12

c) Folic acid, Vitamin B12 and Vitamin D

d) Vitamin A, Iron and Vitamin C

61. ITCFSAN means

a) International Training Centre for Food Safety and Applied Nutrition

b) Indian Training Centre for Food Safety and Applied Nutrition

c) Institute Training Centre for Food Safety and Applied Nutrition

d) International Training Centre for Food Safety and Nutrition

62. Kaizen means

a) Continuous production　　b) Continuous management

c) Continuous improvement　　d) Continuous process

63. The corner stones of ITCFSAN are
   a) Training with Impact
   b) Training to manage risk
   c) Supporting towards self compliance
   d) All of the above

64. Green tea is
   a) Fermented tea b) Semifermented tea
   c) Unfermented tea d) None of the above

65. Oxytoxin, Vasopressin are examples of
   a) Peptide hormones b) Goitrogen
   c) Zymogen d) Parotid

66. Which amino acid is imino acid
   a) Proline b) Histidine
   c) Tyrosine d) Glutamic acid

67. Iodine number of fatty acid denotes its
   a) Degree of unsaturation b) Solubility in water
   c) Chain length d) Molecular weight

68. Pasteurization of egg should be done at the temperature of
   a) $60 - 62^0$ C b) $60 - 72^0$ C
   c) $60 - 82^0$ C d) $60 - 92^0$ C

69. Yellow orange colour in saffron is due to
   a) Xanthophyll b) Crocetin
   c) Chlorophyll d) None of these

70. PAC stands for
   a) Pacific Association Cooperation b) Pacific Accreditation Cooperation
   c) Pacific Accreditation Committeee d) None of these

71. Kimchi is a product of which country
   a) Japan b) China
   c) India d) Korea

72. Process by which fat removed from tissue by heat known as
   a) Larding b) Rendering
   c) Hydrolysis d) Cloning

73. Chemical name of Ajinomoto is
   a) Ascorbic Acid b) Tryptophan
   c) Calciferol d) Monosodium Glutamate

74. Sub-standard food means

a) It does not meet the specified standards but not so as to render the article of food unsafe

b) Unsafe food

c) Manufactured without license

d) All of the above

75. Indian Cardamom Research Institute is situated at

a) Myladumpara b) Kochi

c) Trivandrum d) Palakkad

76. What is a food recall

a) Action taken to remove a marketed food

b) Action taken to sale the food on priority

c) Action taken to final dispose of food by company

d) All of the above

77. Elimination of all forms of bacteria is called

a) Pasteurisation b) Sterilization

c) Blanching d) Appertization

78. A portion of a material selected from a larger quantity of a material is called

a) Lot b) Sample

c) Lot size d) None of these

79. The term nutraceutical is coined by

a) Defelice b) Went

c) Dixon d) William

80. Identification of Hazards is _____ principle of HACCP

a) 1st b) 2nd

c) 3rd d) 4th

81. What is lactose intolerance

a) Difficulty in digesting vitamins b) Difficulty in digesting Lactose

c) Difficulty in digesting proteins d) Difficulty in digesting fat

82. The purpose of FFRC is to provide

a) Information and technical assistance on standards of fortified foods

b) Quality assurance and control for production of fortified foods

c) Assure safe and wholesome food for all

d) All of the above

83. What means the process of addition of hydrogen to an edible vegetable oil using a catalyst to produce a fat with semi-solid consistency

a) Hydrogenation b) Coagulation

c) Transmission d) Pasteurization

84. Which device is used to detect the odour and flavour of food

a) Electronic nose b) E-tongue

c) Texture analyser d) GC

85. Deficiency of which vitamin is associated with Neural Tube Defects

a) Vitamin B3 b) Vitamin B6

c) Vitamin B9 d) Vitamin B12

86. Which of the following is amphoteric in nature

a) Carbohydrates b) Proteins

c) Fats d) Fibres

87. What is the mixture of probiotics and prebiotics called

a) Symbiotics b) Dibiotics

c) Synbiotics d) None of the above

88. What kind of infectious agents are Prions which caused the mad cow disease

a) Bacteria b) Virus

c) Pathogenic protein d) Protozoa

89. Carrageenan is extracted from

a) Soyabean b) Milk

c) Red edible sea weed d) None of the above

90. Blackening of pickle occurs due to formation of

a) Hydrogen sulfide b) Bromates

c) Oil d) Vinegar

91. Crystallization for long time leads to which size of crystals

a) Small b) Large

c) No crystals formed d) None of the above

92. Which of these is essential for preventing dental caries

a) Flouride b) Calcium

c) Vitamin D d) Vitamin C

93. Butyrorefractrometer reading indicate

a) Fat adulteration b) Melamine adulteration

c) Aflatoxin adulteration d) Histamine adulteration

94. Prevention of Food Adulteration Act 1954 came into force on

a) 1st June 1955
b) 1st March 1955
c) 1st April 1999
d) 2nd March 1988

95. NCCP stands for

a) National congress of hazard critical points
b) National commission on plants
c) National Codex Contact Point
d) None of these

96. For tenderization of meat, the enzyme used is

a) Papain
b) Rennin
c) Lipase
d) All

97. Offences and penalties comes under Chapter

a) Chapter 6
b) Chapter 9
c) Chapter 5
d) Chapter 4

98. When Right to Information Act (RTI) was passed

a) Oct 2005
b) Oct 2006
c) Aug 2005
d) Aug 2008

99. Headquarters of Indian Institute of Packaging

a) Mumbai
b) Chennai
c) Kolkata
d) Delhi

100. Societies registration Act enacted

a) 1860
b) 1855
c) 1866

Answers

1.	Aseptic canning	51.	Genetically modified organism
2.	Corn	52.	Both A & C
3.	Nicholas Appert	53.	Vitamin A
4.	Eugenol	54.	Beriberi
5.	Apple	55.	Probiotics
6.	Papaya seed	56.	Pantothenic acid
7.	1.5%	57.	Vitamin K
8.	2 hours	58.	4
9.	Stigma	59.	Vitamin D
10.	198	60.	Iron, Folic acid and Vitamin B12

11.	Sugarcane	61.	International Training Centre for Food Safety and Applied Nutrition
12.	Calf	62.	Continuous improvement
13.	Cocoa Shipment method	63.	All of the above
14.	Cfu/ml	64.	Unfermented tea
15.	Hazard Analysis Critical Control Point	65.	Peptide hormones
16.	*Glycyrrhiza glabra*	66.	Proline
17.	Pepper	67.	Degree of unsaturation
18.	Nagpur	68.	60- 62^{0}C
19.	Diacetyl	69.	Crocetin
20.	Avidin	70.	Pacific Accreditation Cooperation
21.	Lycopene	71.	Korea
22.	Cold Sterilization	72.	Rendering
23.	Risk prevention	73.	Monosodium Glutamate
24.	Amino acid	74.	It does not meet the specified standardsbut not so as to render the article of food unsafe
25.	Microbiological Risk assessment	75.	Myladumpara
26.	Pressure	76.	Action taken to remove a marketed food
27.	Sensory analysis	77.	Sterilization
28.	Diabetes mellitus	78.	Sample
29.	Chalky bread	79.	Defelice
30.	One – third	80.	1st
31.	WHO	81.	Difficulty in digesting lactose
32.	APEDA	82.	All of the above
33.	Persons and families purchasing and receiving food in order to meet their personal needs	83.	Hydrogenation
34.	Chapter 7	84.	Electronic nose
35.	Section 70	85.	Vitamin B9
36.	Amertume	86.	Proteins
37.	100 rads	87.	Synbiotics
38.	Water	88.	Pathogenic protein
39.	Fat	89.	Red edible sea weed
40.	*L. monocytogenes*	90.	Hydrogen sulphide

41.	Iron	91.	Large
42.	Itmay darken the product	92.	Fluoride
43.	Delhi	93.	Fat adulteration
44.	Clear solution	94.	1st June 1955
45.	Bacillus subtilis	95.	National Codex Contact Point
46.	Protect the health of the cosumers and ensure fair practices in the food trade	96.	Papain
47.	7	97.	Chapter 9
48.	Folic acid	98.	Oct 2005
49.	Bowel movements	99.	Mumbai
50.	Food fortification	100.	1860

CHAPTER-3

Mock Test 2

1. Normally _____ is used for packaging of butter

a) Polypropylene
b) Polyethylene
c) Aluminium foil
d) Parchment paper

2. Chairman of APEDA is appointed by

a) State government
b) Central Government
c) Director
d) MPEDA

3. DMI stands for

a) Directorate of foreign trade
b) Directorate of Marketing and Inspection
c) Direct metabolic index
d) None of these

4. Central coffee research Institute situated at

a) Balehonnur
b) Kodaikanal
c) Myladuthurai
d) Yelagiri

5. FSSAI initiated Diet 4 life programme for

a) Diet for school children
b) Healthy diet for adolescence
c) Comprehensive platform towards IEM management
d) Safe and sustainable diet

6. Spice Board has the provision of quality evaluation services under following schemes

a) Technology upgradation
b) Quality upgradation
c) Research and product development
d) All of these

7. HACCP was first used in 1960s by

a) Nestle
b) ITC
c) Pillsburry
d) TATA consumer products

8. Vancomycin is produced by

a) *Streptomyces orientalis*
b) *Streptomyces fradiae*
c) *Streptomyces rimosus*
d) All of the above

9. FSSAI operates under which Ministry?

a) Ministry of Agriculture
b) Ministry of consumer
c) Ministry of commerce
d) Ministry of Health and Family Welfare

10. Full form of ADI is

a) Acceptable Daily Intake
b) Altered Daily Intake
c) Acceptable Diet Intake
d) None of these

11. Which of these substances, naturally present in plant foods, inhibits the uptake of iodine by the thyroid gland

a) Phytate
b) Oxalate
c) Goitrogen
d) Tannin

12. What Does Green Dot on food packet stands for?

a) Vegetarian food
b) Non-Vegetarian Food
c) Organic Food
d) Fortified Food

13. The first synthetic sweetening agent used as

a) Sucralose
b) Saccharine
c) Aspartame
d) Cyclomates

14. Establishment of FSSAI comes under section

a) Section 3
b) Section 5
c) Section 4
d) Section 1

15. Power to remove difficulties comes under section

a) Section 101
b) Section 99
c) Section77
d) Section 44

16. Itai-Itai disease outbreak in Japan was attributed to which heavy metal poisoning

a) Lead
b) Cadmium
c) Copper
d) Mercury

17. A small transparent container which holds sample during spectrophotometric analysis is called

a) Cascade
b) Cuvette
c) Crucible
d) Quartz

18. The principal flavouring agent of mint is?

a) Eugenol
b) Methanol
c) Menthol
d) Vanilla

19. Salt or Sugar is added to foods for longer shelf life as they

a) Create acidic medium
b) Bind to water
c) Kill microorganisms
d) Dissolve the cell walls

20. What does FSSAI do
    a) Laying down science based standards for articles of food
    b) To regulate manufacture, storage, distribution, sale and import of food
    c) To facilitate food safety
    d) All of the above
21. Food recall procedures comes under section
    a) Section 28 b) Section 29
    c) Section 44 d) Section 17
22. _____ is another term for biosynthesis
    a) Catalyst b) Anabolism
    c) Metabolism d) Catabolism
23. White revolution/operation flood started in year
    a) 1950 b) 1960
    c) 1970 d) 1980
24. ISO 9000- Quality Systems came in year
    a) 1977 b) 1987
    c) 1997 d) 1999
25. Which of the following organization was set up jointly by FAO & WHO
    a) Codex alimentarius b) FSSAI
    c) EU d) USDA
26. During baking a brown crust develops on outside of loaf of bread as a result of
    a) Dextrinisation b) Coagulation
    c) Putrification d) Saponification
27. Barley malt is used for the preparation of
    a) Wine b) Beer
    c) Brandy d) Rum
28. Tofu is processed products from
    a) Soyabean b) Bean
    c) Kidney bean d) Cluster bean
29. Punishment for unsafe food comes under section
    a) S. 59 b) S. 58
    c) S. 77 d) S. 44
30. Penalty for failure to comply with the direction of FSO comes under section
    a) S. 55 b) S. 54
    c) S. 45 d) S. 59

31. Removal of inedible parts or defective parts of foods and cutting to a size appropriate for further processing is called

a) Chopping
b) Trimming
c) Grading
d) Sorting

32. Minamata disease outbreak in Japan was attributed to which heavy metal poisoning

a) Lead
b) Cadmium
c) Copper
d) Mercury

33. Baking powder is adulterated with

a) Citric acid
b) Chicory
c) Ghee
d) Coal tar dyes

34. The class of drugs used to treat allergic reactions is called

a) Beta blockers
b) Histamines
c) Antihistamines
d) Antibiotics

35. What is the full form of BPA, a chemical present in plastics

a) Butylene A
b) Bisphenol A
c) B Phenylalanine
d) B paraffin

36. Which toxic chemical is present in the green portions of potatoes

a) Solanine
b) Starch
c) Chlorophyll
d) None of the above

37. What is the Antinutritional factor in cotton seed

a) Tannin
b) Trypsin inhibitor
c) Gossypol
d) Saponins

38. Carmoisine is a food additive used as a

a) Liquifing agent
b) Moisturising agent
c) Flavour
d) Colour

39. Term of office, Salary, allowances comes under section

a) Section 7
b) Section 6
c) Section 5
d) Section 4

40. The circle in 'Jaivik Bharat' logo represents

a) Holistic wellness
b) Organic foods
c) Both A & B
d) None of the above

41. Colour code for the food safety display board on a retail store is

a) Yellow
b) Purple
c) Grey
d) Brown

83. Pectinesterases causes the hydrolysis of

a) Methyl ester linkage of pectin to yield pectic acid
b) Pectic acid to pectin
c) Protopectin to pectic acid
d) Protopectin to pectin

84. Fats are hydrolyzed by

a) Hydrolases
b) Oxidases
c) Microbial lipase
d) Pectinases

85. Desulfotomaculum nigrificans can reduce

a) Sulfur to sulfide
b) Sulfate to sulfide
c) Sulfide to sulfur
d) None of them

86. Asepsis is

a) Reducing the populations of microorganisms
b) Identifying methods of destruction
c) Sterility checks
d) Keeping out microorganisms

87. Delay in microbial decomposition can be achieved by

a) Asepsis
b) Filtration
c) Radiation
d) All the above

88. Prevention of self-decomposition can be accomplished by

a) Blanching
b) Washing
c) Chemicals
d) Heat

89. Which of the following is not a preservation factor?

a) To restrict oxygen
b) Radiation
c) Heat
d) Mechanical damage

90. The rapid and constant rate of multiplication of an organism occurs during the

a) Lag phase
b) Exponential phase
c) Stationary phase
d) Survival phase

91. Microbial decomposition of foods can be prevented by

a) Recontamination
b) Killing microbes
c) Scalding
d) None of them

92. Restriction of access of microorganisms to a product cannot be achieved by using

a) Heat
b) HCl
c) H_2O_2
d) H_2O

93. The widely used application of asepsis is

a) Clean handling
b) Decontamination
c) Packaging
d) Radiation

94. Heat is used to

a) Inactivate microbes
b) Inhibit growth of microbes
c) Kill microbes
d) Restrict the growth of microbes

95. 'Bacteriaproof' filter is made of

a) Sintered glass
b) Diatomaceous earth
c) Unglazed porcelain
d) All the above

96. Yogurt contains mixed lactic acid culture containing

a) *Lactobacillus bulgaricus* and *Streptococcus thermophilus*
b) Lactobacillus bulgaricus and propionibacterium
c) Lactobacillus bulgaricus and leuconostoc
d) None of the above

97. The process to increase in volume caused by whipping air into the ice cream mix during freezing is called

a) Homogenization
b) Aging
c) Overrun
d) Hardening

98. How many vertical and horizontal panels in scientific panels

a) 7 and 10
b) 9 and 10
c) 10 and 11
d) 14 and 10

99. Net protein utilization is

a) Biological value/ Digestibility
b) Biological value x Digestibility
c) Digestibility / Biological value
d) Digestibility + Biological value

100. Sugar free means

a) Less than 0.1g per serving
b) Less than 0.5g per serving
b) Less than 0.9g per serving
d) None of these

Answers			
1.	Parchment paper	51.	Violet – purplish
2.	Central Government	52.	Khesari dhal
3.	Directorate of Marketing & Inspection	53.	Van der waals
4.	Balehonnur	54.	Saponification
5.	Comprehensive platform towards IEM Management	55.	2.0 – 2.5%
6.	All ofthese	56.	Blanching
7.	Pillsburry	57.	Chilling
8.	*Streptomyces orientalis*	58.	Humectant
9.	Ministry of health & Family Welfare	59.	Chapter. 5
10.	Acceptable Daily Intake	60.	Section . 23
11.	Goitrogen	61.	S. 85
12.	Vegetarian food	62.	18.5 to 22.9
13.	Saccharine	63.	All of the options
14.	Section 4	64.	Vanaspati
15.	Section 101	65.	Polarimeter
16.	Cadmium	66.	Gas Chromatography
17.	Cuvette	67.	Bloom gelometer
18.	Menthol	68.	Tyramine
19.	Bind to water	69.	50 MHz
20.	All of the above	70.	400 – 2000MHz
21.	Section 28	71.	915 MHz
22.	Anabolism	72.	0.00024
23.	1970	73.	2
24.	1987	74.	Calendaring
25.	Codex Alimentarius	75.	540^{0}C
26.	Dextrinisation	76.	Potatoes
27.	Beer	77.	All of the above
28.	Soyabean	78.	Both a and b
29.	S.59	79.	No color change in milk
30.	S.55	80.	Molds
31.	Trimming	81.	Microbial growth
32.	Mercury	82.	Oxidation of organic acids
33.	Citric acid	83.	Methyl ester linkage of pectin to yield pectic acid

34.	Antihistamines	84.	Microbial lipase
35.	Bisphenol A	85.	Sulfate to sulfide
36.	Solanine	86.	Keeping out Microorganisms
37.	Gossypol	87.	All of the above
38.	Colour	88.	Blanching
39.	Section 7	89.	Mechanical damage
40.	Both A &B	90.	Exponential phase
41.	Grey	91.	Killing microbes
42.	Pulsed Electric Field	92.	H_2O
43.	Between 40^0F & 140^0F	93.	Packaging
44.	Vitamin C	94.	Inactivate microbes
45.	Unorganised Sector	95.	All of the above
46.	Coagulase activity	96.	*Lactobacillus bulgaricus* & *Streptococcus thermophilus*
47.	All of these	97.	Overrrun
48.	Buffering agent	98.	10 &11
49.	World War II	99.	Biological value × Digestability
50.	S.35	100.	Less than 0.5g per serving

CHAPTER-4

Mock Test 3

1. Nisin is produced by strains of
   a) *Streptococcus lactis*
   b) *Pseudomonas*
   c) *E. Coli*
   d) *Clostridium*
2. The inner parts of whole healthy tissues of living plants and animals are
   a) Low in microbial content
   b) Sterile
   c) High in microbial content
   d) Both a & b
3. *Pseudomonas* grows well in food containing
   a) Vitamins
   b) Organic acids
   c) Antibiotics
   d) Nitrates
4. Many kinds of molds are
   a) Proteolytic
   b) Inhibit breakdown of proteins
   c) Lipolytic
   d) None of these
5. Proteolytic organisms utilize hydrolysis products of
   a) Proteins
   b) Peptides
   c) Amino acids
   d) All of the above
6. Osmophilic orgainsms like yeasts grow best in
   a) Low concentrations of sugar
   b) High concentrations of sugar
   c) Low concentrations of salt
   d) High concentrations of salt
7. The aw for pure water is
   a) 1.00
   b) 9.99
   c) 0.9823
   d) 0.1
8. Organisms that grow over a wide range of $p^H$are
   a) Bacteria
   b) Yeasts
   c) Thermophillic anaerobes
   d) Molds
9. Avidin is present in
   a) Meat
   b) Fish
   c) Eggs
   d) Fruits

10. Browning of sugar syrups results in the production of
    a) Phenols
    b) Furfural
    c) Alcohol
    d) Ketones
11. The fungus known as bread mold is
    a) *Mucor*
    b) *Penicillium*
    c) *Rhizopus*
    d) *Aspergillus*
12. The organism used in the 'amylo' process for the saccharification of starch is
    a) *P. Digitatum*
    b) *A. niger*
    c) *R. Stolonifer*
    d) *M. rouxii*
13. *Trichothecium* is commonly called
    a) Pink mold
    b) Black mold
    c) Red mold
    d) Green mold
14. Dairy mold is
    a) *Trichothecium*
    b) *Geotrichum*
    c) *Thamnidium*
    d) *Penicillium*
15. The genus *Photobacterium* causes
    a) Phosphorescence of meat
    b) Spoilage of cheese
    c) Spoilage of alcoholic beverages
    d) Stormy fermentation of milk
16. The yellow-orange pigment of which genus causes discoloration on the surface of meat?
    a) *Flavobacterium*
    b) *Gluconobacter*
    c) *Escherichia*
    d) *Erwinia*
17. *E. Carotovora* causes
    a) Ropiness in beer
    b) Bacterial soft rot
    c) Discoloration of foods high in salt
    d) Ripening of cheese
18. *Aeromonas hydrophila* is a
    a) Plant pathogen
    b) Spoilage organism of fruits
    c) Human pathogen
    d) None of the above
19. Red pigmentation on spoilt food is caused by
    a) *Pseudomonas*
    b) *Clostridium*
    c) *Salmonella*
    d) *Serratia*
20. Pigmented *Propionibacter* causes
    a) Color defects in breads
    b) Color defects in juices
    c) Color defects in cheese
    d) Color defects in meat
21. Carcasses of animals may be contaminated with
    a) *Mycobacterium*
    b) *Pediococcus*
    c) *Proteus*
    d) *Salmonella*

22. The number of miroorganisms in air depends on

a) Sunshine
b) Humidity
c) Amount of suspended dust
d) All the above

23. The microbial load shed by a human being per minute is

a) $10^3 - 10^4$
b) $10^1 - 10^3$
c) $10^6 - 10^8$
d) $10^4 - 10^5$

24. During processing, foods can get contaminated because of

a) Workers
b) Equipment
c) Packaging materials
d) All of them

25. Which of the following is based on the review of airborne contamination by Heldman (1974)?

a) The microbial populations are different in processing plants
b) The population levels are not related to the activity of the workers
c) Populations in a plant are not related to the air quality outside the plant
d) The microbial populations of different processing plants are similar

26. Water used for soft drinks are treated with

a) Sand filters
b) Chlorination
c) UV rays
d) Both b and c

27. The bacterium causing the surface taint of cheese, *Pseudomonas putrifaciens*

a) Comes primarily from water
b) Comes from air
c) Comes from sewage
d) Comes from soil

28. An important source of heat-resistant spore-forming bacteria is from

a) Air
b) Sewage
c) Soil
d) Water

29. Coliform bacteria, anaerobes, *Enterococci,* other intestinal bacteria and viruses are generally

a) Present in soil
b) Present in sewage
c) Present in water
d) Present in animals

30. Mechanical damage to fruits and vegetables by birds open the way

a) To microbial spoilage
b) To chemical spoilage
c) To spread infectious diseases
d) None of the above

31. Durum wheat is suitable for production of:

a) Bread
b) Biscuits
c) Chapatti
d) Pasta

32. Tetra-pack is an example of which of the following packaging material?

a) Paper
b) Plastic
c) Composite
d) Metal

33. Any package food which does not conform to the requirements under the PFA is deemed as :
   a) Misbranding
   b) Mismatching
   c) Misguiding
   d) Misleading
34. The objective of heating milk to about 65°C before homogenization is to inactivate
   a) Invertases
   b) Lactases
   c) Lipases
   d) Glucose oxidase
35. Which of the following microbe is used in the production of blue cheese?
   a) *Streptococcus thermophiles*
   b) *Lactobacillus bulgaricus*
   c) *Penicillium roqueforti*
   d) *Rhizopus stolonifer*
36. A microbial kill of 99.99 % is equivalent to :
   a) 2 log cycle
   b) 4 log cycle
   c) 6 log cycle
   d) 3 log cycle
37. Cereal grains are deficient in :
   a) Methionine
   b) Isoleucine
   c) Leucine
   d) Lysine
38. For bread making, flour should have a protein content of:
   a) 8-10 %
   b) 10-12 %
   c) 12-14 %
   d) >14 %
39. Balancing of vegetable prior to freezing is done to :
   a) Maintain colour
   b) Improve texture
   c) Prevent microbial activity
   d) All of these
40. Which harmful component can be found in PET bottles?
   a) Lead
   b) Aluminium
   c) Phthalate
   d) Styrene monomers
41. Berries and Sauerkraut are classified as
   a) High-acid foods
   b) Acid foods
   c) Medium-acid foods
   d) Low-acid foods
42. Moist heat at 60°C for 5 to 10 minutes kills most
   a) Thermophillic bacteria
   b) Yeasts
   c) Sclerotia
   d) Molds
43. TDT is
   a) Thermal death transfer
   b) Transferred death time
   c) Thermal death time
   d) Thermal delayed time
44. Heat penetration in processing can be hastened by
   a) Using glass containers
   b) Rotation and agitation
   c) Layering of foods
   d) Using larger cans

45. The 'Father of canning is'

a) Nicholas Appert
b) Spallanzani
c) Lopez
d) Peter Durand

46. Enamel coating in cans containing zinc oxide cannot be used to store

a) Berries
b) Beets
c) Meat
d) Corn

47. Propellant gas used for pressurized packaged foods include

a) Oxygen
b) Carbon dioxide
c) Hydrogen sulfide
d) Sulfur gas

48. Heating of cans can be done

a) In a boiling water bath
b) Using a steamer
c) In oven heat
d) All the above

49. Meat, fish, etc., are grouped under

a) Low-acid foods
b) Medium-acid foods
c) Acid foods
d) High-acid foods

50. An exposure at 60°C for 10 to 15 minutes kills

a) Ascospores
b) Oospores
c) Basidiospores
d) None of them

51. The fatty acids with shortest chain length, found in nature.

a) Palmitic acid
b) Ricinoleic acid
c) Butyric acid
d) Erucic acid

52. The digestive enzymes of cellular compounds are confined to

a) Lysosomes
b) Ribosomes
c) Peroxisomes
d) Polysomes

53. Evaporated milk is connected to approximately what times the solid of normal whole milk ?

a) 2.25 times
b) 6.25 times
c) 7 times
d) 8.5 times

54. Since ancient times, people near lake chad in Africa used which of the following as food.

a) *Anaebana sp*
b) *Bacillus sp*
c) *Spirulina*
d) *Saccharomyces sp*

55. The first transgenic plant to be produced

a) Rice
b) Maize
c) Cotton
d) Tobacco

56. Freezing point depression is

a) Electrical property
b) Optical property
c) Thermal property
d) Textural property

57.Freezing point of bovine milk is

a) -0.512^{0}C and -0.550^{0}C
b) 2^{0}C
c) 3^{0}C
d) 4^{0}C

58. Oil Refining is a step

a) After oil extraction
b) Before oil extraction
c) Between oil cooking and flaking in Pre-Press solvent extraction
d) None of the mentioned

59. Whey is the by-product in the manufacture of

a) Skimmed milk
b) Butter
c) Cheese
d) Yogurt

60. Most variable constituent of milk is

a) Proteins
b) Fat
c) Lactose
d) Minerals

61. The temperature in cellar storage is lower than

a) 15°C
b) 5°C
c) 1°C
d) 25°C

62. Freezer burn is produced when

a) Thawing is not done
b) Ice crystals melt
c) Foods are desiccated
d) Ice crystals evaporate from the surface

63. Lethal effects are caused due to

a) Freezing at 4°C
b) Flocculation of essential proteins
c) Freezing using liquid nitrogen
d) Both c and d

64. Storage death refers to

a) Death and gradual reduction in microorganisms
b) Death of cells
c) Death of tissues
d) Death of cells and reduction in nutritional levels

65. Cold shock results in

a) Alterations of lipids in the membrane
b) Increased permeability of membranes
c) Syneresis
d) Increased microbial count

66. The process of freezing foods using liquid nitrogen is called

a) Lyophillization
b) Dehydrofreezing
c) Cryoinjury
d) Sharp freezing

67. The rapid slowing of chemical and enzymatic reactions in foods is achieved by
a) Quick freezing
b) Sharp freezing
c) Dehydrofreezing
d) None of them

68. The unfrozen, concentrated solutions of sugars and salt produces a viscous material called
a) Osmotic solution
b) Liquid water
c) Metacryotic liquid
d) None of them

69. Mushiness of fruits on thawing results in physical damage during
a) Freezing
b) Air-blast freezing
c) Immersion in water
d) Storage in ice

70. Chilling storage enables the preservation of products for
a) A longer period of time
b) A limited period of time
c) A period of two months
d) None of them

71. Which of the following is not a factor in the control of drying?
a) The temperature employed
b) The relative humidity of the air
c) The velocity of the air
d) The concentration of heat

72. Thermoduric streptococci are predominant in
a) Dried milk
b) Fruits and nuts
c) Spoiled eggs
d) Vegetables

73. 99% of bacteria are removed by
a) Blanching
b) Sweating
c) Smoking
d) Sun drying

74. Sulfuring helps
a) Conserve vitamin C
b) Maintain an attractive color
c) Repel insects
d) All of the above

75. 'Sweating' is storage for
a) Re-addition of moisture to a desired level
b) Reduces moisture
c) Increases moisture
d) None of the above

76. Foam mat drying is used for
a) Liquid food
b) Powdered food
c) Dehydrated food
d) Dried fruits

77. The simplest dryer is the
a) Kiln
b) Oven
c) Sun
d) Microwave

78. Sodium carbonate is used as an alkali dip before sun drying for
  a) Cereals
  b) Nuts
  c) Vegetables
  d) Grapes

79. Intermediate-moisture foods are those
  a) That contain 20–40% moisture
  b) That have non-refrigerated shelf life
  c) That can be eaten without preparation
  d) All the above are true

80. The chief bacteria on dried vegetables are
  a) Enterobacter
  b) Bacillus
  c) Clostridium
  d) All of them

81. Sorbic acid is known
  a) To inhibit yeasts and molds
  b) To destroy insects
  c) To remove bacteria
  d) To eliminate disease-causing agents

82. Vinegar is used in
  a) Mayonnaise
  b) Pickled sausages
  c) Pickles
  d) All the above

83. Wood smoke contains
  a) Compounds deleterious to molds
  b) Active substances that reduce yeasts
  c) Volatile compounds that are bacteriostatic
  d) Flavoring compounds that have no effects on foods

84. Washing foods or equipment is achieved by
  a) Adding acids
  b) Adding halogens
  c) Adding phosphates
  d) Adding salt water

85. Butyl thiocyanate is an active principle in
  a) Horse radish
  b) Cabbage
  c) Turnips
  d) Garlic

86. A mold inhibitor used as a spray to kill airborne microbes is
  a) Caprylic acid
  b) Sorbic acid
  c) Propylene glycol
  d) Vanillic acid

87. Fumes f burning sulphur is used to treat
  a) Dark-colored vegetables
  b) Light-colored fruits
  c) Meat
  d) Eggs

88. Propionic acid is found naturally in
   a) Butter
   b) Milk
   c) Malt extract
   d) Swiss cheese

89. The organic acid used in drinks, jams, jellies, and syrups is
   a) Oxalic acid
   b) Tartaric acid
   c) Citric acid
   d) Acetic acid

90. Excess addition of which of the following causes high osmotic pressure with plasmolysis of cells?
   a) Salt
   b) Sugar
   c) Organic acid
   d) Both a and b

91. Purines and pyrimidines absorb radiations at wavelengths of
   a) 260 nm
   b) 200 nm
   c) 250 nm
   d) 270 nm

92. The effectiveness of UV rays are influenced by
   a) Time
   b) Intensity
   c) Penetration
   d) All of the above

93. UV irradiation in the food industry is used for the treatment of
   a) Water for beverages
   b) Knives for slicing
   c) Only a
   d) Both a and b

94. The drawback of using X-rays in food preservation is
   a) Their low efficiency
   b) High cost of production
   c) They are toxic
   d) Both a and b

95. The rays that are directional and less penetrating are
   a) Gamma rays
   b) Cathode rays
   c) X-rays
   d) Beta rays

96. Side reactions due to radiations results in
   a) Undesirable color
   b) Change in physical properties
   c) Undesirable tastes
   d) All of the above

97. Low-level irradiation can be used on fresh fruits to
   a) Kill insects
   b) Kill molds
   c) To inhibit the growth of bacteria
   d) None of them

98. The general nutrition of an irradiated food will be
   a) As good as that of a food processed by any other means
   b) Not as good as that of a food processed by any other means
   c) Food quality deteriorates
   d) The food attracts spoilage organisms

99. In which food does the destruction of glutathione occur?

a) Fruits
b) Vegetables
c) Meat
d) Milk

100. Spores of *C. Botulinum* have been found to be resistant to

a) Beta rays
b) Gamma rays
c) Cathode rays
d) X-rays

Answers

1.	*Streptococcus lactis*	51.	Butyric acid
2.	Both a&b	52.	Lysosomes
3.	Nitrates	53.	2.25 Times
4.	Proteolytic	54.	Spirulina
5.	All of the above	55.	Cotton
6.	Low concentrations of sugar	56.	Thermal Property
7.	1.00	57.	-0.512°C and -0.550°C
8.	Molds	58.	After oil extraction
9.	Eggs	59.	Cheese
10.	Furfural	60.	Fat
11.	*Rhizopus*	61.	15°C
12.	*M. rouxii*	62.	Ice crystals evaporate from the surface
13.	Pink mold	63.	Both C & D
14.	*Geotrichum*	64.	Death & gradual reduction in Microorganisms
15.	Phosphorescence of meat	65.	Alterations of lipids in the mem-brane
16.	*Flavobacterium*	66.	Dehydrofreezing
17.	Bacterial soft rot	67.	Quick freezing
18.	Human pathogen	68.	Metacryotic liquid
19.	*Serratia*	69.	Freezing
20.	Color defects in cheese	70.	A limited period of time
21.	*Salmonella*	71.	The concentration of heat
22.	All the above	72.	Dried milk
23.	$10^3 – 10^4$	73.	Blanching
24.	All of them	74.	All of the above
25.	The microbial populations of differ-ent processing plants are similar	75.	Re – addition of moisture to a desired level

26.	Both B and C	76.	Liquid food
27.	Comes primarily from water	77.	Kiln
28.	Soil	78.	Grapes
29.	Present in sewage	79.	All the above are true
30.	To microbial spoilage	80.	All of them
31.	Pasta	81.	To inhibit yeasts & molds
32.	Composite	82.	All the above
33.	Misbranding	83.	Volatile compounds that are bacteriostatic
34.	Lipases	84.	Adding halogens
35.	*Penicillium roqueforti*	85.	Horse radish
36.	4 log cycle	86.	Propylene glycol
37.	Lysine	87.	Light colored fruits
38.	10 -12%	88.	Swiss cheese
39.	All of these	89.	Citric acid
40.	Pthalate	90.	Both A & B
41.	High – Acid foods	91.	260 nm
42.	Molds	92.	All of theabove
43.	Thermal Death time	93.	Both a and b
44.	Rotation & Agitation	94.	Both A & B
45.	Nicholas Appert	95.	Cathode rays
46.	Meat	96.	All of the above
47.	Carbon Dioxide	97.	Kill insects
48.	All of the above	98.	As good as that of a food processed by any other means
49.	Low – acid foods	99.	Meat
50.	Ascospores	100.	Gamma rays

Part – 8

Solved Previous Year Question Papers

CHAPTER-1

CENTRAL FOOD SAFETY OFFICER - 2022

"There are two days in the year that we can't do anything, yesterday and tomorrow" -Mahatma Gandhi

1. What is the full form of PFA

a) Preservation of Food Adulteration
b) **Prevention of Food Adulteration**
c) Prevention of Food Act
d) Protection of Food Adulteration

2. Which department of Food and Agriculture Organization (FAO) provides support to entire FAO organization?

a) Technical cooperation Department
b) Economic and Social Development Department
c) Agriculture and Consumer Protection Department
d) **Corporate Services, Human resources and Finance Department**

3. What is the purpose of ISO 14031?

a) Environmental Assessment of sits and organizations
b) Environmental labels and declarations
c) **Environmental performance evaluation**
d) Environmental communication

4. What does FDCA stands for

a) Foreign Drug and Cosmetic Act
b) **Food Drug and Cosmetic Act**
c) Fuel Drug and Cosmetic Act
d) Feed Drug and Cosmetic Act

5. When did Food Safety and Standards Regulations come into force?

a) 1st January, 2006
b) 13th February, 1986
c) **5th August, 2011**
d) 6th December, 1998

6. In which year European Union (EU) joined the Codex Alimentarius Commission (CAC)?

a) 2001
b) 2007
c) **2003**
d) 2005

7. Critical Control Points (CCP) helps to control

a) Quality checklist
b) **Hazard risk**
c) Novel Product development
d) Quality Assurance

8. A system which identifies, evaluates, and controls hazards that are significant for food safety is

a) Personal Security
b) Food Protection
c) **Hazard analysis and Critical Control Point**
d) Food defense

9. Who represents India in International Organization for standardization (ISO)?

a) Food and Agriculture Organization (FAO)
b) World Health Organization (WHO)
c) Agricultural and Processed Food Product Export Development Authority (APEDA)
d) **Bureau of Indian Standards (BIS)**

10. What does TACCP stands for?

a) Time Assessment and Critical Control Point
b) Temperature Assessment and Critical Control Point
c) Technology Assessment and Critical Control Point
d) **Threat Assessment and Critical Control Point**

11. Which International food standard body jointly established Codex Alimentarius Commission?

a) **FAO and WHO**
b) FAO and WTO
c) ISO and WHO
d) WTO and WHO

12. Baking powder is adulterated with

a) Ghee
b) Coal tar dyes
c) **Citric acid**
d) Chicory

13. Cumin seeds are commonly adulterated with

a) Citric acid
b) Lead chromate
c) Starch
d) **Stalky and woody matter**

14. What does USDA stands for

a) United States Department of Animals
b) United States Department of Aquaculture
c) **United States Department of Agriculture**
d) Union States Department of Agriculture

15. Under which products order specification for vanaspati, margarine and shortenings are laid down

a) Milk and Milk Products Order, 1992
b) Fruit Products Order,1955
c) **Vegetables Oil Products Control Order, 1947**
d) Meat Food Product Order, 1973

16. GDP stands for

a) Group Domestic Product
b) General Domestic Product
c) **Gross Domestic Product**
d) Good Domestic Product

17. The main headquarters of food safety and standards Authority of India (FSSAI) is located at

a) **New Delhi**
b) Mumbai
c) Hyderabad
d) Chennai

18. What is the purpose of ISO 9000 - 2000

a) **Quality management systems – Fundamentals and Vocabulary**
b) Quality management Systems – Guidelines for performance improvements
c) Quality management – Guidelines for quality plans
d) Quality management systems – Requirements

19. ISO has how many membership categories?

a) **3**
b) 5
c) 1
d) 7

20. In which year government of India established Ministry of Food Processing Industries (MOFPI)?

a) 2005
b) 1995
c) **1998**
d) 2001

21. Which foods have been recognized in India as suitable vehicles for foof fortification?

a) Salt, Sugar, Oil, Milk, Corn
b) Salt, Wheat, Corn, Rice, Milk
c) **Salt, Wheat, Rice, Milk, Oil**
d) Salt, Milk, Oil, Sugar, Rice

22. Which is not a cluster initiative of FSSAI?

a) **Swachh Bharat Abhiyaan**
b) Clean Street Food Hubs
c) Clean and fresh Fruit and Vegetables Market
d) BHOG

23. Foundation phase of induction training for newly recruited officers, contains ___ units

a) Ten
b) Twelve
c) **Six**
d) Eight

24. What is the normal cut-off for BMI to Asian – Indian?

a) **18.5 – 22.9**
b) >25
c) <18.49
d) 23.0-24.9

25. What is the full form of CHA ?

a) Custom House Authoriy
b) Central House Authority
c) **Custom House Agent**
d) Central Head Agent

26. Deficiency of which vitamin causes neural tube defect?

a) Nicotinic acid
b) **Folic acid**
c) Fatty acid
d) Ascorbic acid

27. One excellent source of omega – 3 fatty acids

a) **Flax seed**
b) Cream
c) Vanaspati
d) Beef

28. Who is responsible for conducting a survey of the state's food manufacturing and processing facilities?

a) Food Analyst
b) Adjudicating Officer
c) **Commissioner of food Safety of the state**
d) Food Safety Officer

29. What is the full form of GSFA?

a) General Standard for Food Antibiotics
b) **General Standard for food additives**
c) General Standard for food Adulteration
d) General Standard for food Aflatoxins

30. What is the full form of "NOTS"?

a) Nature of Transforming Substances
b) Nature of Toxic Substances
c) Naturally Occurring tasty substances
d) **Naturally occurring toxic substances**

31. The Prevention of Food Adulteration Act was made in

a) **1954**
b) 1967
c) 1973
d) 1955

32. One example of non – perishable food is

a) Gram flours
b) **Dried beans**
c) Semolina
d) Eggs

33. At least _____of the establishments in clean street food hub should selling regional

a) **80 percent**
b) 60 percent
c) 75 percent
d) 50 percent

34. Which section of the Food Safety and standards Regulations 2011 notifies the food safety for infant nutrition

a) 2.1.3
b) 1.1.9
c) **2.1.9**
d) 1.1.6

35. How long is the import license valid?

a) 1-2 years
b) 1-3 years
c) **1-5 years**
d) 1-4 years

36. Which is not a part of serve safe initiative?

a) Hygiene + certification
b) Food Safety supervisor
c) Food Safety Display Boards
d) **Food Service Manager**

37. Who keeps track of all inspection by food safety officers and the measures they take?

a) Food Safety Officer
b) Commissioner of Food Safety
c) Adjudicating officer
d) **Designated officer**

38. The International Standard for Laboratory Accreditation is

a) OSO 17049
b) ISO17025
c) ISO17098
d) **ISO 17025**

39. What is the full form of AGMARK?

a) **Agricultutral Mark**
b) Agricultural Business Marketing
c) Agarian Mark
d) Agricultural Media

40. The training curriculum for FSO is___days long

a) 45
b) 30
c) 35
d) **40**

41. The cholesterol content of food given in the Indian food composition tables is determined by

a) High Performance Liquid Chromatography

b) Ion – exchange Chromatography

c) Thin Layer Chromatography

d) **Gas Liquid Chromatography**

42. Which of the following is INCORRECT regarding hand washing facilities required under Good Manufacturing Practices?

a) Hand washing notices should be pasted on walls near hand washing stations

b) Hand drying and sanitizing facility should be provided

c) Taps should be designed to prevent hand contact

d) **Non – perfumed soap bars should be used for hand washing**

43. Emerging methods of food preservation include the following EXCEPT

a) High Pressure Processing

b) **Irradiation**

c) Pulsed electric field

d) Ultrasonic food processing

44. The alcohol content of wine during fermentation and the ripeness of fruits before harvesting is assessed by using a

a) Penetrometer

b) **Refractometer**

c) Volumeter

d) Compressimeter

45. The fourth step in a HACCP plan is to

a) Identify hazards

b) **Construct process flow diagram**

c) Describe the product

d) Established monitoring action

46. Which of the following statements in INCORRECT with respect to the number 5 mentioned in a recycle logo at the bottom of a plastic container?

a) Which type of food/beverages it can be used for

b) It's safety for use

c) It tells us which monomer unit/resin the container is made from

d) **How many times the container can be reused**

47. Which of the following statements in INCORRECT with respect to microbial enzymes

a) They are produced by bacteria, yeast and mold

b) They are cost effective to produce

c) They are easy to produce

d) **They are less stable compared to plant and animal enzymes**

48. Trans fats are present in

a) **Margarine**
b) Egg yolk
c) Butter
d) Red palm oil

49. How many kcal/g do organic acids present in fruits and vegetables provide

a) 2
b) 7
c) 0
d) **3**

50. Which grain can a gluten intolerant person safely consume

a) Triticale
b) **Buck wheat**
c) Rye
d) Barley

51. To preserve the green colour while cooking green leafy vegetables, it is advisable to cook them

a) In an alkaline medium
b) In an covered pan
c) **Uncovered for a few minutes to allow volatile acids to escape**
d) By boiling in adequate water and discarding the water

52. Oligosaccharides which encourage the growth of beneficial microorganisms in the gut are called

a) Dietary fibre
b) **Prebiotics**
c) Long chain carbohydrates
d) Probiotics

53. The health clam which is not permitted on a nutraceutical package is

a) Anti-ageying claims
b) Health maintenance claims
c) Immunity Booster claims
d) **Prevention and cure of disease claims**

54. The action to remove food from the market at any stage of the food chain, including that possessed by consumers is called

a) Food recovery
b) Responsible food handling
c) **Food recall**
d) Food Traceability

55. Total polar compounds are formed from

a) Oil is emulsified
b) Oil is inter esterified
c) Oil is fully hydrogenated
d) **Oil is reheated often above 180°C while frying**

56. How much vitamin A should fortified milk contain

a) 50µg RE to 75µg RE/Litre 500µg
b) RE to 750µg RE/Litre
c) **270µg RE to 450µg RE/Litre**
d) 6µg RE to 9.9µg RE/Litre

57. Micronutrients are better absorbed and more bioavailable from

a) Vitamin and mineral tablets

b) **Natural foods recommended in 'My food plate for the day'**

c) Vitamin and mineral supplements

d) Fortified food products

58. The technological function of calcium propionate in bread is as a/an

a) **Preservative** b) Anticaking agent

c) Nutrient supplement d) Raising agent

59. The test to confirm presence of sesame oil in vanaspati in sufficient

a) Peroxide value testb) Tri-ortho-cresyl-phosphate test

c) Holde's test d) **Baudouin test**

60. Time-Temperature Indicators, Biosensors, Ripeness Indicators and Radio Frequency Identification are some quality indicators which may be used in

a) **Intelligent Packaging** b) Active Packaging

c) Eco-Friendly Packaging d) Nano Packaging

61. A condition which certain foods trigger an abnormal immune response is called a

a) Food infestation b) Food infection

c) **Food allergy** d) Food poisoning

62. The number of double bonds present in a carbon chain of α – Linolenic acid (ALA) is

a) **3** b) 2

c) 6 d) 5

63. The date after which a food product is not advisable to be marketed as it's quality may have diminished but may still be safe to consume it's

a) Use by date

b) Recommended last consumption date

c) **Best before date**

d) Expiry date

64. The plant enzymes bromelain, ficin and papain in are

a) α-amylases b) **Proteases**

c) Glucoamylases d) Esterases

65. As per regulations, the limits for the presence of impurities of animal origin in pulses shall not exceed

a) 0.25 percent
b) **0.01 percent**
c) 0.50 percent
d) 1.00 percent

66. Maintaining the temperature of food in the range of 0^0C to 8^0C is called

a) **Chilling**
b) Cooling
c) Freeze drying
d) Freezing

67. A method of quantitative chemical analysis used to determine the mass on concentration of a substance by measuring a change in it's mass is

a) **Gravimetric analysis**
b) Colorimetric analysis
c) Fluorometric analysis
d) Volumetric analysis

68. Which of the following is NOT a physical method of food preservation

a) **Fermentation**
b) Freezing
c) Sterlization
d) Pasteurization

69. The microbial enzyme fungal lactases are used in the dairy industry while manufacturing milk products to

a) Add a distinct flavor to cheese
b) Accelerate ripening of cheese
c) Coagulate milk
d) **Lower the sugar content**

70. A laboratory which develops methods of testing provides valiation and technical support and evaluates performance is designated as a

a) Recognized food laboratory
b) **Reference food laboratory**
c) Referral food laboratory
d) Notified food laboratory

71. Removal of inedible parts or defective parts of foods and cutting to a size appropriate for further processing is called

a) Sorting
b) Grading
c) **Trimming**
d) Chopping

72. Which one of the following food colors is not permitted to be used in food

a) Tartrazine
b) **Malachite Green**
c) Annato
d) Brilliant Blue FCF

73. Which one of the following statements is INCORRECT with regard to soaking dehusked pulses in water and discarding it before cooking

a) Phytic acid content decreases
b) Cooking time is minimized

c) Oligosaccharide content is reduced

d) **Water soluble vitamin content increases**

74. Polycyclic aromatic Hydrocarbon are formed during cooking from all of the following EXCEPT

a) Grilling of meat
b) Cooking directly on gas flame
c) Smoke from fossil fuels
d) **Maillard browning**

75. The daily dietary nutrient intake level that is sufficient to meet the nutrient requirements of nearly all healthy individuals is called

a) **Recommended Dietary Allowance**
b) Tolerable Upper level
c) Requirement Daily Allowance
d) Estimated Average Requirement

76. As per regulations, the use of permitted synthetic food colors in canned cherris is

a) Permitted but should not exceed 200 ppm

b) **Permitted but should not exceed 200 ppm**

c) Permitted but should not exceed 50 ppm

d) Not permitted

77. Which one of the following is NOT a complex carbohydrate

a) Glycogen
b) Mucilage
c) Starch
d) **Lignin**

78. The vitamin which can combine with free oxygen radicals and protect the integrity of the cell membrane is

a) Vitamin K
b) Vitamin D
c) Vitamin B_{12}
d) **Iron**

79. Which nutrient helps in preventing Microcytic Anaemia

a) Vitamin K
b) Folic acid
c) Vitamin B12
d) **Iron**

80. A burnt or caramel flavor in milk is caused by

a) *Saccharomyces cerevisiae var .ellipsoideus*

b) *Clostridium thermosaccharolyticum*

c) ***Streptococcus lactis var. maltigenes***

d) *Brevibacterium erythrogenes*

CHAPTER-2

Technical Officer FSSAI - 2022

1. What does GMP stands for

a) Good Management Practices
b) **Good Manufacturing Practices**
c) Good Managerial Practices
d) Good Making Practices

2. Where is the headquarters of FSSAI located?

a) **New Delhi**
b) Mumbai
c) Kolkata
d) Chennai

3. When did European Union (EU) join the Codex Alimentarius?

a) 1999
b) 1995
c) 2000
d) **2003**

4. In food Industry, GAP stands for

a) Great Agriculture Practices
b) **Good Agricultural Practices**
c) Great Agriculture Protocols
d) Good Agricultural Protocols

5. GFSI stands for

a) Global Feed Safety Initiative
b) Global Fuel Safety Initiative
c) **Global Food safety Initiative**
d) Global Fruit Safety Initiative

6. Where is the headquarter of Bureau of Indian Standards (BIS) located?

a) Chennai
b) Kolkata
c) **New Delhi**
d) Chandigarh

7. Under which act APEDA (Agricultural and Processed Food Product Export Development Authority) was established 1985?

a) Export (Quality Control and Inspection) Act
b) **APEDA Act**
c) PFA Act
d) Environment Protection Act

8. Which term is used to assure that the food is acceptable for human consumption according to its intended use

a) Toxicity
b) Adulterants
c) Hazards
d) **Food Safety**

9. What is the full form of ISI

a) Industrial Standards Institute
b) International Standards Institute
c) **Indian Standards Institute**

10. ISO 22000 describes which management system

a) Quality Management
b) Environmental Management
c) Animal Management
d) **Food Safety Managment**

11. What is the full form of FSSAI

a) Feed Safety and Standards Authority of India
b) Food Security and Standards Authority of India
c) **Food Safety and Standards Authority of India**
d) Feed Security and Standards Authority of India

12. What is the full form of WTO ?

a) **World Trade Organization**
b) World Transport Organization
c) World Textile Organization
d) World Tariff Organization

13. Which ISO Standard is related to quality management system?

a) ISO 45001
b) **ISO 9000**
c) ISO 22000
d) ISO14000

14. In which year government of India establish Ministry of Food Processing Industries?

a) **1988**
b) 1972
c) 1980
d) 1964

15. Which voluntary certification scheme known as ISI mark for processed foods

a) **BIS**
b) FPO
c) AGMARK
d) MFPO

16. What is the second principle of Hazard Analysis Critical Control Point (HACCP) System

a) **Identify Critical Control Points**
b) Establish Monitoring Procedures for critical limits
c) Establish Critical limits at each CCP
d) Conduct a hazard analysis

17. Which of the following Administrative Ministry are responsible for the implementation of fruit Products Order, 1955?

a) Ministry of Civil Supplies and Consumer affairs

b) Ministry of Health and Family Welfare

c) **Ministry of Food Processing, Govt of India**

d) Ministry of Industry, Govt of India

18. Milk is adulterated with

a) Coal tar dyes
b) Citric acid
c) Sand
d) **Water and Starch**

19. Which scheme is employed by manufactures who need ISI mark (BIS standard Mark) within 30 days as per the government notification?

a) Registration scheme for self Declaration of conformity

b) **Tatkal scheme**

c) Foreign manufactures Certification scheme

d) ECO Mark scheme

20. What is the role of Agriculture and Consumer Protection Department of the FAO?

a) Promotes the management of forestry resources

b) Promotes economic development through the internal production and trade

c) Promotes the management of fishing and Aquaculture

d) **Promotes Agriculture to reduce poverty and ensuring safe food production**

21. The 3rd day of the 5 days training program for designated officer focuses on

a) Need for food safety
b) Licensing and Registration
c) **Packaging and Labelling and FSMS**
d) Surveillance and Monitoring

22. What is SNF in milk?

a) Saturated Not Fat
b) Safe Nutritious Food
c) **Solids Not Fat**
d) Skimmed-N-Fresh

23. The principle of FIFO adopted in clean street hub refers to

a) **First in First out for ingredients**
b) First interested in Offers
c) First in for order
d) First in for offers

24. FSSAI has incorporated third party audit for FBO's. This will help in the following except

a) Assure safe food to consumers

b) Strengthen food safety surveillance system

c) **Encourage preparation of healthy food**

d) Encourage self-compliance

25. Upon arrival of the food consignment for import, the importer shall fine

a) FSSAI clearance certificate
b) **Integrated declaration form**
c) Custom duty
d) The import license

26. What is the full form of SoFTeL

a) Strengthening of Fat testing Laboratories
b) Strengthening of flour testing Laboratories
c) Strengthening of fast testing Laboratories
d) **Strengthening of food testing laboratories**

27. Which of the following is true regarding WHO?

a) **Stands for WHO established in Geneva Switzerland on 7th April 1948**
b) Stands for WHO established in Geneva Switzerland on 7th April 1949
c) Stands for WHO established in Rome, Italy on 7th April 1949
d) Stands for WHO established in Rome, Italy on 7th April 1948

28. Food Safety display boards are colour for different kinds of food businesses,Which of the following business is NOT matched with the colour code

a) Green – Fruit and Vegetable retail
b) Purple - Restaurant
c) Blue – Milk retail
d) **Grey – Liquor retail**

29. ISO 22000 lays process specifications for

a) Food Export Management System
b) **Food Safety Management System**
c) Safe Food Management System
d) Food Import Management System

30. Balance shelf life means

a) The remaining period upto Best Before/date of expiry for any food on the shelf life
b) The period between the date of manufacture and best before/date of expiry
c) **The period between the date of import and best before/ date of expiry**
d) The period between the release of stock in the market and best before/ date of expiry

31. According to FSS rules, ____ shall be responsible for inspection of food business, obtaining samples and sending them to the food analyst

a) Commissioner
b) **Food Safety Officer**
c) Designated Officer
d) Assistant commissioner

32. Under Section (42) 2 of the FSS Act 200 the FSSAI has notified how many laboratories in September 2017:

a) 18
b) **16**
c) 14
d) 20

33. Food containers should kept at least ____ above the ground in the clean street hub project

a) 5 cm
b) 20cm
c) **15 cm**
d) 10 cm

34. What is the full form of RUCO?

a) Repurpose unused Cooking Oil
b) **Repurpose used cooking Oil**
c) Reuse unused cooking Oil
d) Reuse used Cooking oil

35. Licensing and registration of food business in FSSAI are covered under which section

a) Section 30
b) Section 9
c) **Section 31**
d) Section 13

36. The term Hidden hunger refers to

a) **Micronutrient deficiency**
b) Malnutrition
c) Inadequate food intake
d) Macronutrient deficiency

37. SNF@ workplace Initiative aims at the following EXCEPT

a) Promoting general health and well being
b) Providing FSSAI trained health and wellness coordinator
c) **Providing resources such as the Pink book**
d) To combat increase in obesity and NCDs

38. An initiative of the GOI and FSSAI to transform the country's food system to ensure safe, healthy and sustainable food to all is known as

a) Eat healthy India Movement
b) Combat Malnutrition Movement
c) Eat safe India Movement
d) **Eat right India Movement**

39. Double fortified salt is fortified with

a) Iodine and Vitamin A
b) Iodine and Calcium
c) **Iodine and Iron**
d) Iodine and Vitamin D

40. FSSAI was established in

a) 2006
b) **2008**
c) 1954
d) 2018

41. Foods which have the potential to prevent disease and promote good health are called

a) Organic foods
b) GM foods
c) Special foods
d) **Nutraceuticals**

42. The date beyond which packaged food product may still be perfectly safe to eat though its quality may have diminished is

a) **Best before date**
b) Use by date
c) Date of discounted sale
d) Expiry date

43. Epidemic dropsy is caused by

a) **Argemone oil**
b) Mustard oil
c) Lathyrus sativus
d) Mycotoxins

44. An in-house reference sample for which one or more property values have been established by the user laboratory is called the

a) Test sample
b) **Control sample**
c) Spiked sample
d) Blind sample

45. The vitamin which helps in the conversion of Tryptophan to Niacin is

a) Pantothenic acid
b) Thiamine
c) **Pyridoxine**
d) Biotin

46. Which of the following CANNOT be called a non- communicable Diseases?

a) **Hepatitis**
b) Cancer
c) Diabetes
d) Atherosclerosis

47. Most foods have a water activity above

a) **0.95**
b) 0.9
c) 0.85
d) 0.65

48. Surface ropiness in milk is caused by

a) *Leuconostoc spp*
b) *Clostridium perfringens*
c) *Pseudomonas fluorescens*
d) ***Alcaligenes viscolactis***

49. Food Safety Management system related Documents and records which are mandatory are

a) Visitor record
b) Approved supplier list
c) **Medical fitness certificate for food handlers**
d) Equipment breakdown maintenance report

50. Which of the following statements is INCORRECT with respect to the Enterobacteriaceae family?

a) **It is a large family of gram positive bacteria**

b) They are present in the human intestinal tract

c) Pathogens like *E.coli, Salmonella* and *Enterobacter* are same of the genera in the class

d) Faecal coliforms which can grow at 45^{0}C belong to this class

51. Vitamin required for the synthesis of collagen is

a) Pantothenic acid
b) Riboflavin
c) Vitamin K
d) **Ascorbic acid**

52. Which of the following dietary fibres is form of a non-carbohydrates source

a) Mucilage
b) Pectin
c) Algae
d) **Lignin**

53. "My plate for the Day" which promotes health, prevents hidden hunger and protects from diseases developed in the year

a) **2018**
b) 2021
c) 2015
d) 2011

54. A powerful chemical released when an allergen enters the body causing symptoms of allergy

a) Antibody
b) **Histamine**
c) Antigen
d) Antihistamine

55. The model used in the preparation of Soya sauce is

a) ***Aspergillus oryzae***
b) *Penicillium chrysogenum*
c) *Rhizopus stolonifer*
d) *Aspergillus tamarii*

56. Which one of the following statements is INCORRECT for sprouted pulses?

a) Sprouting increases digestibility
b) Sprouting increases availability of nutrients
c) Sprouting increases the content of B-complex and C vitamins
d) **Sprouting increases the shelf - life**

57. With respect to probiotics which of the following statements is INCORRECT?

a) Probiotic bacteria are added to processed foods for their health benefits
b) They colonize the large intestine and can combat harmful bacteria
c) **They survive pasteurization and cooking temperatures**
d) They are live microorganisms present in some foods which we eat

58. With respect to irradiation of food, which one of the following is INCORRECT:

a) Food in sealed containers can be irradiated

b) Radura symbol should be displayed on the label

c) **Can be used as a substitute for GMP**

d) Sensory characteristics do not change significantly

59. Walnuts are rich source of

a) Butyric acid
b) **Alpha – linolenic axid (ALA)**
c) Stearic acid
d) Ricinoleic acid

60. Fats perform the following functions except for one function. Which function does fat NOT perform?

a) **Stimulates peristalsis and eliminated fecal waste**
b) Helps absorb fat soluble vitamins
c) Provides thermal insulation
d) Adds satiety value and flavour

61. Functional properties of lipids include all of the following EXCEPT

a) **Adding bulk**
b) Aerating
c) Prevents product from sticking
d) Development of flavour

62. As compared to conventional methods of extraction, green extraction technologies have the following advantages EXCEPT

a) High quality extract
b) Safe products
c) **Time consuming**
d) Low environment impact

63. On the basis of their shelf life, potatoes and Onions are called as

a) Perishable
b) Stable
c) **Semi – Perishable**
d) Non - Perishable

64. The enzyme which increases the bioavailability of thiosulfinates is

a) Diastase
b) Aryl sulphatase
c) Inulase
d) **Allinase**

65. Which one of the following statements is INCORRECT with respect to mass spectrometry?

a) It is used to determine a particle mass

b) Can measure difference between mass of different isotopes of the same atom

c) **Can determine the amino acid profile of a protein**

d) Can determine types of elements in compounds

66. With respect to quality control to correct errors and prevent repetition, 5 W's need to be answered, Which one of the following is not one of them?

a) Where was it made
b) What error was made
c) Why was it made
d) **Whom was it reported to**

67. Which of the following statements is INCORRECT with respect to Algal toxins in shellfish and fish in oceans?

a) They have no smell or taste

b) Enter the body of fish and shellfish and can be retained

c) Cause symptoms of food poisoning, tingling and paralysis

d) **Are eliminated by cooking and freezing**

68. With respect to Non – communicable Diseases which one of the following statement is INCORRECT?

a) They are also called Life –Style related diseases

b) **They cannot be prevented**

c) Excessive intake of saturated fats and cholesterol should be avoided

d) Obesity predisposes a person to Non- communicable diseases

69. The essential amino acid in short supply in cereals is:

a) Phenylalanine
b) Methionine
c) Isoleucine
d) **Lysine**

70. Shelf stable products with a water activity of 0.6 to 0.84 which can be eaten without rehydration are called

a) Low moisture foods
b) High moisture foods
c) Convenience foods
d) **Intermediate moisture foods**

71. Fruits and vegetables are blanched during processing mainly to

a) Remove foreign material like stalks and soil

b) Reduce processing time

c) Destroy insects and pesticides residues

d) **Eliminate enzymes and microorganisms**

72. Which one of the following statements is incorrect with respect to microbial enzymes?

a) They offer huge economics benefits to the industry

b) They have better stability than plant or animal enzymes

c) They are produced through fermentations

d) **Use of enzymes or microorganisms in food is a recent development**

73. What is the tagline for the Eat Right India movement ?

a) Ek Kadam Swatcha Ki Aur
b) Jago Grahak, Jago
c) Sahi Poshan- Desh Roshan
d) **Sahi Bhojan, Behtar Jeevan**

74. The best practices for frying food include all of the following EXCEPT?

a) Using oils which have a high smoke point

b) Using stainless steel frying pans

c) **Mixing the used cooking oil with new oil in the oil container**

d) Removing food particles from oil frequently before they clear

75. With reference to food fortification in India, which of the following statement is correct?

a) **Some commonly consumed foods are fortified**

b) Fortification aims at bridging the protein calorie gap

c) Fortified foods provide 100% RDA

d) Fortification of food is a new concept

76. Another term for provitamin is

a) Preformed vitamin

b) Active form of vitamin

c) **Precursor**

d) Coenzyme

77. Active packaging systems use oxygen scavengers while packaging grated cheese to

a) Retain Vitamin C

b) **Prevent mold growth**

c) Decreases level of condensation

d) Prevent enzymatic browning

78. In – house procedures for continuous monitoring of operations and systematic day-to-day checking of produced data for reliability in the analysis laboratory is called

a) Quality management

b) **Internal Quality control**

c) External audit

d) External Quality Control

79. Allergens cross –contact in food operations can be prevented by:

a) Mentioning ingredients used in recipes on the menu card

b) Cooking all protein rich foods thoroughly

c) **Following safe food handling and storage practices**

d) Mentioning know food allergens on the packages label

80. The toxin produced by *Clostridium botulinum* is an

a) Enterotoxin

b) **Neurotoxin**

c) Hepatotoxin

d) Hemolysin

CHAPTER-3

MRB – Tamil Nadu Food Safety Officer Exam – 2022 (Session – 1)

1. Low Sodium Food labelling refers to ___________ or less of sodium per standard serving

a) 35 mg
b) **140 mg**
c) 5 mg
d) 200 mg

2. Which of the following is a non-permitted colour as per FSSAI regulations?

a) **Metanil Yellow**
b) Sunset Yellow FCF
c) Erythrosine
d) Carmosine

3. Cholinesterase sensors are most intensively used to detect

a) Food borne pathogens
b) Toxins
c) **Pesticides**
d) Antibodies

4. Altered gas composition inside the packaging is monitored and maintained at a preset level by means of scrubbers and inflow of gases in

a) Modified humidity packaging
b) Modified atmosphere packaging
c) **Controlled atmosphere packaging**
d) Active packaging

5. A sachet coated with iron powder and calcium hydroxide scavenges

a) Nitrogen
b) Oxygen
c) **Both Oxygen and Carbon dioxide**
d) Carbon dioxide

6. Solid-phase micro extraction is a ————— preparation techniques

a) **Solvent free sample**
b) Solid free sample
c) Gas free sample
d) Liquid free sample

7. The action to remove food from the market at any stage of the food chain, including that is processed by the consumers

a) **Food Recall**
b) Food analyse
c) Food auditing
d) Food surveillance

8. Packaging with ——————water vapour permeability material protects against water loss during storage and distribution

a) **Low**
b) High
c) Excess
d) Medium

9. Nitrates play a role in the colour of

a) **Meat**
b) Honey
c) Vegetables
d) Fruits

10. When designing the food industry "Hygiene" parameter will be measured by

a) **Number of Micro-organisms per ml of finished product**
b) Number of nutrients present
c) Ton of steam per ton of sugar produced
d) Percentage of food loss

11. Expand LISA

a) **Longitudinally Integrated Safety Assurance**
b) Latitudinal Integrated Survey Assurance Latitudinal Integrated Survey Assurance
c) Latitudinal Inspection Safety Area Latitudinal Inspection Safety Area
d) Longitudinal Instrumentation Survey Access Longitudinal Instrumentation Survey Access

12. Fatty acid composition from extracted oil/oil samples can be determined by following detector

a) Electron capture detector
b) UV detector
c) Thermal conductivity detector
d) **Flame ionisation detector**

13. The technology that employs the intelligent combination of different hurdles or preservation techniques to achieve multi-target preservation effects is called

a) Process technology
b) **Hurdle technology**
c) Food technology
d) Enzyme technology

14. The detector used in Liquid Chromatography (LC) is ___________ to measure the Food Preservatives.

a) **Ultraviolet Detector**
b) Refractive Index Detector
c) Fluorescence Detector
d) Mass Detector

15. Which one of the following bacterial pathogen is cold tolerant?

a) *Escherichia coli*
b) ***Yersinia enterocolitica***
c) *Salmonella sp*
d) *Thermus aquaticus*

16. An adulterant found in laddu is

a) Sudan dye
b) Turmeric
c) Lead chromate
d) **Metanil Yellow**

17. ———— provides quality assurance without shelf testing of the produce.

a) **Good Manufacturing Practices (GMP)**
b) Hazard Analysis and Critical Control Point (HACCP))
c) Total Quality Management (TQM)
d) Standard Operating Procedure (SOP)

18. AGMARK headquarters is in which city

a) Hyderabad
b) **Faridabad**
c) Ahmedabad
d) Allahabad

19. Storage method which include use of gases to replace air around non respiring foods without further controls after storage or packaging is termed as

a) Controlled atmosphere storage
b) **Modified atmosphere storage**
c) Gas-exchange preservation
d) Equilibrium modified atmosphere

20. Egg allergy develops when the egg protein bind to ____________ antibodies

a) Ig D
b) Ig A
c) **Ig E**
d) Ig G

21. ——— produces hydrocyanic acid on hydrolysis by enzymes present in food.

a) Saponins
b) **Cyanogenic glycosides**
c) Isothiocyanates
d) Glycosides

22. __ is widely used in restaurants in insulated cups for hot beverages and takeout containers

a) Polyphenol
b) Polythene
c) Polyethylene
d) **Polystyrene foam**

23. Which of the following organizations declared ozone as GRAS for food use in 1997?

a) **US-FDA**
b) FSSAI
c) FAO
d) FSIS

24. The first principle of HACCP is to

a) Establish critical limits
b) **Conduct hazard analysis**
c) Establish documentation
d) Determine critical control points

25. Milk and Milk Product Order (MMPO) was introduced during the year

a) 1998
b) 1955
c) 1973
d) **1992**

26. The training which food industry employees should receive as part of HACCP programme

a) **GMP's**
b) Specification
c) Production
d) Chemical control

27. Generally applied frequency in industrial equipments in microwave heating

a) 1540 MHz
b) **2450 MHz**
c) 4450 MHz
d) 3360 MHz

28. —— is an attractive technology for thermal processing applications of foods.

a) Radiation
b) Heat
c) **Ohmic heating**
d) Solar heating

29. A mold inhibitor used as a spray to kill airborne microbes is

a) **Propylene glycol**
b) Vanillic acid
c) **Sorbic acid**
d) Caprylic acid

30. As per PFA Rules 1955, the maximum limit of artificial sweetener in carbonated water and soft drink concentration is

a) 200 ppm
b) 300 ppm
c) **100 ppm**
d) 400 ppm

31. Which of the following is one of the mechanical properties of packaging films?

a) Temperature
b) **Tensile strength**
c) Pressure
d) Humidity

32. An example of food borne intoxication of microbial origin is

a) ***Clostridium perfringens***
b) *Salmonella enterica*
c) *Campylobacter jejuni*
d) ***Staphylococcus aureus***

33. Which of the following food packaging materials is commonly known to exhibit gas barrier properties?

a) Polyethylene terephthalate
b) Low-density polyethylene
c) **Polyvinylidene chloride**
d) High- density polyethylene

34. ———— hydrolyse hydrogen peroxide from milk prior to cheese production.

a) Glucoamylase
b) **Catalase**
c) Lactase
d) Lipase

35. ___________ is used to alter the eating qualities of foods by changing the surface colour, flavour and aroma

a) Dielectric heating
b) Ohmic heating
c) Both (A) and (B)
d) **Infrared Radiation**

36. ___________ is an extensive list of practices that, if not met, could cause an adulterated food product

a) Verification procedures
b) **Good manufacturing practices**
c) Analysis procedures
d) Critical control point

37. Codex Alimentarius Commission was established in the year ___________

a) 1962
b) 1965
c) 1968
d) 1960

38. The process of applying heat under controlled conditions to remove water normally present in food is called

a) Pasteurization
b) **Dehydration**
c) Canning
d) Sterilization

39. Microorganisms are susceptible to UV light between ________ and ___________ nm

a) 280 – 300 nm
b) **200 – 280 nm**
c) 250 – 280 nm
d) 300 – 320 nm

40. Food Safety Officer's powers is explained in ___________ Section of Food Safety and Standards Act 2006 and Regulation 2011

a) Section 43
b) Section 51
c) Section 26
d) **Section 38**

41. In Kjeldhal method of nitrogen estimation, the indicator is

a) Phenolphthalein
b) Metanil yellow
c) **Methyl red**
d) Methylene blue

42. Which of the following is not one of the key themes of Eat Right India Initiative of Food Safety and Standards Authority of India?

a) Eat Healthy
b) Eat Sustainable
c) Eat Safe
d) **Eat Clean**

43. In countries all over the world, fortification of white flour with ___________ is required, and it has proven to be an effective public health strategy

a) Calcium
b) Iodine
c) **Folic acid**
d) Protein

44. Which is used as an alternative for Non biodegradable plastic films?

a) Biaxially oriented Polypropylene
b) **Biopolymer films**
c) Laminates
d) Low density polyethylene

45. The functional ingredient added to food to lower cholesterol is

a) Lactulose
b) Calcium citrate malate
c) Raffinose
d) **Soya**

46. The anti-caking agent added in fortified salt should not exceed more than __________ per cent.

a) 2.4
b) 3.5
c) 3
d) **2**

47. As per Food Safety and Standards (Fortification of Foods) Regulations, 2018, double fortified salt shall be fortified with iodine and

a) Zinc
b) Potassium
c) **Iron**
d) Magnesium

48. The foods contain Monosodium Glutamate (MSG) shall bear the label saying "This package contains Monosodium Glutamate its unfit for ____________"

a) **infants below 12 months**
b) school children
c) old age people
d) adults

49. Choose the best statements which explain the Hazard Analysis Critical Control Points

a) Appreciation of sanitation and Food hygiene
b) **Prevention and elimination of food safety risk**
c) Ensuring the good manufacturing practices guidelines
d) Understanding of microbial growth and survival

50. Name the compound that can be very effective in slowing down fat Oxidation

a) **Antioxidants**
b) Minerals
c) Enzymes
d) Trace metals

51. The containers generally preferred for most heat processed foods are

a) Glass
b) **Tin Cans**
c) Clay
d) Silver

52. In FSSAI-Food license number is 14 digit number (eg. 1XX XXXX XXXX 001), first digit '1' number denotes license or registration then 2 and 3 digit number denotes to which state license, so the code for "Tamil Nadu" is

a) 56
b) **24**
c) 35
d) 12

53. A Food Business in India importing their food ingredients from different countries to India should have a

a) **Central License**
b) Registration
c) International License
d) State License

54. Enzyme lipase is likely to attack fat globules

a) Before Homogenization
b) After pasteurization
c) Before cream separation
d) **After Homogenization**

55. Bacteria grow best in the water activity of

a) Less than 0.7
b) **0.9 and above**
c) 0.8 – 0.9
d) 0.7 – 0.8

56. The fungus identified in spoiled food by its sickle-shaped conidia is

a) *Mucor*
b) *Aspergillus*
c) *Penicillium*
d) ***Fusarium***

57. Discoloration of fat portion is due to

a) Hydrogenation
b) **Oxidation**
c) Homogenization
d) Carboxylation

58. Chlorogenic acid, responsible for allergic reaction, is present in

a) Lemon
b) Beer
c) **Coffee**
d) Mushroom

59. The presence of a blood clot in the coronary artery that blocks normal flow of blood to the heart is called

a) Hypertension
b) Atherosclerosis
c) **Coronary thrombosis**
d) Anaemia

60. ____________ film is not to be used for wrapping sweets.

a) **Polyvinyl Chloride (PVC)**
b) Polymer
c) Petroleum
d) Polyethylene

61. Which of the following thermal processing techniques kills only the pathogenic microorganism in food?

a) Sterilization
b) **Pasteurization**
c) Canning
d) Blanching

62 In addition to preservation, fermentation of food has additional benefits like ———

a) improved flavour
b) more nutritious
c) synthesis of several vitamins
d) **All of the answers**

63. Name the food that is a good source of Lutein and Zeaxanthin

a) Apple
b) Tomato
c) Guava
d) **Corn**

64. As per food safety and standards (Prohibition and Restrictions on sales) Regulation 2011, AGMARK certification is mandatory except for

a) Multi Source Edible Oil (MSEO)
b) Ghee
c) **Honey**
d) Fat Spread

65. — vegetable should not be stored for the long term under refrigeration conditions

a) **Potato**
b) Green leafy
c) Bitter gourd
d) Tomato

66. Glycerol and mixed fatty acids are formed during microbial spoilage of

a) **Lipid**
b) Pectin
c) Peptone
d) Cellulose

67. The closeness of agreement between a test result and the accepted reference value is called as

a) Precision
b) target value
c) **accuracy**
d) true value

68. Central Advisory Committee does not contain which of the member?

a) Chairperson of Scientific Committee
b) **Designated Officers of all District**
c) Commissioner of Food Safety
d) Member Representative from Food Industry

69. In Cryogenic freezing liquid ___________ of extremely low boiling point is used

a) Hydrogen
b) Oxygen
c) Carbon
d) **Nitrogen**

70. ___________ anaemia is caused due to the deficiency of Vitamin B12

a) Sickle cell
b) Haemolytic
c) Aplastic
d) **Perinicious**

71. Asepsis means

a) Identifying methods of destruction
b) Sterility checks
c) Reducing the populations of microorganisms
d) **Keeping out microorganisms**

72. Micro organism involved in Spoilage of Canned Fruits

a) ***Byssochlamys fulva***
b) *Pseudomonas putrefaciens*
c) *Bacillus stearothermophilus*
d) *Clostridium botulinum*

73. Choose the correct order in beer production

a) Malting – Aging – Mashing – Boiling – Fermentation – Finishing
b) Boiling – Mashing – Malting –Fermentation – Aging – Finishing
c) **Malting – Mashing – Boiling – Fermentation – Aging – Finishing**
d) Mashing – Malting – Boiling – Fermentation – Aging – Finishing

74. Which bacteria is used to control Psychrotrophic spoilage?

a) ***Lactobacillus***
b) *Pediococcus*
c) *Pseudomonas*
d) *Bifidobacterium*

75. Identify the nutraceutical derived from black cumin seed

a) **Thymoquinone**
b) Eugenol
c) Gambogic acid
d) Diosgenin

76. Over consumption of Food and Drug Administration (FDA) approved non nutritive sweeteners can lead to

a) Constipation
b) **Gut Dysbiosis**
c) Dyspepsia
d) Myalgia

77. The defect "Whiskers" in meat is caused by

a) *Cladosporium*
b) *Sporotrichum*
c) *Penicillium*
d) ***Rhizopus***

78. ISO standard for General requirements for the competence of Testing and calibration laboratories is

a) ISO/IEC 17011 : 2017
b) **ISO/IEC 17025 : 2017**
c) ISO 17034 : 2016
d) ISO 9001 : 2015

79. The efficacy of HACCP system relies on

a) Lead Auditor
b) Employees
c) **Management and Employees**
d) Management

80. Which day is celebrated as World Food Safety Day?

a) **07 June**
b) 02 October
c) 12 December
d) 21 January

81. "Jaivik Bharat" logo of FSSAI is related to

a) Food for exports
b) Milk and milk products
c) Imported food
d) **Organic foods**

82. To kill bacterial growth and moulds by using recently invented ———— in food safety systems

a) **UV radiation**
b) Tritium
c) Sulfur - 32
d) Uranium - 238

83. ——— is the selection from a population of a finite number of units to be analyzed

a) Data
b) Variables
c) **Random samples**
d) **Samples**

84. An organization shall conduct ___________ at planned intervals to determine whether the GMP system conforms to the planned arrangements and meets the requirements of the standards.

a) Fake inspections
b) Strict actions
c) **Internal audits**
d) Surprise visits

85. Toxins produced by ———— are neurotoxic, but not enterotoxic.

a) *Clostridium perfringens*
b) *Shigella*
c) ***Clostridium botulinum***
d) *Salmonella*

86. Cold sterilization is

a) Sterilization by ice
b) Sterilization by liquid nitrogen
c) Sterilization by freezing
d) **Sterilization by irradiation**

87. The energy value (conversion value) used for fats to calculate energy value of food is ————.

a) 27 kJ/g
b) 47 kJ/g
c) 17 kJ/g
d) **37 kJ/g**

88. Which of the following protein is well balanced and is considered to have a biological value of 96?

a) **Egg**
b) Milk
c) Cereal
d) Soyabean

89. Which of the commodities can be fortified under Food Safety and Standards (Fortification of Food), Regulation, 2018?

a) Rice, Salt, Tea
b) **Wheat, Milk, Oil**
c) Rice, Tea, Wheat
d) Wheat, Rice, Sugar (Chosen option)

90. A system to control the safety of a manufactured product's is determined

a) ISO 9000
b) CCP
c) **HACCP**
d) GMP

91. Calculation of Standard deviation expresses the variation between

a) measured value and true value
b) measurements
c) **replicate measurements**
d) mean value and true value

92. Fats are hydrolysed by

a) Oxidases
b) Hydrolases
c) **Microbial lipase**
d) Pectinase

93. Polyvinyl chloride used in clear food packaging, cooking oil containers leads to

a) Liver damage
b) Cancer
c) Skin Allergy
d) **Endocrine disruptors**

94. The total polar compounds in unused or fresh vegetable oil or fat shall not be more than

a) 20%
b) 10%
c) 25%
d) **15%**

95. The polymorph in chocolate is subjected to a special heat treatment process known as

a) Blanching
b) **Tempering**
c) Beating
d) Moulding

96. SNF % of standard milk

a) **8.5**
b) 9.7
c) 9.2
d) 4.5

97. What is the tagline of FSSAI?

a) **Inspiring trust, assuring safe and nutritious food**
b) Eat healthy, be healthy
c) Food : you can trust
d) Trusted science for safe food

98. Production of vinegar is regulated under ———————— order

a) Meat products control
b) Milk and Milk products
c) **The fruit products**
d) Vegetable products control

99. Botulism is a food borne intoxication associated with

a) ***Clostridium***
b) *Vibrio*
c) *Shigella*
d) *Salmonella*

100. Which of the food challenge is the "Gold Standard" method for food allergy testing?

a) Single Blind challenge
b) Open oral method
c) **Double blind placebo controlled**
d) Food elimination test

CHAPTER-4

Telengana State PSC FSOAZ - 2022

1. Scombroid poisoning is mainly due to the formation of

a) Serotonin
b) Prolamine
c) Histamines
d) Valine

2. The estimation of the probabibity of the occurrence of adverse events in food production is known as

a) Risk characterization
b) **Risk assessment**
c) Risk management
d) Risk communication

3. The antinutritional factor present in egg white is

a) Ovalbumin
b) **Avidin**
c) Lecithin
d) Ovomucin

4. The sequence in the risk assessment is

a) Hazard Identification, Dose response assessment, Exposure assessment, Risk characterization
b) Risk characterization, Hazard Identification, Dose response assessment, Exposure assessment
c) **Hazard identification, Exposure assessment, Dose response assessment, Risk characterization**
d) Hazard identification, Dose response assessment, Risk characterization, Exposure assessment

5. The spread of typhoid and paratyphoid fever through food and water is mainly due to contamination with

a) *Campylobacter sp*
b) *Pseudomonas sp*
c) *Shigella sp*
d) ***Salmonella sp***

6. Match the following

Type of milk	**Concentration of constituents**
1. Evaporated milk	A. 10-12% fat and 36% total solids
2. Condensed milk	B. 80% fat and 2% total solids

3. Sweetened condensed milk — C. 7.5 % milk fat and 25% total solids

4. Butter — D. 8.5% fat and 28% total solids

a) 1-B, 2-A, 3-C, 4-D

b) 1-A, 2-C, 3-B, 4-D

c) **1-C, 2-A, 3-D, 4-B**

d) 1-C, 2-D, 3-A, 4-B

7. The bacteria known as the buffet germ is

a) *E. coli*

b) ***Clostridium perfringens***

c) *Enterococcus*

d) *Campylobacter*

8. Food Safety and Standards Act 2006 has become operational in the entire country from

a) 2010

b) 2012

c) 2009

d) **2011**

9. Neural tube defects are mainly due to the deficiency of

a) **Folic acid**

b) Pyridoxine

c) Thiamine

d) Pantothenic acid

10. Consider the following sentences

1. The germicidal effectiveness of the benzoates is higher in the acidic foods
2. The Paraben compounds are effective over broader spectrum of microbes
3. Propionates are used in bakery products
4. Sulphur dioxide is used to preserve fruit juices and dried fruits

Which of the statements are correct

a) 1, 3 & 4 are correct

b) **1, 2, 3 & 4 are correct**

c) 2, 3 & 4 are correct

d) 1,2 & 3 are correct

11. Consider the statement ''illness transmission by the fecal - oral route" means

1. From beast, to food, to human
2. From unwashed hands, to food, to mouth
3. By fomites, to food, to human
4. By contaminated water, to food, to human

Which of the following statements is/are correct

a) 2,3 & 4

b) 1,2 & 4

c) **1, 2, 3 & 4**

d) 1, 2 & 3

12. Classes of wheat contains the highest content of gluten is

a) Soft wheat

b) **Durum wheat**

c) Dry wheat

d) Winter wheat

13. An irregular triangular patch with silver greyish foamy surface on the Conjunctiva is known as

a) **Bitot's spot**
b) Corneal xerosis
c) Keratomalacia
d) Conjunctival xerosis

14. Which among the following organisms is used to index the sanitisation?

a) ***E.coli***
b) *Leuconostoc*
c) *Salmomnella*
d) *Campylobacter*

15. Mastitis is mainly due to

a) *Clostridium* spores
b) ***Staphylococcus aureus***
c) *Micrococcus*
d) *Enterococcus*

16. Koilonychias is atypical clinical symptom of

a) **Iron deficiency**
b) Calcium deficiency
c) Vitamin A deficiency
d) Iodine deficiency

17.Monosaccharides linked together by ___ linkages to form disaccharides

a) Ester bonds
b) Peptide bonds
c) Van der waals forces
d) **Glycosidic linkages**

18. Consider the following sentences about polymerisation of oils

1. Decreases the smoke point of the oils
2. Causes increased absorption of fat by the food
3. Development of dark color
4. Decreases in viscosity and foaming capacity

Which of the following statements are correct

a) 1, 2, 3 & 4
b) **1, 2 & 3**
c) 1, 3 & 4
d) 2, 3 & 4

19. Combined method of roasting and stewing in airtight pan is called as

a) Grilling
b) Sauteing
c) **Braising**
d) Broiling

20. Principles of food fortification

1. Restoration to normal level to replace the nutrient lost during processing
2. To maintain the above natural level in the food
3. To improve public health
4. To make a food complete by itself

Which of the following statements are correct

a) 2, 3 & 4
b) **1, 2, 3 & 4**
c) 1, 2 & 3
d) 1, 3 & 4

21. The deficiency symptom of essential fatty acids is

a) Glositis
b) **Phrynoderma**
c) Scabies
d) Eczema

22. Body mass index

1. Measures muscle fat mass in relation to height of an adult body
2. Reflects adiposity
3. Also known as Quetelet index
4. Calculated by (Height in cm – 100)

Which of the following statements are correct

a) 1, 3 & 4
b) **1, 2 & 3**
c) 1, 2 & 4
d) 2, 3 & 4

23.Starch becoming less soluble like in it's original state is called

a) **Retrogradation**
b) Gelation
c) Dextrin
d) Syneresis

24. Which of the following causes hydrolytic rancidity in oils

a) **Lipase**
b) Peroxides
c) Aluminium
d) Carotenoids

25. The energy obtained from 10g of oil is

a) 900 K.cal
b) **90 K.cal**
c) 9 K.cal
d) 270 K.cal

26. Isovaleric and Isobutyric acid cause ______ in meat

a) Sliminess
b) **Cheesy odour**
c) Green discoloration
d) Dark red color

27. Skimming of milk or addition of skimmed milk to ordinary milk will leads to

a) Change in the protein content
b) **Change in the fat content**
c) Change in the all above nutrients
d) Change in the carbohydrate content

28. Which of the following are the most capable of using polysaccharidesas their food

a) **Molds**
b) Protozoans
c) Virus
d) Bacteria

29. Addition of potassium sorbate, Sodium benzoate or sodium phosphate is done during ___ of fish

a) Smoking
b) Freeze dehydration
c) Chilling
d) **Salting**

30. The chief objectives of the Codex Alimentarius are

a) Protection of the consumer health
b) Provides food processing technology
c) Enforcing the decision of the member nations
d) Facilitation of International trade

Which of the following statements are correct

a) **1 & 4**
b) 3 & 4
c) 1 & 2
d) 2 & 3

31. In microbiological experiment Stomacher is a

a) **Homogenizer of food samples**
b) Colony counter
c) Specific membrane filter
d) Culturing media for the growth of microbe

32. The mandate of provision of 100 days of guaranteed wage employment in a financial year is done by

a) **MGNREGA**
b) PDS
c) NFBS
d) NFFWP

33. Lipid soluble, yellow-orange-red pigments found in higher plants are called

a) **Carotenoids**
b) Betalains
c) Anthocyanins
d) Desmoids

34. Facultative anaerobes are the bacteria that can

a) Grows at high and low concentration of salts
b) Grows at higher osmotic environment
c) Produces gas bacteria
d) **Grows in presence and absence of oxygen**

35. The products containing living microorganisms is defined as

a) **Probiotics**
b) Prebiotics
c) Antibiotics
d) Synbiotics

36. Cryolite industry people are at risk of

a) Chronic toxicity of fluorine
b) Endemic fluorosis
c) **Occupational fluorosis**
d) Acute toxicity of fluorine

37. The basis for biomedical concept of health is

a) Web of Disease concept
b) **Germ theory of disease**
c) Supernatural theory of disease
d) Tridosha theory of disease

38. The standards formulated on physical and chemical characteristics of food is done by

a) PFA standards
b) **AGMARK standards**
c) FPO standards
d) BIS

39. Which among the following can metabolize cholesterol are believed to be capable of reducing serum cholesterol levels in humans?

a) ***Lactobacillus acidophilus* strains**
b) *Pseudomonas* strains
c) *Alcaligenes* strains
d) *Achromobacter* strains

40. Which of the following can be used to differentiate of *E.coli* from *Enterobacter sp*

a) Production of Niacin from tryptophan
b) **Production of Indole from tryptophan**
c) Production of urea from tryptophan
d) Production of creatinine from tryptophan

41. International Organization for Standardization (ISO) is a

a) Governmental organization
b) Quasi – Governmental Organization
c) **Non - governmental Organization**
d) Organization established by developing countries

42. Heating milk followed by immediate cooling to increase the keeping quality is known as

a) Clarification
b) Sterlization
c) **Pasteurization**
d) Homogenization

43. The sweetened condensed milk is more susceptible to ____ spoilage

a) **Osmophilic yeasts**
b) Psychotrophic bacteria
c) Thermoduric yeasts
d) Thermophilic bacteria

44. The discs which cracks down the unsound kernel for rejection is called

a) Magnetic seperator
b) Scourer
c) Disc separator
d) **Entoleter**

45. The most common dust disease in India

a) Bagassosis
b) **Silicosis**
c) Asbestosis
d) Byssinosis

46. The successive growth curve, features of exponential and stationary phases with the lag phase in between is seen in

a) Symbiotic growth
b) Synergistic growth
c) Antagonistic growth
d) **Diauxic growth**

47. Ripe fruits are rich in

a) Maltose
b) Raffinose
c) **Sucrose**
d) Glucose

48. Undissolved residual portion left after extraction of milk from soy is called as

a) Tempeh
b) **Okara**
c) Tofu
d) Natto

49. Pectins are polymers of galacturonic acid connected by

a) β 1-6 linkages
b) α 1-4 linkages
c) β 1-4 linkages
d) α 1-6 linkages

50. Identifying missing cases and thereby supplementing to the notified cases is known as

a) Feedback
b) Surveillance
c) Monitoring
d) **Sentinel surveillance**

51. The layer which seperates the germ or embryo from the endosperm of the grain is

a) Pericarp
b) **Scutellum**
c) Aleurone
d) Bran

52. The components in the food, that are derived through microbial metabolic activity of food nutrients, possessing health benefits are known as

a) Proteomics
b) Eugenics
c) **Biogenics**
d) Metabolomics

53. Carcasses contain an average of _____ bacterial cells/inch

a) 0.1 bacterial cells/inch
b) 100 bacterial cells/inch
c) 1.0 bacterial cells/inch
d) **10 bacterial cells/inch**

54. Match the type of microorganism with suitable pH for the maximum growth

Type of microorganism	pH range for maximum growth
1. Yeasts	A. 6.0- 8.0
2. Bacteria	B. 3.5 -4.0
3. Fungi	C. 4.5-6.0

a) **1-C, 2-A, 3-B**
b) 1-B, 2-A, 3-C
c) 1-A, 2-B, 3-C
d) 1-B, 2-C, 3-A

55. Which concept of health states "the dynamic equilibrium between man and environment

a) Psychosocial
b) Biomedical concept
c) **Ecological concept**
d) Holistic

56. Consider the following statements of the spiral plating over standard platingMore Agar is used

1. Fewer plates, dilution blanks and pipettes are required
2. 3-4 times more samples/hour can be examined
3. Little training is necessary for its operation
4. It is not appropriate for used with liquid foods such as milk

a) 1,4 & 5 statements are correct
b) 1,2 & 4 statements are correct
c) 3,4 & 5 statements are correct
d) **2,3 & 4 statements are correct**

57. The temperature obtained in autoclaving is

a) 850ºC
b) **120ºC**
c) 65ºC
d) 100ºC

58. Which of the following contains high fibre

a) Rice
b) Wheat
c) Egg
d) **Millets**

59. Lathyrism is caused due to high consumption of

a) Bengal gram dal
b) Red gram dal
c) Masoor dal
d) **Khesari dal**

60. The polymerized end product of the enzymatic browning is

a) Orthoquinones
b) Orthidiphenol
c) **Melanin**
d) DOPA

61. The antinutrients present in the vegetables interferes the absorption of Vitamin C which can lead to

a) Xeropthalmia
b) Osteomalacia
c) Beri- Beri
d) **Scurvey**

62. The oxygen carrying compound of the muscle is

a) Transferrin
b) Haemoglobin
c) Cytochrome
d) **Myoglobin**

63. Halotolerant bacteria can grow/survive at

a) Pasteurization temperature
b) Refrigerated temperature
c) Low pH
d) **High Salt concentrations**

64. The gram negative rods, which are characterized by their creation of yellow to red pigments in Agar belongs to

a) *Pseudomonas*
b) ***Flavobacterium***
c) *Micrococcus*
d) *Staphylococcus*

65. According to Iceberg disease theory, the floating tip represents

a) Latent cases
b) **Clinical cases**
c) Undiagnosed cases
d) Pre Symptomatic cases

66. Partiallyfermented tea is called

a) **Oolong**
b) Souchang
c) Orange Pekoe
d) Red tea

67. Water absorption capacity of the flour is done by

a) Pelshenke test
b) Amylograph
c) Extensograph
d) **Farinograph**

68. Agar droplet method was proposed by

a) McCrady
b) R S Breed
c) **Sharpe and Kilsby**
d) Gilchrist

69. In microbial modeling systems the term "D" represents the time for

a) **One log units of inactivation**
b) Ten log units of inactivation
c) Thousand log units of inactivation
d) Hundred log units of inactivation

70. Match the following

Quality parameter	**Equipment used**
1. Butter content of milk	A. Refractometer

2. Sugar content | B. Butyrometer
3. Colour intensity | C. Penetrometer
4. Tenderness | D. Spectrophotometer

a) **1-B, 2-A, 3-D, 4-C**
b) 1-B, 2-D, 3-A, 4-C
c) 1-D, 2-A, 3-B, 4-C
d) 1-C, 2-A, 3-B, 4- D

71. One of the easy ways of getting adequate vitamin C per day is through regular eating of

a) Grapes
b) **Guava**
c) Banana
d) Apple

72. Which of the following is a structural protein

a) Myosin
b) **Collagen**
c) Gamma Globulin
d) Actin

73. Match the following programme with nutrient deficiency

Deficiency	**Nutrient deficiency**
1. NIDDCP	A . Vitamin A
2. NPPNB due to VAD	B. Iodine
3. WIFS	C. Dietary diversity
4. Kitchen garden	D. Iron

a) 1-C, 2-A, 3-D. 4-B
b) **1-B, 2-A, 3-D, 4-C**
c) 1-C, 2- D,3-A, 4-B
d) 1-A, 2-C, 3- B, 4 -D

74. Consider the following statements

Microbial contamination of food from the air can be reduced by

1. Removing the potential sources
2. Using filteredair
3. Using positive air pressure
4. Reducing humidity level

Which of the statements are correct

a) 1, 2 & 4
b) **1, 2, 3 &4**
c) 1, 2 & 3
d) 1 & 2

75. Hypogeusia and hyposmia are remarkable deficiency symptoms of

a) **Zinc deficiency**
b) Magnesium deficiency
c) Selenium deficiency
d) Calcium deficiency

76. Hydrogenation of glucose, galactose and mannose under high pressure and temperature in the presence of catalyst results in the formation of

a) Starches
b) Sugar acids
c) **Sugar alcohols**
d) Sugar granules

77. Iron absorption is interfered by

a) Cyanogenic glycosides
b) Goitrogenes
c) Saponines
d) **Tannins**

78. Which method is more suitable to collect the dietary intake data of the large population

a) Food weighment method
b) **24 –hour recall method**
c) Diet history method
d) Food diary method

79. Consider the following with respect to Trypsin inhibitors

1. Present in pulses
2. They are fatty acids and prevents the activity of trypsin in the gut
3. Release of methionine is hampered
4. Can be inactivated at autoclave temperatures

Ans

a) **1,3 & 4**
b) 2,3 &4
c) 1, 2, 3 & 4
d) 1, 2 &3

80. For every increase in 152 metre of altitude, the boiling point of water

a) Increases by 1^0C
b) **Decreases by 1^0C**
c) Decreases by 10^0C
d) Increases by 10^0C

81. The washed maize which is milled to a gritty textured product is called

a) **Masa**
b) Corn flakes
c) Tortilla
d) Corn flour

82. The spontaneous exudation of fluid from a gel is called

a) Dextrinization
b) **Syneresis**
c) Emulsification
d) Gelatinization

83. The most frequently applied inactivation model in retorted foods is

a) **Thermal deaths models**
b) Irradiation models
c) Pulsed electrical field model
d) Ultra –high – pressure models

84. The anaerobic bacteria do not increase until the onset of rigormortis because of

a) Low OR/R in pre rigor meat
b) **High O/R in pre rigor meat**
c) High O/R in post rigor meat
d) Low O/R in post rigor meat

85. In sensory evaluation, the test where two identical and one different samples presented simultaneously for determination of odd sample is

a) **Triangle test**
b) Ranking test
c) Duo – trio test
d) Paired Comparision test

86. The spoilage is characterized by a flat container, darkened products with the odor of rotten eggs is called

a) Flat sour spoilage
b) Thermophilic Anaerobe (TA) spoilage
c) **Sulfide Stinker Spoilage**
d) Spoilage due to insufficient heating

87.The water activity at which the spoilage bacteria do not grow

a) Below aw = 1.80
b) Above aw = 1.80
c) **Below aw = 0.91**
d) Above aw = 0.91

88. Stirring and mixing of liquid chocolate at 180°F is called

a) Curing
b) **Conching**
c) Defatting
d) Roasting

89. Which organism preferentially metabolize amino acids instead ofglucose, can be rapidly and produce undesirable odors in meat

a) ***Acinetobacter***
b) *Pseudomonas*
c) *Lactobacillus*
d) *Brochothrix*

90. Which of the the following pathogen causes Botulism

a) ***Clostridium***
b) *Bacillus*
c) *Staphylococcus*
d) *Salmonella*

91.Monosodium glutamate is a

a) Preservative
b) Texturizer
c) **Flavour enhancer**
d) Tenderizer

92. Measure of egg protein quality based on the height of its egg white (albumen) in relation to the weight of the egg is

a) **Haughs Unit**
b) White Index
c) Yolk Index
d) Candling

93. The benefit of consuming normal yogurt is due to

1. The reduced amounts of lactose in yogurt, as compared to milk
2. The supply of lactose from the dead cells

3. The supply of β-galactosidase

Which of the statements are correct

a) 1, 2 & 3
b) 2 & 3
c) 1 & 3
d) **1 & 2**

94. Distribution of fat between the muscle fibre bundles is known as

a) Ageing
b) Ripening
c) **Marbling**
d) Rigor mortis

95. Pneumoconiosis is a

a) Heart disease
b) **Lung disease**
c) Skin disease
d) Kidney disease

96. Ciguatoxin is mainly caused by the consumption of

a) **Reef fish with algal toxins**
b) Egg with fungal toxins
c) Poultry meat bacterial toxins
d) Beef viral toxins

97. In anthocyanins, increase in no.of hydroxyl groups yields____ colour and methoxy groups give___ colour

a) Red, orange
b) Yellow, white
c) White, green
d) **Blue, red**

98. The most important cellulose derivative for food application is

a) **Carboxy methyl cellulose**
b) Micro crystalline cellulose
c) Hydroxy propyl methyl cellulose
d) Methyl cellulose

99. Mycotoxins are toxins produced by

a) Bacteria
b) **Fungi**
c) Algae
d) Virus

100. Lye peeling is done by dipping in boiling

a) Calcium carbonate solution
b) Sodium benzoate solution
c) **Sodium hydroxide solution**
d) Potassium permanganate solution

101. Match the following

Modified starch	**Functional property**
1. Pre gelatinized property	A. Gum Jellies
2. Acid hydrolyzed starch	B. Thickeners in dry soup powders

3. Cross linked starches
4. Oxidized starches

C. Starch batters for fish and meat
D. Instant puddings

a) 1-A, 2-B, 3-D, 4-C
b) 1-C, 2-A, 3-B, 4-D
c) **1-D, 2-A, 3-B, 4 – C**
d) 1-B, 2-D, 3-A, 4-C

102. PDCAAS=

a) Protein digestibility + Amino acid score
b) Protein digestibility/ Amino acid score ×100
c) Protein digestibility/ Amino acid score
d) **Protein digestibility × Amino acid score**

103. Dermatitis, dementia and diarrhea are the typical deficiency symptoms of

a) Thiamine
b) Pyridoxine
c) **Niacin**
d) Riboflavin

104. Cream and butter are more susceptible to spoilage by ___ enzymes

a) Catalases
b) Galactidases
c) **Lipases**
d) Proteinases

105. Frustration, insecurity, lack of job satisfaction, poor human relationships are considered as causative factors of

a) **Psychosocial hazards**
b) Biological hazards
c) Physical hazards
d) Mechanical hazards

106. "Black spot" on beef and freezing mutton are developed by

a) *Aspergillus niger*
b) *Staphylococcus aureus*
c) ***Cladosporium herbarum***
d) *Talaromyces flavus*

107. Match the following nutritional deficiency with symptoms

Nutrient
1. Kwashiorkor
2. Iodine
3. Vitamin C
4. Riboflavin

Clinical symptoms
A. Cretinism
B. Angular stomatitis
C. Moon face
D. Bleeding gums

a) 1-C, 2-D, 3-A, 4-B
b) 1-B, 2-A, 3-D, 4-C
c) 1-A, 2-C, 3-B, 4-D
d) **1-C, 2-A, 3-D, 4-B**

108. A good source of most of the B- Complex vitamins

a) Milk and milk products
b) Green leafy vegetables
c) **Bran of cereals**
d) Root vegetables

109. Consider the following sentences

Assertion: Polyols have very high humectancy and plasticizing power

Reasoning: The products made with polyols will be soft, moist and low in water activity

a) Assertion and reasoning are correct, but reasoning is not explaining the assertion

b) Assertion is correct

c) **Assertion and reasoning are correct, reasoning is explaining the assertion**

d) Reasoning is correct

110. The substances interfere with iodine uptake are known as

a) **Goitrogens** b) Haemagglutinins

c) Saponins d) Tannins

111. The indispensable fatty acids for humans are

a) Partially hydrogenated vegetable oils

b) Saturated fatty acids

c) Palmitic acid and arachidonic acid

d) **Linoleic acid and alpha linolenic acid**

112. World consumers right day is celebrated on

a) 15th March b) 22nd December

c) 5th June d) 14th October

113. The meal through mid-day meal programme, expected to provide per day is

a) 2/3 of energy and 1/4 of protein RDI of the children

b) 1/2 of energy and 2/3of protein RDI of the children

c) **1/3 of energy and 1/2 of protein RDI of the children**

d) 1/2 of energy and 1/3of protein RDI of the children

114. Consider the following statements

Statement 1: The specific gravity of un-adulterated milk is 1.026

Statement 2: Milk adulterated with water will have freezing point close to zero

Ans

a) Both the statements are correct and statement 2 explaining statement 1

b) **Both the statements are correct and statements 2 is not explaining statement 1**

c) Statement 1 is correct d) Statement 2 is correct

115. The desirable flavor in the milk yogurt is due to the formation of

a) Formaldehyde b) **Acetaldehyde**

c) Methylene d) Glycerin

116. The central AGMARK Laboratory is located at

a) Nagpur　　b) New Delhi

c) Kolkata　　d) Hyderabad

117. Hydrogen ion concentrations in a system is known as

a) O/R　　b) E^{O}

c) Aw　　d) **pH**

118. Raw papaya is used in meat cooking for

a) **Tenderization**　　b) Emulsifying

c) Thickening　　d) Marination

119. The iron requirements is highest for

a) **Pregnant women**　　b) Adolescent boy

c) Lactating women　　d) Adolescent girl

120. Consider the following statements

1. Germination of pulses
2. Provides more essential amino acids
3. Decreases calcium, Zinc and iron
4. Causes activation of enzymes

Increases vitamin content

a) 2, 3 & 4 are correct　　b) **1, 3 & 4 are correct**

c) 1, 2 & 4 are correct　　d) 1,2 &3 are correct

121. Vegetarian meat is an example for

a) Enriched food　　b) **Simulated food**

c) Synthetic food　　d) Fortified food

122. To delay microbial spoilage fresh meats are stored at

a) **<5°C**　　b) <15°C

c) <10°C　　d) <20°C

123. Consider the following statements

Statement 1: Microbial growth is accomplished through enzymatic reactions

Statement 2: With every 10°C rise in temperature, the catalytic rate of an enzymes doubles and reduced to half by decreasing the temperature by 10°C

Statement 3: Microbial cells die rapidly at high temperatures and relatively slowly at lower temperatures

Ans

a) Statement 2 only explains the statement 1

b) Statement 3 only explains the statement 1

c) All the Statements are correct independently

d) **Statement 2 & 3 explains the statement 1**

124. The direct epifluorescent filter technique is used for estimating bacterial counts in

a) Fruit juices
b) **Raw milk**
c) Cereal based batters
d) Canned vegetables

125. Prevention of the emergence or development of risk factors in countries or population groups, before its appearance is called

a) Secondary prevention
b) Primary prevention
c) Teritary prevention
d) **Primordial prevention**

12.The principle of drying the material by sublimation is followed in

a) Drum drying
b) **Freeze drying**
c) Foam mat drying
d) Spray drying

127. Which type of the water can be used in food processing unit

a) Potable water
b) Recycled water
c) Tube well water
d) **Chlorinated potable water**

128. Partial sealing of a can facilitates the escape of dissolved or free air is known as

a) Peeling
b) Processing
c) Exhausting
d) **Clinching**

129. The major nutritional programme addressing the health and nutritional needs of under six children in India

a) **ICDS SCHEME**
b) Mid – day meal programme
c) Antyodaya anna yojana
d) Food for work programme

130. The technique involved in PCR method, in assessing the food quality is

a) Enzymatic assay
b) Bioluminescense reactions
c) Titration reactions
d) **DNA amplification**

131. The proportion of clinical cases resulting in severe clinical manifestations of a biological agents is called

a) Infectivity
b) Contagious
c) Pathogenicity
d) **Virulence**

132. Which of the following is food safety risk management tool

a) Codex Alimentarius
b) **HACCP**
c) GMP
d) GAP

133. The pungency of chilli extract is expressed as

a) Degree Brix
b) IBU
c) **Scoville value**
d) Pyruvate scale

134. Material used as substitute for the coffee and often blended to give taste to coffee is

a) Caffeine
b) Tea
c) **Chicory**
d) Cocoa

135. Which of the following B vitamin RDA'S requirements is based on protein requirement

a) **Pyridoxine**
b) B_{12}
c) Thiamine
d) Folic acid

136. Consider the following statements with regards to Amylase rich food (ARF)

1) Are highly suitable as weaning foods
2) Increases the total solid concentration
3) Helps to make high viscous recipes
4) High energy dense preparations

Which of the following statements is /are correct

a) 1,2 & 3
b) **1 & 4**
c) 2 & 4
d) 1 & 2

137. Match the following Antiseptics and dosage recommended for food preservation

Antiseptic	Dose
1. Sugar	A. 2%
2. Salt	B. 0.2%
3. Acetic acid	C. 15%
4. Benzoates	D. 70%

a) 1-D, 2-A, 3-B, 4-C
b) **1-D, 2-C, 3-A, 4-B**
c) 1-B, 2-C, 3-D, 4-A
d) 1-C, 2-A, 3-B, 4-D

138. The concept of primary health care system as a basic unit for health was provided by

a) Central advisory board for health

b) Govt. of India act 1935

c) Royal commission

d) **Bhore commitee**

139. The principal compound which contributes aroma to the aromatic rice is

a) Oryzonol

b) B glucans

c) **Acetyl 1-1 pyrroline**

d) Formaldehyde

140. Cereals like rice and wheat are rich in amino acid___

a) Lysine

b) Phenyl alanine

c) Tryptophan

d) **Methionine**

141. Alimentary Toxic Aleukia (ATK) is caused by

a) ***Fusarium sporotrichiodies***

b) *Penicillium islandicum*

c) *Claviceps purpurea*

d) *Aspergillus flavus*

142. Which of the following is rich source of lycopene

a) **Tomato**

b) Potato

c) Kale

d) Avocado

143. Ergotism is caused by

a) *Penicillium islandicum*

b) *Aspergillus flavus*

c) ***Claviceps purpurea***

d) *Fusarium sporotrichioides*

144. The antimicrobial property of mustard oil is due to the presence of

a) Thiosulfinate

b) Benzoic acid

c) Sorbic acid

d) **Isothiocyanate**

145. Cut potatoes are immersed in salt water to prevent

a) Non- enzymatic browning

b) Rancidity

c) **Enzymatic browning**

d) Lipase activity

146. Match the following

Food Testing Laboratory	Location
1. Food Research and Standardization laboratory	A. Pune
2. Central food Laboratory	B. Ghaziabad
3. Public health laboratory	C. Mysore
4. Central food technological Research Institute	D. Kolkata

a) 1-D, 2-A, 3-B, 4-C

b) 1-A, 2-D, 3- B, 4- C

c) 1-D, 2-B, 3-A, 4-C

d) **1-B, 2-D, 3-A, 4- C**

147. The nutrient profiles which are extensively used in the laboratory for the biochemical identification of unknown microorganisms isolated from foods

a) **Carbohydrate metabolism**
b) Protein metabolism
c) Fat metabolism
d) Mineral metabolism

148. Food laws and food codes are the integral parts of

a) **Codex Alimentarius**
b) General Agreement on Trade and Tariff
c) Hazard Analysis Critical Control Point
d) Good Management Practices

149. Match the following

Food stuff	**Common adulterant**
1. Tea	A. Tamarind seed powder
2. Pepper	B. Dal husk
3. Coffee	C. Vanaspathi
4. Ghee	D. Papaya seeds

a) **1-B, 2-D, 3-A, 4-C**
b) 1-B, 2-A, 3-D, 4-C
c) 1-D, 2-B, 3-A, 4-C
d) 1-A, 2-D, 3-B, 4-C

150. During malting of barley, the increase in giberellic acid will causes

a) Decrease in cyclic amino acids sugars
d) Decrease in reducing sugars
c) **Increase in reducing sugars**
d) Increase in cyclic amino acids

CHAPTER-5

Kerala Food Safety Officer Exam - 2020

1. Freeze drying takes place at

a) The triple point

b) **Below the triple point**

c) Above the triple point

d) At zero degree Celsius

2. Use of several methods like temperature (high or low), control of acidity, control of water activity for preservation of food is known as

a) **Hurdle technology**

b) Mixed technology

c) Stumbling technology

d) Multiple technology

3. Cause and effect diagram is also known as

a) Quality circles

b) **Fish bone diagram**

c) Five force diagram

d) Kaizen diagram

4. The process in which a specially designed hermetic centrifuge is used to separate bacteria and especially the spores formed by specific bacteria strains, from milk is known as

a) Sterilization

b) Pasteurisation

c) Aseptic packaging

d) **Bactofugation**

5. The most common bacterial cultures involved in acidic fermentation are

a) ***Lactobacillus, Leuconostoc, Lactococcus* and *Streptococcus***

b) *Lactococcus, Bifidobacterium, Lactobacillus* and *Leuconostoc*

c) *Lactococcus, Rhizopus, Lactococcus* and *Streptococcus*

d) *Lactobacillus, Leuconostoc, Lactococcus* and *Aspergillus*

6. Which of the following statements are true

1.Foods high in sugar and other solutes dry more slowly.

2. As drying progresses the concentration of solutes in water increases causing the drying rate to slow.

3. Water that is most difficult to remove is that is chemically bound in the form of hydrates.

4. Drying at high pressure occurs at lower temperature.

a) 1, 2, 3, 4

b) **1, 2, 3**

c) 1, 3, 4

d) 1, 2, 4

7. Foods processed using high-pressure technology, gamma irradiation, high electric field pulse and thermosonication are known as

a) **Minimally processed foods** b) UHT processed foods
c) Aseptically processed foods d) All of the above

8. Food items should be subjected to micro frequencies such that, the dielectric constant is __________ and loss factor is ______

a) Maximum, minimum b) Maximum, maximum
c) **Minimum, minimum** d) Minimum, maximum

9. In which of the following ways does absorption of gamma radiation takes place

a) Photoelectric effect b) Compton effect
c) Pair production d) **All of the mentioned**

10. Which among the following claims is prohibited

a) **Unsubstantiated claims** b) Claims of Veg./Non-veg.
c) Claims of quality3 d) None of the mentioned

11. What is "carryover" principle?

a) Additives added in the raw materials are not present in the final products
b) **Antioxidant added to oil is present in all oil based products made from it**
c) All of the above
d) None of the above

12. Difference of Green Tea from Black Tea is that

a) The oxidation process is omitted
b) The tea leaves are steamed in a pan before rolling to prevent oxidation by enzymes
c) **The oxidation process is omitted and the tea leaves are steamed in a pan before being rolled to prevent oxidation by enzymes**
d) None of the mentioned

13. When a deviation from critical limits happens what should be done ?

a) Documentation of corrective actions
b) Stop the line and inform the supervisor
c) Reassess the HACCP plan d) **All of the above**

14. Which type of packaging is appropriate for fruits ?

a) **Ethylene absorbers** b) Oxygen absorbers
c) Carbon-di-oxide absorbers d) Nitrogen producing

15. Which of the following is true about death time curve method to sterilize canned food ?

a) **It tells us the time and temperature to sterilize canned food**

b) It tells us about the heat penetration of the container

c) It tells us about the heat conductivity of the container

d) All of the mentioned

16. Which method is most energy efficient for making ghee ?

a) Desi method

b) Creamery butter method

c) Direct cream method

d) **Pre-stratification method**

17. What will be the over run, if 400 litre of mix produces 740 litre of ice cream ?

a) 60%

b) **85%**

c) 30%

d) 100%

18. What is the major defect that occurs in UHT milk during storage ?

a) Darkening of colour

b) **Age gelation**

c) Cooked flavour

d) Absence of beneficial bacteria

19. During cheddar cheese manufacture, rennet split the kappa-casein at the junction of

a) Phenyl alanine-histidine

b) Methionine-lysine

c) Histidine-lysine

d) **Phenyl alanine-methionine**

20. UHT processed milk is aseptically packaged at

a) 5^0C

b) 10^0 C

c) **20^0C**

d) 40^0C

21. The usual method of stunning cattle is by using

a) **Captive bolt pistol**

b) Electrical stunning

c) CO2 anaesthesia

d) None of the above

22. Which Vitamin is not available in egg ?

a) Vitamin A

b) Vitamin B

c) **Vitamin C**

d) Vitamin D

23. A meat borne bacterial infection

a) Taeniasis

b) Toxoplasmosis

c) Sarcocystis

d) **Salmonellosis**

24. A cured meat product

a) Sausage

b) **Bacon**

c) Keema

d) Cutlet

25. The method of preservation of egg using sodium silicate

a) Thermal processing
b) **Water glass method**
c) Lime sealing
d) Oil coating

26. The certified copies may be produced in proof of the contents of which document ?

a) All kinds of documents
b) Private documents
c) **Public documents**
d) Government documents

27. 'Consumer' under the Food Safety and Standards Act, 2006 is the

a) Person who consumes food
b) Person and family who consume food
c) Person who purchases and receives the food
d) **Person and families who purchases and receives food**

28. The head office of the Food Safety and Standards Authority of India is at

a) Mumbai
b) **Delhi**
c) Calcutta
d) Kochi

29. The enactment of Information Technology Act, 2000 resulted in the introduction of which provision under Indian Evidence Act, 1872 ?

a) **S. 65A**
b) S. 64A
c) S. 63A
d) S. 62A

30. Who is responsible for the inspection of food business, drawing and sending samples for food analysis under Food Safety and Standards Act, 2006 ?

a) Commissioner of Food Safety
b) Food Analyst
c) **Food Safety Officer**
d) Live Stock Inspector

31. Which of the following is correct ?

a) **The accused can file written statements under S. 233 Cr.P.C. in support of his defence**

b) S. 250 Cr.P.C. empowers the magistrate to discharge an accused in a warrant case instituted otherwise than on a police report.

c) In a summary trial under S. 235 Cr.P.C. the maximum period of imprisonment that can be imposed is two years.

d) The bail bond executed for the appearance before the higher court under S. 437 Cr.P.C. shall be five years.

32. The magistrate can take cognizance of offence upon

a) Receiving information through telephone or e-mail
b) **A police report**

c) Information received from a police officer

d) All the above

33. Under S. 439 Cr.P.C., which court has the power to release any person on bail and by a subsequent order cause him to be rearrested ?

a) High Court

b) Sessions Court

c) **Both High Court and Sessions Court**

d) Magistrate Court and Sessions Court

34. The High Court may confer on any magistrate invested with the powers of a magistrate of the second class power to try summarily any offence which is punishable with imprisonment for a term not exceeding

a) **6 months**

b) 3 months

c) 1 year

d) 7 years

35. Under S. 374 Cr.P.C. who can file appeal to the Supreme Court ?

a) **Any person convicted on a trial held by a High Court in its extraordinary original criminal jurisdiction**

b) The prosecution which could not succeed in the trial in High Court

c) Both A) and B)

d) None of the above

36. Any person who manufactures for sale or distribute any article of substandard food for consumption is liable to the extend of

a) 2.5 lakhs rupees and 6 months imprisonment

b) 2.5 lakhs rupees only

c) 5 lakhs of rupees and 6 months imprisonment

d) **5 lakhs rupees**

37. The Food Safety Appellate Tribunal shall consists of

a) 5 members

b) 3 members

c) **1 member**

d) Any of the above

38. The defences which may be allowed in prosecution under the Food Safety and Standards Act is under

a) S. 78

b) S. 79

c) S. 81

d) **S. 80**

39. Where in a case the sample container received by the Food Analyst is found to be in broken condition, he shall

a) **Inform the designated officer within seven days**

b) Inform the designated officer within reasonable period of time

c) Inform the commissioner within seven days

d) Inform the commissioner within reasonable period of time

40. The secondary evidence is defined under which provision of Indian Evidence Act ?

a) S. 66 b) S. 44

c) S. 36 d) **S. 63**

41. In which of the following separation techniques the separation is based on the net charge of the molecule ?

a) Affinity chromatography b) **Ion exchange chromatography**

c) Molecular exclusion chromatography d) Isopyenic centrifugation

42. An example for triose is

a) Glucose b) Ribulose

c) Xylulose d) **Glyceraldehyde**

43. The exoskeleton of insects (chitin) is composed of

a) **N-Acetyl glucosamine** b) N-Acetyl muramic acid

c) N-Acetyl galactosamine d) Glucose-6-phosphate

44. Of the following, which amino acid is an imino acid ?

a) Histidine b) Glutamic acid

c) **Proline** d) Tyrosine

45. The proteolytic enzyme trypsin, hydrolyses the peptide bonds in which

a) Amino group is contributed either by lysine or arginine

b) **Carbonyl function is contributed either by lysine or arginine**

c) Carbonyl function is contributed either by phenylalanine or tyrosine

d) Amino group is contributed either by phenylalanine or tyrosine

46. Which of the following is not an antioxidant ?

a) Vit. C b) Vit. E

c) Carotenes d) **Vit. B6**

47. Iodine number of fatty acids denotes its

a) **Degree of unsaturation** b) Chain length

c) Molecular weight d) Solubility in water

48. Cold Sterilization means perseveration of food by

a) Sterilizing at – 179°C b) **Radiation**

c) Sterilizing at 0°C d) Lyophylization

49. In humans the basal metabolic rate accounts for about __________ percentage of the daily calorie expenditure.

a) **60 – 75**
b) 40 – 55
c) 25 – 40
d) 80 – 90

50. The Respiratory Quotient (RQ) is the ratio of

a) O_2 consumed/CO_2 eliminated
b) H_2O consumed/CO_2 eliminated
c) **CO_2 eliminated/O_2 consumed**
d) CO_2 eliminated/H_2O consumed

51. Biological Value of a protein is influenced by

a) Amino acid composition
b) Vitamin and mineral content
c) Preparation (cooking)
d) **All the above**

52. The absorption maxima Lambda max max of a compound is dependent on

a) Structure of the compound
b) pH of the solvent in which the compound exist
c) The polarity of the solvent
d) **All the above**

53. The purpose of guard column in HPLC systems is to

a) Protect the peristaltic pump
b) **Protect the main column**
c) Protect the injection port
d) Protect the detector

54. All free radicals have _________ in their orbitals.

a) Paired valence electron
b) **Unpaired valence electrons**
c) No valence electron
d) None of the above

55. Of the following which is not an artificial sweetener ?

a) Saccharin
b) Sodium cyclamate
c) **Butylated hydroxyanisole**
d) Acesulfame

56. Which is mordant in Grams staining ?

a) Crystal Violet
b) Safranin
c) Alcohol
d) **Iodine**

57. The immersion oil used in microscopy will

a) Decrease the numerical aperture
b) **Increase the refractive index**
c) Decrease the refractive index
d) None of the above

58. Aflatoxins are

a) Produced by certain fungi
b) Cancer causing agent
c) Causes immunosuppression
d) **All the above**

59. Botulinum toxins are

a) **Neurotoxic**
b) Teratogen
c) Carcinogenic
d) Mutagen

60. MSA (Mannitol Salt Agar) is generally used for the detection of

a) *E. Coli*
b) ***Staphylococcus aureus***
c) *Bacillus sp*
d) *Aspergillus niger*

61. Enzyme used in fruit juice clarification is

a) Peroxidase
b) Dismutase
c) Catalase
d) **Pectinase**

62. Rotating Biological contactors are employed

a) Primary treatment of waste water
b) **Secondary treatment of waste water**
c) RBC isolation
d) Solid waste management

63. This is not a method of enzyme immobilization

a) Encapsulation
b) Adsorption
c) Nanomaterial immobilization
d) **PAGE**

64. HACCP stands

a) Health Analysis and Critical Control Point
b) Hazard Analysis and Critical Care Point
c) Hazard Analysis and Crucial Control Point
d) **Hazard Analysis and Critical Control Point**

65. Which GM crop is approved in India ?

a) Bt Corn
b) Bt Brinjal
c) **Bt Cotton**
d) GM Tomato

66. The trap which is used widely to kill rice field rats is

a) Snap trap
b) Remote triggered trap
c) **Pot trap**
d) Automatic trap

67. A dull hollow sound when tapped is the maturity index of _________ crop.

a) Papaya
b) Pineapple
c) Sapota
d) **Watermelon**

68. Bheema is a high yielding variety of _________ mushroom.

a) Paddy straw mushroom
b) Button mushroom
c) Oyster mushroom
d) **White milky mushroom**

69. A chemical safely sprayed on bags of stored grains in godowns

a) Carbosulfan
b) **Malathion**
c) Dimethoate
d) Quinalphos

70. Which of the following is not an advantage of blanching ?

a) **For precooling**
b) To preserve colour
c) To preserve flavor
d) To inactivate enzymes

71. Who among the following was the Anglo-Indian representative in the Indian Constituent Assembly ?

a) Morris Johns
b) **Frank Anthony**
c) Sardar Vallabha Bhai Patel
d) K. M. Munshi

72. Which Article of the Indian Constitution deals with Right to Life ?

a) Art. – 14
b) Art. – 19
c) Art. – 20
d) **Art. – 21**

73. Who among the following is returning officer for the election of President of India ?

a) **Secretary General of Lok Sabha**
b) Chief Election Commissioner
c) Chief Justice of India
d) Prime Minister of India

74. What is the subject matter of Article 40 of Indian Constitution ?

a) Uniform Civil Code
c) Prohibition
c) Right to Education
d) **Panchayati Raj**

75. By which Amendment Secularism incorporated in the Preamble of Indian Constitution ?

a) 24th
b) 74th
c) **42nd**
d) 44th

76. Which Article of Indian Constitution deals with Grama Sabha ?

a) **Article 243**
b) Article 248
c) Article 233
d) None of the above

77. Which among the following are in the centre list of 7th Schedule of Indian Constitution ?

1. Markets and fairs
2. Insurance
3. Taxes on Profession
4. Banking

a) 1 and 2
b) 1 and 3
c) **2 and 4**
d) 3 and 4

78. In which year Balwant Rai Mehta Committee was appointed ?

a) 1947 b) **1957**
c) 1967 d) 1987

79. Identify the subject matter of the second chapter of the Indian Constitution.

a) **Citizenship** b) Union and State
c) Fundamental Rights d) Executive

80. Which among the following Act is related to Article 17 ?

1. Nirbhaya Act, 2013
2. Protection of Civil Rights Act in 1976
3. Armed Forces (Special Powers) Act, 1958
4. Citizenship Amendment Act, 2019

a) 1 and 2 b) **2 only**
c) 3 only d) 3 and 4

81. Which among the following pairs of months will have the same calendar ?

a) April – November b) **January – October**
c) July – October d) June – August

82. The difference between 75% of a number and 20% of the same number is 378.4. What is 40% of that number ?

a) **275.2** b) 274
c) 267.2 d) 266

83. Neha walked 9 m in the East, then she turned to her right and walked 4 m. Again she turned to her left and moved 3 m. Then she turned to her left and walked 9 m. How far is she and in which direction from the starting point ?

a) 13 m, South – West b) **13 m, North – East**
c) 15 m, North – East d) 15 m, South – West

84. If eye = ice, lips = rose and brows = black, what is coded as 'forehead' ?

a) Sindoor b) Flower
c) Jasmine d) **Frontier**

85. A committee of 3 members is to be selected out of 3 men and 2 women. What is the probability that the committee has atleast one woman ?

a) 1/ 10 b) 9 /20
c) **9/ 10** d) 1 /20

86. Vaunt : Flaunt : : Disparate : ?

a) Similar b) Homogeneous
c) **Contrast** d) Alike

87. What will be the next term in the following – DCXW, FEVU, HGTS, ?

a) AKPO
b) ABYZ
c) **JIRQ**
d) LMRS

88. In how many different ways can the letters of the word 'PUNCTUAL' be arranged

a) 64
b) 40320
c) 960
d) **20160**

89. Find out the wrong term in the series. 2, 3, 4, 4, 6, 8, 9, 12, 16

a) **9**
b) 12
c) 16
d) 8

90. In a certain code if C = 3 and SCHOOL = 12, then LAMB = ?

a) 28
b) 12
c) **7**
d) 8

91. My brother _______ the answer to the question.

a) is know
b) know
c) Knowing
d) **knows**

92. I think I will buy these shirts. _______ me really well.

a) They were fitting
b) **They fit**
c) They are fitting
d) They have fit

93. Where _______ the book ?

a) **did you keep**
b) did you kept
c) kept you
d) none of these

94. At five o'clock yesterday evening I _______ for the bus

a) were waiting
b) **was waiting**
c) Wait
d) waiting

95. Anne _______ ill for two weeks. She is still in hospital

a) Was
b) had been
c) Is
d) **has been**

96. How did you come ? _______ bus ?

a) In
b) on
c) Through
d) **by**

97. Choose the correct sentence from the following

a) I am not agree with what you say
b) **He is doing a course in linguistics**
c) Children makes a lot of noise
d) He speak English well

98. Which of the following is the opposite of diligent ?

a) Active
b) smart
c) hard working
d) **lazy**

99. What is the one word substitute for one who is not sure about God's existence ?

a) **Agnostic**
b) Atheist
c) Theist
d) None of these

100. What does the idiom kick the bucket mean ?

a) **to die**
b) to hit someone with a bucket
c) to cry
d) none of these

CHAPTER-6

Central Food Safety Officer Exam – Solved Question Paper - 2019

1. In a certain code language TROUBLE is written as GNDWQTV. How would the word TEACHER be written in the same code language?

a) THJEDHV
b) TGJEDGV
c) TGIFDGV
d) **TGJECGV**

2. Which closed nuclear plant was commissioned again in 2019?

a) Kalpakam, Tamil Nadu
b) Tarapur, Maharashtra
c) Rawatbhata, Rajasthan
d) **Kudankulam, Tamil Nadu**

3. Which regions in India are specially considered for the Special Area Games Support Programme by the Sports Authority of India?

a) Village youth
b) Girls and Women
c) Youth under 18 years
d) **Hill and Coastal areas**

4. Select the most appropriate Antonym of the word AUTHENTIC

a) Real
b) Genuine
c) **Spurious**
d) Original

5. Select the most appropriate synonym of the word EXAGGERATE.

a) Demonstrate
b) Appreciate
c) **Inflate**
d) Eradicate

6.______ is a tool built into Microsoft Excel to summarize, sort, recognise, group, count, total or average data stored in a database.

a) Filtering and sorting
b) Data analysis
c) **Pivot table**
d) Power view

7. Which of the following is not a valid email address?

a) Rekha.Menon@Gmail.com
b) NARASIMHA@OUTLOOK.com
c) Vikas@vikas.in
d) **Aniruddha.Banerjee@ms.ind**

8. The ' Word Count ' in Google docs does not have one of the following options. Which one is it

a) Pages
b) **Paragraphs**
c) Characters
d) Word

9. To use exact same font type, size, and colour in the title of all the slides in a PowerPoint presentation, you will :

a) Use slide sorter
b) Use file master
c) Use format brush and make titles identical
d) **Use Slide Master**

10. The term GHz is an indicator of which feature of the computer?

a) Number of Pixels
b) Screen Resolution
c) **Speed**
d) Storage

11. Which of the following is an Open Sourced Software?

a) Android
b) Windows
c) Internet explorer
d) **Linux**

12. Technology could be used to connect a computer to a cell phone or headphone without any wires or special connectors.

a) Wifi
b) **Bluetooth**
c) Infrared
d) Cloud

13. ____is a valuable resource for career and business professionals to network; obtain resources and support; and build relationships with potential customers, clients, and partners.

a) Facebook
b) Twitter
c) **LinkedIn**
d) Instagram

14. Agriculture and Processed Food Products Export Development Authority was established by the Government of India in :

a) December, 1985
b) December, 1980
c) **February, 1986**
d) January, 1980

15. In case seized food article is perishable and is unfit for human consumption, the Food Safety Officer should:

a) Send the sample for analysis
b) **After giving notice in writing to FBO, destroy the same**
c) Destroy the same without notifying the FBO
d) Return the same to the FBO, after notifying him in writing

16. The full form of IUU fishing is

a) Illegal, Unreal and Unregulated
b) Imported, Unreported and Unregulated
c) **Illegal, Unreported and Unregulated**
d) Illegal, Unreported and Unregistered

17. BIS certification for drinking water is

a) Binding regulation
b) Obligatory standard
c) **Voluntary standard**
d) Mandatory standard

18. BIS is the National Standards body supported by

a) Ministry of Home Affairs
b) Ministry of Health and Quality of Life
c) Ministry of External Affairs
d) **Ministry of Consumer Affairs, Food and Public Distribution**

19. An important catalyst in the conception of the Codex Alimentarius Commission is

a) **International Dairy Federation**
b) United Nations Economic Commission for Europe
c) World Health Organization
d) Food and Agriculture Organization

20. The Food Authority Comprises of 22 members of which women shall make up to

a) Three fourth
b) **One-third**
c) Two-third
d) Half

21. The Designated officer performs the following functions except

a) Sanction and launch prosecution
b) Issuing and cancelling licenses of FBO's
c) **Seize any article of food**
d) Investigating any complaint against FSO's

22. As per the FSSA 2006 , purchase may have any food article analyzed by

a) **Informing the food business operator at the time of purchase of his intention**
b) Sending purchased food for analysis without informing the FBO
c) Sending two parts to the food safety officer
d) Dividing the sample into three parts

23. Which of the following is not a part of 'risk analyses'?

a) Risk assessment
b) Risk communication
c) **Risk prevention**
d) Risk management

24. Health is defined as a state of complete physical, mental and social well-being and not merely the absence of disease or infirmity by

a) **WHO**
b) UNESCO
c) FSSAI
d) FAO

25. Codex Standards are used to

a) Increase the revenue collection
b) Standardize the products by the manufactures
c) Protect the interest of the food manufactures
d) **Protect the health of the consumers and ensure fair practices in the food trade**

26. 'Adulterant' means

a) Any article obtained from a disease animal
b) Any coloring matter other than that prescribed
c) **Any material employed for the purpose of adulteration**
d) Any article containing any poisonous ingredient

27. The licensing authority for the manufacture of mineral water and packaged drinking water in India is

a) PFA
b) FPO
c) **BIS**
d) AGMARK

28. Maximum residue limits for individual pesticides in or on specific commodities is proposed by

a) JEMRA
b) MRA
c) JECFA
d) **JMPR**

29. The organization responsible for formulating Indian Standards for fresh and processed fish is

a) APEDA
b) MPEDA
c) AGMARK
d) **BIS**

30. Chairperson of the Food Authority should be well versed in the field of

a) Engineering
b) Social science
c) **Food Science**
d) Medicine

31. The Director of APEDA is appointed by

a) Central government
b) State government
c) Food Authority
d) **APEDA**

32. The full form of MRA is

a) **Microbiological Risk Assessment**
b) Marine Risk Assessment
c) Micro Risk Assessment
d) Major Risk Assessment

33. An autonomous commercial policy instrument, directed to promote and sustain mutual trade and to develop economic co-operation among countries is termed as

a) **Certificate of clearance**
b) Certificate of origin
c) Certificate of authenticity
d) Certificate of assurance

34. The function of MPDA is include

a) Making international trade easy
b) Provide infrastructural facilities for seafood import trade
c) Promotion of international marine products in Indian markets
d) **Inspection of marine products, its raw material, fixing standards and specifications**

35. "Risk Management" is a process that includes

a) Hazard identification
b) Interactive exchange of information and opinion
c) Hazard characterization
d) **Evaluation of policy alternatives**

36. "Food business" means

a) Sale of food or food ingredients for no profit
b) A person by whom the business is carried on
c) **Sale of food ingredients for profit or not and whether public or private**
d) Sale of food or food ingredients for profit

37. To promote safe and healthy food, FSSAI has launched a training toolkit for health under the scheme

a) Jaago Grahak jaago
b) Swachh Bharat
c) Satvik khaana
d) **Ayushman Bharat**

38. Dehradun-based Indian Institute of Petroleum has pilot tested to convert used cooking oil into:

a) Bio-ethanol
b) **Bio-aviation turbine fuel**
c) Bio-diesel
d) Bio-methanol

39. "Food" means any substance that is

a) Processed and intended for human consumption

b) Unprocessed and intended for human consumption

c) Genetically modified or engineered food intended for human consumption

d) **Processed or unprocessed which is intended for human consumption**

40. Trans fats can be avoided by

a) **Avoiding 'Vanaspati' ghee for Cooking**

b) Choosing meat and dairy products

c) Consumption of baked/processed foods like biscuits/fan, cake, and chips

d) Leaving food in the oil for a long time

41. 'Consumer' is defined as

a) **Persons and families purchasing and receiving food in order to meet their personal needs**

b) A single family that consumes food

c) Persons receiving food to sell or to meet their personal needs

d) A person who purchases food

42. Milk and Milk Product Order was promoted by the Government of India under the provisions of

a) Food safety and Standards Act

b) FSSAI

c) **Essential Commodities Act**

d) Ministry of Home Affairs

43. 'IFS Quick Access' is a system developed by

a) **FSSAI**

b) WHO

c) FAO

d) UNO

44. Third party private auditing of FBO will

a) More frequent regulatory inspections by central or state licensing authority

b) Increase the gap between regulators led enforcement and field level non-compliance

c) **Reduce the food safety inspections conducted by licensing authorities**

d) Facilitate free of cost auditing for FBO's

45. The project 'clean street food' is an initiative taken up under a 360° approach to

a) **Food Safety and Healthy Nutrition**

b) Safety

c) Food adulteration

d) Hygiene

46. 'Risk assessment' means a scientifically based process consisting of

a) 8 steps
b) **4 steps**
c) 10 steps
d) 6 step

47. The head office of FSSAI is situated in

a) Mumbai
b) Bangalore
c) **Delhi**
d) Chennai

48. 'Ingredient' means

a) An extraneous matter present in the final product
b) A substance that gets modified in the end product
c) **Any substance used to prepare food**
d) A food additive used in food preparation

49. A healthy food contains trans fatty acids content of

a) **<0.2 gram per serving**
b) < 1 gram per serving
c) >1 gram per serving
d) >0.2 gram per serving

50. A system integrating all Food Safety Standards and Regulations for providing quick access to vertical as well as horizontal standards called

a) **Indian Food Standards Quick Access**
b) FSSAI
c) FSSA
d) International Food Standards

51. The objective of clean street hub includes

a) Making eat out places free of crime
b) Making eat out places free of even teasers
c) **Rigorous implementation of hygiene and safety in the eat out places**
d) Popularizing Indian Cuisine

52. Online service, namely, the "Food Product Approval System" is developed to

a) Regulate manufacture, storage, distribution, sale and import of food article
b) **Identify if a food product requires approval from FSSAI**
c) Ensure safe and wholesome food for human consumption
d) Develop food standards, regulations, and guidelines

53. "Hazard" means a

a) Biological or chemical agent in food which can cause an adverse health effect
b) Biological or Physical agent in food which can cause an adverse health effect

c) Biological, chemical or physical agent in food which can be beneficial or may cause an adverse health effect

d) **Biological, chemical or physical agent in food which can cause an adverse health effect**

54. Authorities jointly responsible for implementation and enforcement of FSSA, 2006

a) FSSAI and central Food Authorities

b) FSSAI and FAO

c) WHO and FAO

d) **FSSAI and State Food Authorities**

55. Example of a 'commercially sterile' product is:

a) Pickles

b) **Canned foods**

c) Boiled milk

d) Fruit juices

56. The standard plate count is not applicable to

a) RTE foods which has only cooked ingredients

b) Deep fried products

c) **Fresh fruits and vegetables**

d) RTE food which has cooked ingredients and some added ingredients where no cooking process has been used

57. At temperatures above freezing, activities of food borne microorganisms can be:

a) Stopped

b) **Slow**

c) Rapid

d) Quick

58. Water soluble vitamins include:

a) Carotenoids

b) **Ascorbic acid**

c) Vitamin D

d) Vitamin K

59. Benzoic acid is mostly used to preserve colored products because:

a) Of its bleaching action

b) **It may darken the product**

c) Of its characteristics aroma

d) It may lighten the product

60. Excess glucose gets stored in liver in the form of

a) Glycogenesis

b) Glycolysis

c) Glucagon

d) **Glycogen**

61. Chemical preservatives is defined as a chemical compound that:

a) **Retard alterations caused by microorganisms in food**

b) Increase the nutritional value of fruit

c) Hasten ripening

d) Speeds up alternations caused by microorganisms in food

62. Fat soluble vitamin include

a) Vitamin C
b) Ascorbic acid
c) **Vitamin A**
d) B complex vitamins

63. Psychrophilic microorganisms grow over the temperature range of:

a) -23 to -29 °C
b) **Sub-zero to 20°C**
c) 0°C
d) >20°C

64. Radiation dose is defined as the:

a) Quantity of radiation energy liberated by the food when it passes through the radiation field during processing

b) Quantity of radiation energy scattered by the food when it passes through the radiation field during processing

c) **Quantity of radiation energy absorbed by the food when it passes through the radiation field during processing**

d) Quantity of radiation energy dispersed by the food when it passes through the radiation field during processing

65. The mineral found in hemoglobin is called as:

a) Sodium
b) Protein
c) **Iron**
d) Calcium

66. Asepsis is a process of

a) **Keeping microorganisms out**
b) Removal of microorganisms
c) Maintenance of anaerobic conditions
d) Adding chemicals

67. Sulphur dioxide is widely used to preserve:

a) Papads
b) **Nectar**
c) Cheese
d) Milk

68. Listeriosis is generally caused by:

a) Hepatitis A virus
b) ***L. monocytogenes***
c) Norovirus
d) *E.coli*

69. One of the major causes for food spoilage are

a) Lack of oxygen
b) Reaction with carbon dioxide
c) Stored at a very low temperature
d) **Gain or loss of moisture**

70. When a food spoils, its texture becomes slimy because of the:

a) Development of nitrogenous compounds

b) Chlorophyll breakdown

c) Development of sulphides

d) **Surface accumulation of microbial cells**

71. According to FSSA rules, class II preservatives includes:

a) Acetic acid
b) Dextrose
c) **Nisin**
d) Glucose

A process where food is first frozen at -18°C on trays and then under high vacuum is called as:

a) Quick freezing
b) Cryogenic freezing
c) **Freeze drying**
d) Dehydro-freezing

73. The "c" in "cGMP" stands for

a) Up to date
b) Commitment
c) **Current**
d) Content

74. Sulphur dioxide cannot be used to preserve naturally colored juices because of its

a) Characteristics flavor
b) Characteristics aroma
c) Liberation of CO2
d) **Bleaching action**

75. If a manufacturing comparing company does not adhere to CGMP regulations:

a) Any drug manufactured by such company will be considered " adulterated"

b) **No action will be taken, if the drugs are safe**

c) The company will be closed instantly

d) It means that there is necessarily something wrong with the drug

CHAPTER-7

State Nutrition Officer - Department of Health Services – 2023

1:-The statistical study of human populations.

A:-**Demography**
B:-Topography
C:-Human Development
D:-Anthropology

2:-The Sustainable Development Goals are:

A:-Ending poverty in all its forms everywhere

B:-Ending hunger, achieving food security, improving nutrition and promoting sustainable agriculture

C:-Ensuring healthy lives and promoting well-being for all at all ages

D:-**All of the above**

3:-The rate that defines the number of deaths of children before their first birthday.

A:-Morbidity
B:-**Infant mortality**
C:-Death rate
D:-Death ratio

4:-Tool to calculate hunger and malnutrition at the regional level in India

A:-Indian Hunger Index (IHI)

B:-**The India State Hunger Index (ISHI)**

C:-Hunger Index India (HII)

D:-Index of Hunger of India (IHI)

5:-What is the Human Development Index (HDI)?

A:-An index that measures development stages of human

B:-**An index that measures key dimensions of human development**

C:-An index that measures human growth

D:-An index that measures development of human body

6:-What is the infant mortality rate of Kerala?

A:-**Comparable to any developed nation.**

B:-Like any other under developed countries

C:-Like other developing countries

D:-Like other states of India

7:-Major areas of epidemiological study include

A:-Disease causation transmission and outbreak investigation

B:-Medical Camps, Disease survey and Investigation.

C:-Screening, biomonitoring and comparisons of treatment effects

D:-**Both (A) and (C)**

8:-What does NIN stands for

A:-National Index of Nutrition B:-**National Institute of Nutrition**

C:-Nutritional Index of Neonates D:-national Insurance for Nutrition

9:-The science of public health is termed as

A:-Public health care B:-**Epidemiology**

C:-Entomology D:-Pomology

10:-What is Gross Enrollment Ratio (GER)?

A:-**Socio economic indicators** B:-Medical status indicators

C:-Health indicator D:-Nutrition indicator

11:-The time spanning between conception and a baby's second birthday which is very crucial

A:-Infancy B:-**First 1000 days**

C:-Toddler D:-Childhood

12:-This scoring system provides a standardized assessment for infants after delivery

A:-**Apgar score** B:-IUGR score

C:-Z score D:-SD score

13:-DHA supplement in prenatal stage is important for

A:-Muscle development B:-Bone development

C:-**Brain development** D:-Vision development

14:-Extra calories required by the lactating women on a daily basis

A:-800 B:-200

C:-300 D:-**500**

15:-It is important to breast feed the neonate

A:-For muscle growth B:-Fat deposit

C:-To gain weight D:-**To boost immunity**

16:-This stimulates the Oxytocin release

A:-**Suckling of the baby** B:-Prolactin release

C:-Pituitary release D:-Making a fist by the baby

17:-The food that should be restricted during pregnancy?

A:-Chocolate B:-Crab and Fish

C:-Ice cream D:-**Rum and wine**

18:- Healthy snacks for Pre school children

A:-Burger
B:-Potatoes chips
C:-**Steamed banana**
D:-Wafers

19:-Pair below works together to help build up the bones of a developing baby

A:-Vitamin A and Calcium
B:-Vitamin B and Calcium
C:-**Vitamin D and Calcium**
D:-Vitamin C and Calcium

20:-An index that correlates with total body fat content or percent body fat, and is acceptable measure of adiposity or body fatness in children and adults.

A:-HI
B:-**BMI**
C:-BMR
D:-MUC

21:-ABCDE in community Nutrition means

A:-Anthropometry, Bioinformatics, Clinical, Dietary and Economical
B:-Anthropometry, Biophysical, Clinical, Dietary and Economical
C:-Anthropometry, Biological Economical, Clinical, Dietary and Economical
D:-**Anthropometry, Biochemical, Clinical, Dietary and Economical**

22:-Anthropometry is classified into two types

A:-Static and Diplomatic
B:-State and Dynamic
C:-**Static and Dynamic**
D:-Still and Dynamic

23:-What is the primary method of dietary assessment used in epidemiological studies?

A:-Diet recall
B:-Diet history
C:-**Food frequency questionnaire**
D:-Food intake interview

24:-Calculate the body mass index (BMI) for a patient whose height is 1.75 m and whose weight is 99 kg.

A:-42
B:-52
C:-62
D:-**32**

25:-A common anthropometric measure for infants is:

A:-Recumbent length
B:-Head circumference
C:-Skin fold
D:-Biceps

Correct Answer:-Question Cancelled

26:-Which of the following is the most frequently used anthorpometric measure to estimate body mass?

A:-**Body weight**
B:-Body volume
C:-Skin fold
D:-Head circumference

27:-Data from FAO food balance sheets can be used to determine

A:-Daily food consumption at an individual level
B:-Daily food consumption at a national level

C:-**Daily food availability for consumption at a national level**

D:-None of the above

28:-Which one of the following methods is a prospective method of dietary assessment?

A:-**Weighed food record** B:-24 Hour dietary recall

C:-Diet history D:-FFQ

29:-Duties of a dietician includes

A:-Creating healthy and nutritious diets for patients

B:-Advising eating healthy food

C:-Monitoring eating habits and diets of individual, family members or both

D:-**All of the above**

30:-This diet is a structured eating plan that restricts daily caloric intake, commonly for weight loss.

A:-**Low calorie diet** B:-High protein diet

C:-High calorie diet D:-Keto diet

31:-Food to be avoided by an obese person

A:-Leafy vegetables B:-Fruits

C:-**Red meat** D:-Milk

32:-The food that in the past people would get by hunting and gathering is also known as

A:-**Paleo diet** B:-Feingold diet

C:-Adams diet D:-Paste diet

33:-A process by which a health professional with special training in nutrition helps people make healthy food choices and form healthy eating habits

A:-Food counselling B:-Nutrition training

C:-**Nutrition counselling** D:-Balanced diet

34:-The method of feeding via the gastro intestinal track

A:-Parental feeding B:-**Enternal feeding**

C:-Breast feeding D:-Bottle feeding

35:-An eating pattern that cycles between periods of fasting and eating

A:-Fasting diet B:-**Intermitted fasting**

C:-30 days diet D:-Healthy diet

36:-A diet for weight loss

A:-**Ketogenic diet** B:-Feingold diet

C:-GFCF diet D:-DASH diet

37:-This survey is done to assess the quantities of food items and nutrients consumed by the family

A:-Diet record B:-Nutri survey

C:-Food records D:-**Family diet survey**

38:-To assess the food intake at institutional level there are two methods

A:-**Inventory method and actual weighment method**

B:-Institution method and survey method

C:-Inventory method and non inventory method

D:-Weighment method and non weighment method

39:- One of the aetiology of peptic ulcer

A:-**Stress** B:-High calorie food

C:-High protein food D:-Low calorie food

40:-Pathological changes may follow damage to the liver

A:-Fatty infiltration B:-Necrosis

C:-Cirrhosis D:-**All of the above**

41:-What is the full form of "INSIMP"?

A:-**Intensive Millets Promotion** B:-Indian Millets Promotion

C:-Intensive Millets Protection D:-Indian Millets Protection

42:-Name the millet nutrient that lowers cholesterol

A:-Vitamin C B:-Biotin

C:-**Niacin** D:-Vitamin A

43:-Who is considered as Father of Green Revolution in the World?

A:-William S Gaud B:-**Norman Borlaug**

C:-M.S. Swaminathan D:-John Bennet Lawes

44:-The national prophylaxis program against nutritional blindness is being implemented in the country since

A:-**1970** B:-1983

C:-1986 D:-1980

45:-What impact does globalisation have on food security?

A:-Globalisation truly has no impact on food security because agriculture is not covered by World Trade Organisation rules.

B:-Developing countries need to create publicly owned food reserves in order to realise the potential benefits.

C:-The only place where food and agriculture have seen globalisation so far is supermarkets.

D:-**Developing nations find it challenging to benefit from the potential of globalisation for enhancing food security because of subsidies and trade restrictions from wealthy nations.**

46:-In the NFHS-4 following information have been added?

A:-Migration in the context of HIV B:-Abortion

C:-Malaria prevention D:-**All of the above**

47:-Which states are called as Goiter belt in India?

A:-**Uttar Pradesh along the belt of Himalayas**

B:-Maharashtra and Madhya Pradesh

C:-Coastal areas of Karnataka and Kerala

D:-Coastal belts of Tamil Nadu and Andhra Pradesh

48:-First formal National Health Policy was formulated in

A:-1999 B:-1985

C:-**1983** D:-2000

49:-Under ICDS which of the following services are not delivered through the Anganwadi center?

A:-Growth monitoring

B:-**Sports training to children below 5 year**

C:-Nutritional supplement D:-Pre-school education

50:-Gomez classification of PEM is based on

A:-Height for age B:-**Weight for age**

C:-Weight for height D:-Mid arm circumference

51:-Recent techniques and advances in Food Preservation

A:-**Hurdle technology** B:-Mixed technology

C:-Stumbling technology D:-Multiple technology

52:-Organic acid used in food preservation include

A:-Nitric acid B:-Phophoric acid

C:-Hydrochloric acid D:-**Sorbic acid**

53:-The reason for food spoilage is

A:-Growth of microorganism such as bacteria, fungus etc.

B:-Autolysis

C:-Oxidation by air D:-**All of the above**

54:-Meat food products order 1973 was promoted under the act:

A:-Essential Service Maintenance Act

B:-Consumer Protection Act, 1986

C:-**Essential Commodities Act, 1955**

D:-Right to Food Act

55:-AGMARK Act 1937 comes under

A:-Department of Consumer Affairs, GOI

B:-**Directorate of Marketing and Inspection**

C:-Department of Legal Metrology

D:-Department of Agriculture and Cooperation

56:-What is an example of a biological hazard?

A:-***Salmonella***
B:-Antibiotics
C:-Pesticide
D:-Metallic objects

57:-Pasteurization of milk effectively kills all the following except:

A:-Fever organisms
B:-Tubercle bacilli
C:-Salmonella
D:-**Bacterial spores**

58:-*Clostridium perfinges* poisoning is associated with

A:-Canned food
B:-**Meat products**
C:-Vegetables
D:-Fish products

59:-What are the intrinsic factors for microbial growth?

A:-Moisture
B:-Redox potential
C:-pH
D:-**All of the above**

60:-Fortification means

A:-To add additives in processed food products
B:-**To add nutrients in food products**
C:-To add oil fat in food products
D:-All of the above

61:-The generic name of polysaccharides is

A:-Pentoses
B:-Cellulose
C:-**Glycans**
D:-Glucans

62:-Inulin is a polymer of

A:-**Fructose**
B:-Glucose
C:-Lactose
D:-Galactose

63:-The ratio of amino acids converted to proteins to the ratio of amino acids supplied, is called as

A:-**NPU**
B:-PER
C:-Biological value
D:-Nitrogen balance

64:-Two chain of DNA are formed by

A:-Sugar deoxy ribulose and sulphate
B:-Sugar and zinc
C:-**Sugar deoxyribose and phosphate**
D:-Copper and deoxyribose

65:-Under anaerobic condition of glycolysis pyruvic acid is converted to

A:-Pyruvic acid
B:-**Lactic acid**
C:-Citric acid
D:-Glucose

66:-Fatty acids are oxidized in the

A:-**Mitochondria** B:-Cytoplast

C:-Lysosome D:-None of the above

67:-During fasting, glucose is phosphorylated mainly by

A:-Glucokinase B:-**Hexokinase**

C:-Both (a) and (b) D:-None of the above

68:-Which of the following substances is being separated using gas-solid chromatography?

A:-Thermally stable organic components

B:-Volatile organic components

C:-Thermally stable inorganic components

D:-**Low molecular weight gaseous species**

69:-Menke's disease is due to an abnormality in the metabolism of

A:-Iron B:-Manganese

C:-Magnesium D:-**Copper**

70:-Dietary fiber denotes

A:-Undigested proteins

B:-**Plant cell components that cannot be digested by own enzymes**

C:-All plant cell wall components

D:-All non-digestible water insoluble polysaccharide

71:-Applied nutrition programme was aided by

A:-UNICEF B:-FAO

C:-WHO D:-**All the above**

72:-_______ provides the clearest picture of acute malnutrition in a population at a specific point in time.

A:-Weight for Age B:-Height for Age

C:-**Weight for Height** D:-All the above

73:- DASH diet is recommended for patients with

A:-Diabetes B:-Cancer

C:-**Hypertension** D:-Acute Respiratory Distress

74:-Which method is suitable for a small group of mothers to present a situation illustrating how they deal with malnourished children?

A:-Problem Solving Method B:-**Role Play Method**

C:-Discussion Decision Method D:-None

75:-Applied nutrition programme was aided by

A:-UNICEF B:-FAO

C:-WHO D:-**All the above**

76:-National Program for Prevention and Control of Cancer, Diabetes, Cardiovascular Diseases and Stroke (NPCDCS) was launched in

A:-2009 B:-2011

C:-**2010** D:-2012

77:-Vitamin A prophylaxis Programme recommended a dose of ________ Vitamin A for children in age group of 1-5 years.

A:-0.3 million IU B:-0.1 million IU

C:-0.4 million IU D:-**0.2 million IU**

78:-Match the year of intervention programmes of malnutrition ICDS

(i) 1971 SNP **(ii)** 1975 WNP

(iii) 1986 MDM **(iv)** 1956

A:-**(ii), (i), (iv), (iii)** B:-(i), (ii), (iii), (iv)

C:-(ii), (i), (iii), (iv) D:-(i), (ii), (iv), (iii)

79:-Message circulated in the form of letter among the intended group of receivers

A:-Announcement letter B:-Calendar

C:-**Circular letter** D:-Leaflet

80:-Which statement is incorrect?

A:-**Discussion is an unorganized conversation**

B:-Discussion promote socialized interaction

C:-Get possible solutions

D:-Leadership and participation are two essential characteristics of discussion

81:-High altitude leads to

A:-Acute Mountain Sickness

B:-High Altitude Pulmonary Oedema

C:-High Altitude Cerebral Oedema

D:-**All the above**

82:-Sports persons have to consume ________ fruits and vegetables.

A:-**500-700 g** B:-250-500 g

C:-700-900 g D:-100-200 g

83:-Catabolic hormones are _______ during and after space flight.

A:-Altered B:-No change

C:-Decreased D:-**Increased**

84:-For athletes all these drugs are banned except

A:-**Amino acids** B:-Anabolic Steroids

C:-Beta 2 Agonists D:-Diuretics

85:-Among the techniques used to assess body composition which has the lowest standard error of estimate.

A:-Hydrodensitometry
B:-Skinfold
C:-Bioelectric Impedance Analysis
D:-**DXA**

86:-For long lasting events ________ pathway provides primary fuel.

A:-Glycolytic
B:-Non oxidative
C:-**Oxidative**
D:-Phosphagen

87:-At high altitude intake of carbohydrate need to be

A:-Low
B:-**High**
C:-Moderate
D:-Adequate

88:-Type of beverage most suitable for sports persons 1-2 hour before activity

A:-**Plain cold water**
B:-Diluted fruit juice
C:-Glucose
D:-Electrolyte drink

89:-Which of the following is not true related to food handling in emergencies?

A:-Type of disaster
B:-Duration of disaster
C:-**Nutritional status of population following disaster**
D:-Size of disaster affected area

90:-For athletes who are physically very active fluid requirements are increased from

A:-5-10 L/day
B:-5 L/day
C:-5 to 16 L/day
D:-15 L/day

Correct Answer:-Question Cancelled

91:-Which is a variable associated with control group?

(i) Independent variable
(ii) Dependent variable
(iii) Effect
(iv) Criterion variable

A:-**(ii), (iii), (iv)**
B:-(i), (ii), (iii)
C:-(i), (iii), (iv)
D:-(ii), (iii), (i)

92:-In which type of interview free environment is given to respondents so that they can express their views freely and the interviewer simply supports the views expressed by the respondent instead of approving or disapproving them?

A:-Focussed interview
B:-Clinical interview
C:-**Non-directive interview**
D:-Structured interview

93:-_______ deals with different meaning of words.

A:-Syntactics
B:-Diction
C:-Grammar
D:-**Semantics**

94:-Choose the ethical problems in research

(i) Beneficence
(ii) Breach of confidentiality
(iii) Plagiarism
(iv) Coercion

A:-(i), (ii), (iv)
B:-(i), (ii), (iii)
C:-**(ii), (iii), (iv)**
D:-(i), (iii), (iv)

95:- Correct sequence in steps of research process

A:-**Validated findings-peer review-Addition to the pool of knowledge**
B:-Addition to the pool of knowledge-peer review-validated findings
C:-Peer review - Validated findings - Addition to the pool of knowledge
D:-Peer review - Addition to the pool of knowledge - Validated findings

96:-Method of collection of data to obtain accuracy in recording the scores

A:-Reliability
B:-Generalisation
C:-Validity
D:-**Objectivity**

97:-Which of the following steps in research are least vulnerable to ethics in research?

(i) Data Collection Procedure
(ii) Data Analysis Procedure
(iii) Defining research variables
(iv) Identify research variables

A:-**(iii), (iv)**
B:-(i), (ii)
C:-(ii), (iv)
D:-(i), (iv)

98:-Sampling which is useful when we are trying to reach population that are inaccessible or hard to find

A:-Quota sampling
B:-Stratified sampling
C:-**Snowball sampling**
D:-Multistage sampling

99:-Which statement on peer review is true?

A:-A method of typesetting in publishing
B:-Process of peer review ensures that a scientific paper is correct
C:-Process by which scientists friends can give advice
D:-**Process by which independent scientists evaluate the technical merit of scientific research**

100:-Choose the correct sequence of steps involved in case study

i. Collecting background information
ii. Determining the present status
iii. Instituting remedial action
iv. Testing the suggested hypothesis

A:-(i), (ii), (iii), (iv)
B:-(ii), (i), (iii), (iv)
C:-(i), (ii), (iv), (iii)
D:-**(ii), (i), (iv), (iii)**

CHAPTER-8

Meghalaya FSO – 2023

PART—A : GENERAL ENGLISH & GENERAL KNOWLEDGE

Directions (Q. Nos. 1–5) : Fill in the blanks with the appropriate preposition from the options given.

1. The telephone and the doorbell rang ______ the same time.

(A) at
(B) in
(C) on
(D) by

2. He is not interested ______ sports and games.

(A) of
(B) by
(C) for
(D) in

3. Is there anything interesting ______ the paper today?

(A) from
(B) on
(C) in
(D) by

4. It is very risky to enter ______ partnership with an unknown person.

(A) with
(B) into
(C) on
(D) to

5. There are tall coconut trees ______ the river.

(A) over
(B) at
(C) along
(D) on

Directions (Q. Nos. 6–10) : In these questions, out of four alternatives given, choose the one which best expresses the meaning of the underlined word.

6. Some people believe that the Third World War is imminent.

(A) possible
(B) likely
(C) certain
(D) impending

7. There were intermittent power cuts in the city on Sunday.

(A) prolonged
(B) continual
(C) sporadic
(D) intervening

8. The car engine has been subjected to exhaustive tests.

(A) complicated
(B) thorough
(C) exclusive
(D) compulsory

9. I have serious misgivings about taking this job.

(A) doubts
(B) objections
(C) fear
(D) difficulties

10. The police have confiscated a large consignment of contraband.

(A) destroyed
(B) seized
(C) grasped
(D) stopped

Directions (Q. Nos. 11–15) : In these questions, out of four alternatives given, choose the one which is opposite in meaning of the underlined word.

11. He is showing signs of senility.

(A) virility
(B) maturity
(C) laziness
(D) exhaustion

12. The speaker had a superficial knowledge of the subject.

(A) artificial
(B) deep
(C) overt
(D) judicious

13. There is always ambiguity in what he says.

(A) lucidity
(B) clarity
(C) transparency
(D) plainness

14. His evasive replies intrigued the investigating officer.

(A) frank
(B) respectful
(C) astonishing
(D) confused

15. They approached the stranger warily.

(A) suspiciously
(B) cautiously
(C) carefully
(D) carelessly

Directions (Q. Nos. 16–25) : Choose the correct meaning for the words or phrases and idioms given below.

16. Rancour means

(A) bitterness
(B) energy
(C) fatigue
(D) tolerance

17. Congenital means

(A) expensive
(B) yielding
(C) industrious
(D) existing at birth

18. Brazen means

(A) pious
(B) shameless
(C) hasty
(D) lethargic

19. Cajole means

(A) to scorn (B) to scold

(C) to coax (D) to ridicule

20. Clandestine means

(A) visualize (B) secret

(C) locate (D) surplus

21. Through thick and thin means

(A) under all conditions (B) thin and fat

(C) large object (D) big and small

22. Take exception to means

(A) difficult (B) different

(C) object to (D) to take with difficulty

23. A white elephant means

(A) elephant with white skin (B) a costly thing

(C) a costly but useful thing (D) a costly but useless thing

24. Put two and two together means

(A) make a formal statement (B) take great care

(C) draw a logical conclusion (D) count very well

25. Sitting on the fence means

(A) unbalanced (B) uncomfortable

(C) coward (D) between two opinions

26. 'Satyameva Jayate' means

(A) the truth alone prevails (B) the truth alone triumphs

(C) only the truth will be established

(D) strive for the truth

27. Which State is *not* included under the Sixth Schedule?

(A) Tripura (B) Assam

(C) Meghalaya (D) Nagaland

28. Which is the first State in India to have water policy?

(A) Gujarat (B) Maharashtra

(C) Assam (D) Meghalaya

29. Which planet in the solar system is called as the green planet?

(A) Earth (B) Pluto

(C) Uranus (D) Venus

30. The State of Meghalaya was created by

(A) the Meghalaya Reorganization Act, 1970

(B) the Assam Reorganization (Meghalaya) Act, 1969

(C) the Sixth Schedule

(D) the North-Eastern Areas (Reorganization) Act, 1971

31. The current President of India (2024) is the

(A) 15th President (B) 16th President

(C) 20th President (D) 21st President

32. World's highest waterfall is the

(A) Angel Falls (B) Victoria Falls

(C) Niagara Falls (D) Jog Falls

33. Match List–I with List–II and select the correct answer using the codes given below the Lists :

	List–I		**List–II**
a.	United Nations	1.	The Secretariat
b.	Sustainable Development Goals	2.	Gender Equality
c.	World Health Organization	3.	1948
d.	International Covenant on Civil and Political Rights	4.	Multilateral treaty

Codes :

	a	**b**	**c**	**d**
(A)	1	2	3	4
(B)	3	4	2	1
(C)	4	3	1	2
(D)	1	3	4	2

34. What is the local name of the Elephants Falls?

(A) Phan Nonglait (B) Kshaid-Lai-Pateng

(C) Kshaid Hati (D) Kshaid Weinia

35. Which is the smallest district in Meghalaya?

(A) Eastern West Khasi Hills (B) South West Garo Hills

(C) South West Khasi Hills (D) West Garo Hills

36. Match List–I with List–II and select the correct answer using the codes given below the Lists :

	List–I		**List–II**
a.	Solar system	1.	Nicolaus Copernicus

	List–I		List–II
b.	Satellites of Jupitar	2.	Galileo Galilei
c.	Earth-centered Universe	3.	Ptolemy
d.	Laws of Planetary Motion	4.	Kepler

Codes :

	a	b	c	d
(A)	1	2	3	4
(B)	1	3	4	2
(C)	2	1	3	4
(D)	3	4	2	1

37. How many minutes does sunlight take to reach the Earth?

(A) 17.3 (B) 20

(C) 8.20 (D) 25.5

38. When was the Election Commission of India founded?

(A) 26th January, 1950 (B) 15th August, 1947

(C) 25th January, 1950 (D) 26th November, 1949

39. The first electronic voting machine was used in

(A) Delhi, 1950 (B) Gujarat, 1982

(C) Maharashtra, 1970 (D) Kerala, 1982

40. Viksit Bharat@2047 is

(A) to celebrate 100 years of Independence

(B) to make India a developed nation

(C) to empower the youth (D) to eradicate poverty

41. The first woman ruler of Delhi Sultanate was

(A) Razia Sultana (B) Mumtaz Mahal

(C) Chand Bibi (D) Jihanara

42. Who is the author of the book, *Discovery of India*?

(A) Mahatma Gandhi (B) Jawaharlal Nehru

(C) APJ Abdul Kalam (D) Rabindranath Tagore

43. Fundamental Rights are enshrined in which part of the Constitution of India?

(A) Part IV (B) Part III

(C) Part II (D) Part V

44. Who is considered as the Father of Indian Constitution?

(A) Dr. B. R. Ambedkar
(B) Dr. Rajendra Prasad
(C) Mahatma Gandhi
(D) Jawaharlal Nehru

45. Durand Line is the boundary line between

(A) India and Pakistan
(B) Pakistan and Afghanistan
(C) India and China
(D) India and Bhutan

46. Which planet is closest to the Sun?

(A) Venus
(B) Earth
(C) Mars
(D) Mercury

47. Which country won the ICC Men's Cricket World Cup 2023?

(A) India
(B) Australia
(C) South Africa
(D) New Zealand

48. Headquarter of World Health Organization is located at

(A) New York
(B) Geneva
(C) Paris
(D) Washington D.C.

49. The currency of Japan is

(A) Dollar
(B) Euro
(C) Yen
(D) Renminbi

50. Sound cannot travel through

(A) Solid
(B) Liquid
(C) Gas
(D) Vacuum

PART—B : FOOD SAFETY STANDARDS & NUTRITION

51. Rheology is the science of

(A) flow and deformation of matter
(B) energy of cosmic ray
(C) environmental pollution
(D) microbiology

52. The cereals, potato and pasta group is a good source of

(A) carbohydrate
(B) vitamin C
(C) calcium
(D) vitamin D

53. Curcumin content in turmeric is determined by using

(A) HPLC only
(B) UV-visible spectrophotometer only
(C) HPLC and UV-VIS spectrophotometer
(D) None of the above

54. Which is *not* involved in dehydration system?

(A) Freeze drying
(B) Vacuum drum drying
(C) Suspended drying
(D) Gamma rays

55. Which of the following has highest calorific value?

(A) Vitamins
(B) Carbohydrates
(C) Fats
(D) Proteins

56. In the SI unit, the unit of density is

(A) g/m^2
(B) kg/cm^2
(C) kg/m^3
(D) None of the above

57. The water activity is measured on a scale of range

(A) 0 to 100
(B) 0 to 14
(C) 0 to 1
(D) 32 to 540

58. Viscosity is a property of

(A) fluid
(B) liquid
(C) gas
(D) All of the above

59. For zero order reaction, the rate with time is

(A) constant
(B) increasing
(C) decreasing
(D) All of the above

60. Food products manufactured using extrusion usually have

(A) high fat content
(B) low starch content
(C) high starch content
(D) high fat and protein content

61. Food additives are used in food processing for

(A) increasing the shelf life
(B) flavour and smell
(C) texture and preservative
(D) All of the above

62. The name of the useful bacteria to produce Beer is

(A) *Acetobacter cerevisiae*
(B) *E.coli*
(C) *Bacillus pumilus*
(D) *Aspergillus oryzae*

63. Niacin is

(A) used in food preservation at high temperature
(B) used in food preservation by fermentation
(C) used in food preservation by irradiation
(D) vitamin B_3

64. Sodium chloride is

(A) organic preservative
(B) class I preservative
(C) Both (A) and (B) are correct
(D) None of the above

65. Which is *not* correct about pasteurization?

(A) Pasteurization is a relatively mild heat treatment process to inactivate enzyme and destroying a large population of vegetative bacterial cell

(B) All pasteurized milk products shall be cooled immediately to temperature of 10 °C or less to prevent multiplication of surviving bacteria

(C) Pasteurized milk should show negative phosphatase test

(D) All of the above

66. A simple method to calculate the relative masses of two materials, that are required to form a mixture of known composition, is the

(A) red square (B) blue square

(C) Pearson square (D) Redyson square

67. The thermal conductivity of food is influenced by

(A) the nature of the food, e.g., cell structure, the amount of air trapped between the cells

(B) moisture content

(C) the temperature and pressure of the surrounding

(D) All of the above

68. Which of the following is *not* a proactive preventive approach to food safety and quality management?

(A) GMP (B) HACCP

(C) TQM (D) FPO

69. Which of the following statements is false about fermented bamboo shoot?

(A) Low in fat and cholesterol

(B) Very high in potassium, carbohydrate and dietary fibre

(C) Rich in vitamins, amino acids and anti-oxidants

(D) Contains high trans fat

70. Tetra pack uses

(A) aseptic packaging technology (B) sun drying

(C) modified atmospheric packaging (D) None of the above

71. Three roles of a manager are

(A) leadership, informational, decision making

(B) misbehaviour, misleading, hiding of documents

(C) good political relation, good listener, good decision making

(D) None of the above

72. Food quality management programme is based on

(A) food quality control with R & D (B) product evaluation

(C) food laws (D) All of the above

73. National Institute of Food Technology Entrepreneurship and Management (NIFTEM) is the brainchild of

(A) The Ministry of Food Processing Industries, Govt. of India

(B) The Ministry of Agriculture, Govt. of Punjab

(C) The Ministry of Commerce, Govt. of Meghalaya

(D) The Ministry of Science and Technology, Govt. of India

74. Which of the following *does not* characterize business activity?

(A) Practice of goods and services (B) Presence of risk

(C) Sales or exchange of goods and services

(D) Salary or wages

75. Wine is a

(A) fermented product (B) fried product

(C) dry product (D) All of the above

76. Food biotechnology means

(A) application of modern genetics, enzymatic, metabolic and systems based biochemical process of food and food related biological systems

(B) food related business

(C) (A) is false but (B) is true (D) None of the above

77. Probiotics, prebiotics and symbiotics are

(A) antioxidants (B) binding agents

(C) nutraceuticals (D) None of the above

78. Which is biotechnological milestone?

(A) Before 6000 BC : Leavening of bread, alcoholic beverages and vinegar from fermented juice

(B) 19th century : Ethanol acetic acid production, sewage treatment, Baker's yeast

(C) 2004 : genetically modified food on market

(D) All are true

79. Find the false one :

(A) Enzymes produced by biotechnology are used in food production and food processing.

(B) Food biotechnology has revolutionized not just the quantity but also the quality of our food supply allowing for enhancement of essential nutrient in everyday diet.

(C) Food biotechnology enhances our economy.

(D) Food biotechnology retards our economy.

80. Which of the following acids is present in vinegar?

(A) Citric (B) Acetic

(C) Tartaric (D) Lactic

81. Which type of food industry would *not* be suitable for Meghalaya?

(A) Dairy industry (B) Wine industry

(C) Natto industry (D) Poultry and meat processing

82. For economic evaluation of Food Plant Operation Management, which of the following is most important?

(A) Past experience
(B) Feasibility study
(C) Comparable facilities
(D) All of the above

83. Food processing in India is concentrated maximum in which sector?

(A) Organized sector
(B) Unorganized sector
(C) Small-scale sector
(D) None of the above

84. What will be the concentration of nitric acid in mole per litre in a sample which has density 1.41 gm $L^{-1}$and the mass percent of nitric acid if being 69%?

(A) 15.44 %
(B) 15.44 N
(C) 15.44 M
(D) 44.15 M

85. Natural vinegar is produced from alcohol by

(A) yeast
(B) mould
(C) bacteria
(D) yeast and bacteria

86. You buy a packet of homogenized toned milk from the market. Homogenization is a process of

(A) filtration
(B) mixing
(C) extraction
(D) All of the above

87. The residual extract for alcoholic beverages is 50 by FSSAI standard. The analysis report of your sample is found as 112. It is due to

(A) filtration defect
(B) distillation defect
(C) evaporation defect
(D) None of the above

88. The Maillard Browning reaction occurs between

(A) sugar and protein
(B) fat and sugar
(C) fat and protein
(D) sugar and water

89. Refrigeration is a process keeping food close to freezing point between

(A) 0°C and 4°C
(B) -18°C and -35°C
(C) 212 K and 270 K
(D) 5°F and 20°F

90. Causes for spoilage of food are

(A) bacteria, mould and yeast
(B) moisture, light and temperature
(C) chemical reactions
(D) All of the above

91. "Processing of food is a segment of manufacturing industry that transforms animal, plant and marine material into intermediate or finished value added food products that are safer to eat." The above statement is

(A) true
(B) false
(C) partially false
(D) partially true

92. Which of the following sentences are true?

1. Sucrose is a reducing sugar.
2. Iron acts as pro-oxidant in vegetable oil.
3. Beta carotene is a precursor of Vitamin E.
4. Saccharine is an artificial sweetener.

(A) 2 and 4 are true (B) 1 and 3 are true

(C) 1 and 2 are false (D) None of the above

93. Which is *not* true about microwave?

(A) Microwave is a radiowave

(B) Frequency ranging from 300 MHz to 300 GHz

(C) Wavelength ranges from 1 mm to around 30 cm

(D) It is used in food cooking

94. The name of the Central Cabinet Minister of Food Processing Industry of India is

(A) Shri Kiren Rijiju (B) Smt. Anita Praveen

(C) Sushri Shobha Karandlaje (D) None of them

95. Foods that have high trans fat are

(A) Margerine, Vanaspati

(B) fried foods and bakery products such as cakes, biscuits and pies

(C) All of the above

(D) None of the above

96. Which is the odd about the quality system in food industry?

(A) HACCP certification (B) ISO : 22000 : 2005

(C) International Food Standard, IFS (1999)

(D) ONGC

97. Residues of pesticides, heavy metals and antibiotics in food affect

(A) public health (B) economically

(C) Both (A) and (B) (D) None of the above

98. Food safety depends on what?

(A) Farm to fork (B) Personal hygiene

(C) Use of safe water and raw materials

(D) All of the above

99. What is the biggest threat to food safety?

(A) Bacteria (B) Residue

(C) Food additive (D) Machinery

100. The prime authority of food safety in India is

(A) BIS (B) FPO

(C) FSSAI (D) ISRO

101. 0.005% is equal to

(A) 50ppm (B) 50 ppb

(C) 0.5ppm (D) 0.005ppb

102. By FSSAI regulations mustard oil can be blended with

(A) rice bean oil (B) any other edible oil

(C) no other edible oil (D) None of the above

103. The equation $ax^2 + bx + c = 0$ is a

(A) non-linear polynomial equation (B) quadratic equation

(C) binomial equation (D) None of the above

104. Which one of the following is used as catalyst in hydrogenation of oil?

(A) Cu (B)Ni

(C) Cd (D) Fe

105. Which of the following is a balanced chemical equation?

(A) $H_2 + O_2 = H_2O$ (B) $H_2 + O_2 = 2H_2O$

(C) $2H_2 + O_2 = 2H_2O$ (D) $H + O = H_2O$

106. Which of the following is *not* related to agriculture?

(A) Green Revolution (B) White Revolution

(C) French Revolution (D) Blue Revolution

107. M. S. Swaminathan was an Indian

(A) agricultural scientist (B) space scientist

(C) physicist (D) chemist

108. The major crops of Meghalaya are

(A) fruits and vegetables, spices, ornamental plants

(B) fruits and vegetables, spices

(C) All of the above (D) None of the above

109. Lakadong turmeric is famous for

(A) highest 7.4% curcumin content (B) high heat conductivity

(C) low antioxidant (D) low reduction rate

110. Rice is a

(A) staple food (B) protein-rich food

(C) vitamin-rich food (D) All of the above

111. Drone bee is used in agriculture sector including

(A) crop mapping (B) pest management

(C) soil analysis, irrigation (D) All of the above

112. Which of the following are used to prevent germination of fungal spores?

(A) Fungicides (B) Insecticides

(C) Nematicides (D) Acaricides

113. The pH of soil for orange cultivation should be

(A) 6.5 to 7.5 (B) more than 7.5

(C) less than 6.5 (D) above 10

114. Which of the following cholesterols is referred to as good cholesterol?

(A) HDL : LDL (B) HDL

(C) LDL (D) None of the above

115. The standard saponification value of mustard oil by FSSAI regulation is

(A) 187 to 196 (B) 168 to 177

(C) not more than 6 (D) 58.6 to 61.7

116. The common forms of DNA technology include

(A) DNA sequencing polymerase chain reaction, DNA cloning and gel electrophoresis

(B) chain initiation, propagation and termination

(C) All of the above (D) None of the above

117. Pectinolytic enzymes are produced by

(A) biotechnology (B) radiation

(C) mechanical flow technology (D) nickel catalyst

118. Biological importance of gluconic acid is

(A) that it imparts a refreshing sour taste in many food items such as wine and juice

(B) as chelating micronutrients

(C) Both (A) and (B) (D) None of the above

119. Bt brinjal is

(A) genetically modified brinjal (B) natural brinjal

(C) hybrid brinjal (D) None of the above

120. Bioresource Development Centre (BRDC), Meghalaya is working for

(A) biotechnological opportunity (B) green economy

(C) green technology (D) All of the above

121. The efficiency (adequacy) of pasteurization of milk is tested by

(A) Phosphatase test (B) Ring test

(C) Buffer test (D) None of the above

122. Milk is the poor source of

(A) Calcium (B) Vitamin C

(C) Vitamin B (D) Vitamin D

123. Main composition of synthetic milk is

(A) water, detergent, vegetable oil and urea

(B) water, proteins and fats

(C) All of the above (D) None of the above

124. Lactose is

(A) milk sugar (B) monosaccharide

(C) polysaccharide (D) None of the above

125. The food components that are essential to maintain the health and contribute to the growth of the body are known as

(A) starch (B) nutrients

(C) vitamin (D) scurvy

126. The feeding intensity of fish determined by calculating gastro-somatic index is equal to

(A) (Weight of the stomach content/weight of the fish) X 100

(B) rate of growth of fish

(C) weight loss by fish (D) None of the above

127. Fish oil is an excellent source of

(A) vitamin C (B) omega-3 fatty acid

(C) calcium (D) iron

128. Formaldehyde is used as preservative for

(A) edible fish (B) biological specimen in laboratory

(C) meat (D) milk

129. Scientists grouped fish into

(A) four main types (B) three main types

(C) two main types (D) five main types

130. Ramsar site in North-East India is

(A) Deepor Beel in Assam (B) Loktak Lake in Manipur

(C) Rudrasagar Lake in Tripura (D) All of the above

131. What is the production process for a single food product?

(A) Batch production (B) Mass production

(C) Continuous-flow production (D) One-off production

132. Who developed frozen food in 1929?

(A) Clarence Seedorf (B) Clarence Birdseye

(C) Nicolas Appert (D) Nicolas Anelka

133. Which instrument measures calories?

(A) Barometer
(B) Thermometer
(C) Odometer
(D) Calorimeter

134. What does MAP stand for?

(A) Modified Atmospheric Packaging
(B) Mixed Additional Packaging
(C) Mild Air Packaging
(D) Mother's Apple Pie

135

138. Obesity occurs

(A) when person's body mass index (BMI) is 25 or above
(B) by doing too much of physical activity
(C) due to unhealthy eating behaviour
(D) All of the above

139. Deficiency of iron causes

(A) anaemia
(B) rickets
(C) night blindness
(D) pellagra

140. Fortified rice in India is fortified with

(A) iodine, vitamin A and vitamin B
(B) calcium, vitamin C and vitamin K
(C) iron, folic acid and vitamin B12
(D) copper, iron and zinc

141. The science most associated with the study of plant grown for food or beautification is

(A) agronomy
(B) forestry
(C) horticulture
(D) physics

142. Which soil particles are the smallest?

(A) Clay
(B) Rock
(C) Sand
(D) Silt

143. The standard for iodine content of iodized salt at consumer level is

(A) 15–30 ppm
(B) 10 ppm
(C) 120 ppm
(D) None of the above

144. Temperature is a factor of

(A) forest
(B) wind
(C) climate
(D) None of the above

145. Mission for integrated development of horticulture (MIDH) is a

(A) centrally sponsored scheme
(B) state sponsored scheme
(C) public-private partnership (PPP) scheme
(D) None of the above

146. The Food Safety and Standards Act, 2006 (Act no. 34 of 2006) received the assent of the President of India on

(A) 26 January, 2006
(B) 15 August, 2006
(C) 23 August, 2006
(D) 28 February, 2007

147. The tolerance limit in cases of pesticides for which MRL have not been fixed is to be considered as

(A) 0.01mg/kg
(B) 0.001 mg/kg
(C) 0.001ppm
(D) 0.001 ppp

148. The fatty acid profile of vegetable oil can be determined by

(A) gas chromatography with FID detector
(B) gas chromatography with ECD detector
(C) ICP-MS
(D) electrometer

149. Under which Section of Food Safety and Standards Act, 2006, a purchaser may analyse the food sample by the food analyst?

(A) Section 40
(B) Section 94
(C) Section 95
(D) Section 101

150. National Accreditation Board of Testing and Calibration Laboratory (NABL) follows the guideline of

(A) ISO/IEC 17025:2017
(B) BIS
(C) FSSAI
(D) None of the above

CHAPTER-9

JPSC Food Safety Officer – 2024 (Paper – I)

1. The working surface of the vending cart should be at least placed above the ground of:

(a) 50 - 60 cm (c) 70 - 80 cm

(d) 80 - 100 cm S1.

2. Which of the following is a compulsory type of legislation?

(a) ISI (b) ISO

(c) FFA (d) All of the above

3. 'Food-o-copeia' is for the purpose of:

(a) Providing standard recipes of 1000 food dishes

(b) Providing reference to food business operators and consumers

(c) Providing information about food standards to consumers

(d) Providing the nutritional contents of food in a manual

4. As per FSS regulations, iron fortified common salt shall be sold only in high-density polyethylene bag of density _____ kg/m^3.

(a) 100 (b) 200

(c) 300 (d) 400

5. Which type of certification is required for organic food products in India?

(a) FSSAI certification (b) ISO 9001 certification

(c) AGMARK certification **(d) India organic certification**

6. If any person or food business operator (except the persons exempted), himself or by any other person on his behalf, who is required to obtain license, manufactures, sells, stores, distributes, or imports any article of food without a license, shall be punishable with imprisonment for a period up to _____ months and a fine up to _____ lakh rupees respectively.

(a) 6, 4 (b) 5, 6

(c) 6, 5 (d) 5, 5

7. When did India become a member of Codex Alimentarius Commission?

(a) 1964 (b) 1968

(c) 1971 (d) 1973

8. What is the purpose of "food recall" in food safety?

(a) To promote a specific brand of food product

(b) To track the sales history of a food items

(c) To remove potentially unsafe food products from the market

(d) To encourage consumers to buy a specific product

9. What does proper labelling inform about food product to consumer and who provides it?

(a) Safe to eat, Third Party Auditor

(b) Safe for consumption, Food Inspector

(c) Safe for consumption, Food Manufacturer

(d) Safe to eat, Retailer

10. Who among the following may, by notification, appoint such persons possessing the qualifications prescribed by the Central Government as he thinks fit, as Food Analysts for such local areas as may be assigned to him by the Commissioner of Food Safety?

(a) Designated Officer (b) Food Safety Officer

(c) Assistant Food Commissioner **(d) Food Commissioner**

11. Bitterness in citrus juices is due to the presence of:

(a) Catechin (b) Isocaumarin

(c) Lecithin **(d) Limonene**

12. Which of the following is not a mandatory requirement for food labelling under the FSS Act?

(a) Name of food product (b) List of ingredients

(c) Net quantity **(d) Date of manufacture or expiry**

13. Potassium metabisulphide is not used for preserving pomegranate juice because:

(a) Of its characteristic aroma **(b) Of its bleaching action**

(c) It may solidify the product (d) It may lighten the product

14. The food business operators exempted from licensing and punishment for carrying out a business without license include:

(a) A petty manufacturer who himself manufactures or sells any article of food

(b) A petty retailer, hawker, itinerant vendor or a temporary stall holder

(c) Small scale or cottage or such other industries relating to food business or tiny food business operator

(d) All of the above S14.

15. As per FSS regulations, the minimum percentage of fat in the cream should be:

(a) 15 (b) 20

(c) 25 (d) 45

16. Who issues 'Eco mark' certificate?

(a) Ministry of Environment **(b) Bureau of Indian Standards**

(c) Ministry of Commerce (d) Ministry of Consumers Affairs

17. The online service, "Food Product Approval System" is developed to:

(a) Regulate import and sale of food articles

(b) Identify if a food product requires approval from FSSAI

(c) Food standards and regulations

(d) Ensure safe and wholesome food

Q18. The minimum legal level for acetic acid in vinegar is:

(a) 4% (b) 5%

(c) 6% (d) 7% S18.

19. According to FSS Act, 2006, to whom the appeal against the report of the Food Analyst will be made?

(a) Food Safety Officer **(b) Designated Officer**

(c) Assistant Food Commissioner (d) Food Commissioner

20. Red colour of the meat is due to the presence of:

(a) Haemoglobin (b) Globulin

(c) Myoglobin (d) None of these S20.

21. What is the maximum permissible limit for trans fats in edible oils and fats as per FSSAI regulations? (a) 5%

(b) 10% **(c) 2%**

(d) 0.2%

22. Pellagra can be cured by feeding:

(a) Folacin **(b) Niacin**

(c) Biotin (d) Riboflavin

23. Prevention of Food Adulteration Act was promulgated in the year:

(a) 1955 (b) 1975

(c) 1954 (d) 1973

24. Antinutrients are also known as:

(a) Primary metabolites (b) Secondary metabolites

(c) Natural toxicants (d) Synthetic toxicants

25. Which test is performed to check the quality of incoming milk for acceptance or rejection?

(a) Standard test (b) Soxhlet test

(c) Quality test **(d) Platform test**

26. The primary goal of "Food Safety Display Board" is:

(a) Display food safety and hygiene practices to be followed by FBO

(b) Display the menu on the digital board

(c) Display the nutritional contents of the food product

(d) Display the latest standards and regulations S26.

27. The other name for 'Pre-requisite Programs' is:

(a) Written programs (b) Implementation

(c) HACCP **(d) GMP**

28. Which State has the maximum number of potential clean street food hubs?

(a) Delhi (b) West Bengal

(c) Uttar Pradesh (d) Maharashtra

29. AGMARK conforms to a set of standards that is approved by:

(a) Agriculture and Manufacturing Authority

(b) Directorate of Marketing and Inspection

(c) Bureau of Indian Standards

(d) Department of Consumer Affairs

30. Bitterness in black pepper is due to:

(a) Capsaicin (b) Anthocyanin

(c) Xanthine **(d) Piperine S30.**

31. What is the significance of Red Circle Symbol present on a Food Packet?

(a) Spicy foods **(b) Non-vegetarian products**

(c) The presence of trans fats (d) Safety and quality of product

32. Any person who whether by himself or by any other person on his behalf manufactures or sells or stores or sells or distributes or imports any article of food for human consumption which is sub-standard, shall be liable to a penalty which may extend to ________ lakh rupees.

(a) 6 **(b) 5**

(c) 4 (d) 1

33. Any biological, chemical or physical factor or condition of food which effectively causes adverse effects on health is called:

(a) Risk **(b) Hazard**

(c) Adulterant (d) Extraneous matter

34. A mild heat treatment of foods that destroys pathogens and extends its shelf life is called:

(a) Baking (b) Blanching

(c) Sterilization **(d) Pasteurization**

35. What is the primary objective of "Food Safety Training Programs for Food Handlers and Professionals"?

(a) To increase the cost of food production

(b) To educate individuals about culinary practices

(c) To enhance awareness about food safety practices and minimize risks

(d) To promote the use of food additives

36. A petty food manufacturer is someone who has a tiny food business with an annual turnover not exceeding Rs.:

(a) 8 lakhs (b) 10 lakhs

(c) 12 lakhs (d) 14 lakhs S36.

37. The ingredients exert tenderizing effect on bakery products are:

(a) Fats and oils (b) Milk and sugar

(c) Salt and yeast **(d) All of the above**

38. An initiative of FSSAI that ensures safe food at railways is:

(a) Safe food on platform **(b) Safe food on track**

(c) Safe food on train (d) Safe food on rail S38.

39. The two main components of GMP essential for the success of the food safety system are:

(a) Education and accomplishment (b) Education and enforcement

(c) Written programs and implementation

(d) Manual and accomplishment

40. Which of the following food businesses falls under the purview of Central Licensing Authority includes?

(a) Dairy units including milk chilling units equipped to handle or process more than 50,000 liters of liquid milk/day or 1500 MT of milk solid per annum.

(b) Vegetable oil processing units and units producing vegetable oil by the process of solvent extraction and refineries including oil expeller unit having installed capacity more than 3 MT/day.

(c) All slaughterhouses equipped to slaughter more than 50 large animals or 150 or more small animals including sheep and goats or 1000 or more poultry birds per day.

(d) Meat processing units equipped to handle or process more than 700 kg of meat per day or 170 MT per annum.

41. World Food Safety Day is celebrated on:

(a) 6th May (b) 12th July

(c) 7th June (d) 8th August

42. Potassium bromate in flour is used as:

(a) Bleaching agent (b) Improver

(c) Both (a) and (b) (d) None of these S42.

43. The word Hygiene is derived from Hygeia, which means :

(a) Name of a Greek Goddess (b) Name of a person

(c) Name of a place (d) None of the above

44. Who among the following has the authority to seize any article of food?

(a) Food Commissioner **(b) Food Safety Officer**

(c) State Government (d) Food Analyst 12 S44.

45. "Verification involves being able to confirm that HACCP elements are working properly." Which of the following is not a method used for verification?

(a) Random sampling (b) Microbiological testing

(c) Performing a mock recall (d) Chemical testing S4.

46. As per FSS Act, 2006, an appeal against the order of rejection for the grant of license shall lie to the following:

(a) Food Commissioner (b) Assistant Food Commissioner

(c) Food Safety Officer (d) Designated Officer S46.

47. With reference to the polythene and foodstuff contact, the Indian standard specification is:

(a) IS: 10146 (b) IS: 10910

(c) IS: 10151 (d) IS: 10142 S47.

48. What is the primary objective of Food Safety and Standards (Packaging and Labelling) Regulations, 2011?

(a) Regulating food production

(b) Ensure accurate labelling of food products

(c) Setting maximum retail prices for food products

(d) Setting labels for export of food products

49. Food Safety and Standards Regulations, 2011 came into force on:

(a) 25th August, 2011 (b) 15th August, 2011

(c) 05th August, 2011 (d) 06th August, 2011

50. In which year the Food Security Act was passed in Parliament?

(a) 2013 (b) 2014

(c) 2015 (d) 2016

51. In which of the following food items use of mono sodium glutamate is not allowed?

(a) Milk and milk products (b) Flours of cereals, pulses and starches

(c) Infant foods (d) All of the above

Q52. 'SaNGRAH' launched by FSSAI is for:

(a) Digital platform to address food safety issues

(b) Facilitating domestic and overseas exporters, importers, etc.

(c) Communicating with State authorities

(d) Ensuring the compliance of food safety standards for trading

53. A common and unified IT portal that provides comprehensive information on standards, regulations, notifications and guidelines is:

(a) Common Digital Dashboard (b) FSSAI IT Platform

(c) Universal Dashboard (d) Multipurpose Digital Dashboard

54. When a Food Safety Officer takes a sample of food for analysis, he shall:

(a) Send one of the part of the sample for analysis to the Food Analyst, two parts to the Designated Officer for keeping these in safe custody and remaining part for analysis to an accredited laboratory

(b) Send two parts of the sample for analysis to the Food Analyst, one part to the Designated Officer for keeping these in safe custody and remaining part for analysis to an accredited laboratory

(c) Send one part of the sample for analysis to the Food Analyst, one part to the Designated Officer for keeping these in safe custody and remaining part for analysis to an accredited laboratory

(d) Send all parts of the sample to an accredited laboratory

55. To control the dissemination of Salmonella spp., egg is pasteurized at which temperature?

(a) 70°C **(b) 64.4°C**

(c) 72.5°C (d) 69°C

56. The FSSAI initiative designed to promote safe and nutritious foods in schools is:

(a) SNF@SCHOOL (b) SAN@SCHOOL

(c) SAFE@SCHOOL (d) FIT@SCHOOL

57. As per FSS Act, 2006, if a license is not issued within _______ months from the date of authorized application or his application is not rejected, the applicant may start his food business after expiry of the said period.

(a) One **(b) Two**

(c) Three (d) Four

58. Lead contamination in infant foods should not be exceeded to:

(a) 0.1 ppm **(b) 0.2 ppm**

(c) 0.3 ppm (d) 0.4 ppm

59. Which of the following is a prohibited food additive under the FSS Act?

(a) Tartrazine **(b) Allura Red AC**

(c) Brilliant Blue FCF (d) Sunset Yellow

60. Which of the following is restricted for sale or expose for sale or have in his possession for the purpose of sale or for use as an ingredient in the preparation of any article of food intended for sale?

(a) Chicory
(b) Argemone
(c) Kesari
(d) Sesame

61. What does the symbol 'F+' on food packets signify?

(a) Foreign foods
(b) Fortified foods
(c) Processed foods
(d) Safe foods

62. Which of the following gas has been strictly prohibited for artificially ripening of fruits?

(a) Ethylene
(b) Acetylene
(c) Propylene
(d) Butylene

63. Which one of the following is the water-soluble vitamin?

(a) Ascorbic acid
(b) Vitamin A
(c) Vitamin D
(d) Vitamin K

64. Which authority is responsible for the enforcement of food safety regulations at the State level of India?

(a) FSSAI
(b) State Food Authority
(c) Ministry of Agriculture and Farmer's Welfare
(d) Both (a) and (b)

65. The Headquarter of AGMARK is located at:

(a) Nagpur
(b) Kanpur
(c) Faridabad
(d) Ahmadabad

66. In general, there are _______ principles of HACCP.

(a) 5
(b) 6
(c) 7
(d) 8

S66.

67. The interactive exchange of information and opinions throughout the risk analysis process concerning risks, risk-related factors and perceptions, among risk assessors, risk managers, consumers, industry, the academic community and other interested parties, including the explanation of risk assessment findings and the basis of risk management decisions, is referred to as:

(a) Risk management
(b) Risk assessment
(c) Risk analysis
(d) Risk communication

68. Which of the following is the major insecticide used in fish and fishery products?

(a) Aldrin
(b) Carbaryl
(c) Chlordane
(d) Dicofol

69. Which material is used for the manufacturing of drinking water packaging bottles?

(a) Polyethylene (b) Polypropylene

(c) Polyethylene terephthalate (d) Polyvinyl propylene

70. Which of the following Act was not prevalent before FSSAI?

(a) MMPO (b) PFA

(c) FPO **(d) Organic Food Regulation**

71. Salmonella bacteria is mostly found in _______ of poultry.

(a) Blood circulatory system (b) Respiratory system

(c) Digestive system (d) Reproductive system

72. As per FSSAI Regulations, the moisture content of Atta (wheat flour) is not more than ______ percent by weight.

(a) 14 (b) 16

(c) 20 (d) 25

73. The basic operational and environmental conditions applied to produce safe foods are called:

(a) HACCP (b) FSSA

(c) FSSAI **(d) GMP**

74. FSSAI license number comprises how many digits?

(a) 8 (b) 10

(c) 12 **(d) 14**

75. Who is in charge of the food safety machinery in various States of India?

(a) Food Safety Officer (b) Adjudicating Officer

(c) Commissioner of Food Safety of State

(d) State Ministry of Health and Family Welfare

76. What can be learned through a food safety surveillance?

(a) Points of contamination

(b) Areas for improvement in food production

(c) Trend in outbreak of food borne diseases

(d) All of the above

77. If any person manufactures or distributes or sells or imports any article of food causing his death, it shall be lawful for the adjudicating officer, the court to direct him to pay compensation of at least not less than ______ lakh to the victim.

(a) 1 (b) 3

(c) 5 (d) 7

78. If internal audit is not conducted as per the Clauses of ISO 17025-2005, the Auditor can issue:

(a) Minor Non-conformance
(b) Major Non-conformance
(c) Improvement Notice
(d) Opportunity for improvement

79. The provision of a single window system for applying for import clearance is called:

(a) FSMS
(b) SWIFT
(c) IEC
(d) FoSTaC

80. Sliminess in spoiled food occurs due to:

(a) Development of nitrogenous compounds
(b) Accumulation of microbial cells
(c) Breakdown of chlorophyll
(d) Developments of amides

81. A food, being a produce of agriculture or horticulture, or animal husbandry and dairying or aquaculture in its natural form, resulting from the growing, raising, cultivation, picking, harvesting, collection or catching in the hands of a person other than a farmer or fisherman is called:

(a) Primary food
(b) Raw food
(c) Unprocessed food
(d) Secondary food

82. Alkaline phosphatase test is linked with:

(a) Meat
(b) Milk
(c) Ghee
(d) Curd

83. Substances which prevent adverse effects of metals catalyzing the oxidative breakdown of foods forming chelates are called:

(a) Sequestering agents
(b) Buffering agents
(c) Binding agents
(d) Oxidizing agents

84. What does the "Eat Right India" movement primarily aim to achieve?

(a) Promoting fast food consumption
(b) Preventing food adulteration
(c) Promoting safe and nutritious food consumption
(d) Banning certain food products

85. How many types of caramel colours are produced in the industry for food application?

(a) Two
(b) Three
(c) Four
(d) Seven

86. Special course in Food Safety Training and Certification Programs is created for:

(a) State and Central licensed food business

(b) Central licensed food business

(c) High-risk food business or business requiring special attention

(d) Food business

87. Where FSSAI organized a Global Food Regulators Summit on 20th - 21st July, 2023?

(a) Pune
(b) Hyderabad
(c) Delhi
(d) Mumbai

88. The Headquarters of FSSAI is located at:

(a) Mumbai
(b) Delhi
(c) Kolkata
(d) Chennai

89. Which of the following is not a naturally existing toxic substance?

(a) Acaric acid
(b) Hypericine
(c) Safrole
(d) Carbaryl

90. GSFA stands for:

(a) General Standards for Food Additives

(b) General Standards for Food Act

(c) General Standards for Food Auction

(d) General Standards for Food Adulterants

91. Which Department under FSSAI is responsible for setting standards for food additives?

(a) Food Additives and Nutrient Standards Department

(b) Food Standards and Labelling Department

(c) Food Licensing and Registration Department

(d) Food Safety Compliance Department

92. A license granted under FSS regulations shall be valid for a period of _______ from the date of issue.

(a) 1 to 3 years
(b) 1 to 4 years
(c) 1 to 5 years
(d) 1 to 6 years

93. Why a person is not allowed to wear accessories in production area?

(a) To avoid physical hazard
(b) To reduce contamination
(c) Subjected to follow GMP
(d) All of these

94. A clean "street food hub" should contain:

(a) 90 or more vendors
(b) 100 or more vendors
(c) 50 or more vendors
(d) 80 or more vendors

95. World Food Day is observed on:

(a) 2 October
(b) 6 October
(c) 16 October
(d) 26 October 25

96. ISO: 22000 is established for the regulation of:

(a) Food Safety Management System
(b) Environment Management System
(c) Quality Management System
(d) Risk Management System

97. Fermented meat sausages commonly have acidities in the range of pH:

(a) 2.5 - 3.5
(b) 4.5 - 5.5
(c) 5.5 - 6.5
(d) None of the above

98. Which one is lacking in milk powder?

(a) Fat
(b) Protein
(c) Vitamins
(d) Carbohydrate

99. The use of which of the following antibiotics and pharmacologically active substances is prohibited in seafood food processing?

(a) Nitrofural
(b) Tetracycline
(c) Trimethoprim
(d) Oxolinic acid S99.

100. With reference to Food Safety and Standard Act, FSMS stands for:

(a) Food Safety Management System
(b) Food Security Management System
(c) Food Standard Management System
(d) Food Safety Maintenance System S100.

CHAPTER-10

JPSC Food Safety Officer - 2024 (Paper - II)

1. Antibiotic "Nisin" is produced by:
   (a) Achromobacter perolens (b) Pseudomonas mucidolens
   (c) Streptococcus lactis (d) *Pseudomonas gnavares*
2. The nutrient responsible for the production of red blood cells:
   (a) Magnesium (b) Vitamin C
   (c) Vitamin B12 (d) Calcium S2.
3. Which of the following is an example of a non-dairy milk alternative?
   (a) Soya milk (b) Almond milk
   c) Coconut milk **(d) All of the above**
4. Zero energy chamber operates on the principle of:
   (a) Evaporative cooling (b) Charle's law
   (c) Thermodynamics (d) Boyle's law 2
5. Which fungus is used for lactic acid production?
   (a) *Fusarium moniliforme* **(b) *Rhizopus oryzae***
   (c) *Aspergillus terreus* (d) *Aspergillus Niger* S5.
6. The major protein in corn is:
   (a) Oryzenin (b) Glutenin
   (c) Hordein **(d) Zein**
7. The chief muscle pigment in meat protein is:
   (a) Myosin (b) Oxymyoglobin
   (c) Haemoglobin **(d) Myoglobin**
8. Safe Quality Food (SQF) 1000 code is designed especially for:
   (a) Big manufacturing units **(b) Primary producers**
   (c) Secondary producers (d) None of these
9. Choose the incorrect statement about BMR out of the following:
   (a) BMR is directly related to surface area
   (b) BMR is increased in warm climate
   (c) BMR is inversely proportional to age
   (d) Males have higher BMR than age-matched females

10. Caramels used in the bakery industry should be:

(a) Positively charged

(b) Half positively and half negatively charged

(c) Negatively charged (d) Neutral

11. Which of the following minerals is important for maintaining healthy bones?

(a) Iron (b) Potassium

(c) Calcium (d) Zinc

12. The mineral important for maintaining proper fluid balance in the body:

(a) Iron (b) Calcium

(c) Sodium (d) Zinc

13. Which of the following is an example of food adulteration?

(a) Adding more vitamins to a fortified cereal

(b) Diluting honey with water (c) Adding extra sugar to a beverage

(d) Increasing the fiber content in bread

14. The sour taste of vinegar is due to:

(a) Acetic acid (b) Lactic acid

(c) Formic acid (d) Citric acid

15. The crystal-clear liquid-based beverage is:

(a) Squash (b) Crush

(c) Cordial (d) RTS

16. Which of the following is a non-climacteric type of fruit?

(a) Pineapple (b) Litchi

(c) Grape **(d) All of the above**

17. Discolouration of milk powder during storage is due to:

(a) Caramelization **(b) Maillard reaction**

(c) Autoxidation (d) Moisture content

18. Indian Gooseberry is also known as:

(a) Grape **(b) Amla**

(c) Lemon (d) Peach

19. Lecithin is a:

(a) Phospholipid (b) Membrane protein

(c) Vitamin (d) Flavonoid

20. Which of the following dairy products is a good source of probiotics?

(a) Butter (b) Cheddar cheese

(c) Greek yogurt (d) Ice-cream

21. Major bactericidal protein in albumin is:

(a) Phosvitin | (b) Ovalbumin
(c) Lysozyme | (d) Conalbumin

22. A classical sign of Zn deficiency is:

(a) Anemia | (b) Goitre
(c) Mottled teeth | **(d) Growth retardation**

23. Which vitamin helps in the absorption of calcium?

(a) Vitamin A | (b) Vitamin B12
(c) Vitamin C | **(d) Vitamin D**

24. The spoilage in eggs is more pronounced by:

(a) Bacteria than molds | (b) Molds than bacteria
(c) Molds and bacteria both | (d) None of the above

25. The vitamin usually added to milk for the purpose of fortification is:

(a) Vitamin A | (b) Vitamin B12
(c) Vitamin D | **(d) Both (a) & (c)**

26. Most spoilage bacteria grow at:

(a) Acidic pH | (b) Alkaline pH
(c) Neutral pH | (d) Basic pH

27. Butter flavor is due to:

(a) Ammonia | (b) Ethylene
(c) Diacetyl | (d) Vanillin

28. Refractometer is used to determine:

(a) Minerals | (b) Acidity
(c) TSS | (d) Vitamins

29. Which process involves separating the fat from milk to create a lower-fat dairy product?

(a) Fortification | (b) Condensation
(c) Fermentation | **(d) Skimming**

30. Turmeric is a:

(a) Tuber | **(b) Rhizome**
(c) Modified root

31. The primary purpose of blanching in food processing is to:

(a) Enhance flavor | (b) Improve texture
(c) Destroy enzymes | (d) Increase nutrient content

32. Which type of fat is considered healthy for the heart?

(a) Saturated fat (b) Trans fat

(c) Monounsaturated fat **(d) Polyunsaturated fat**

33. Which heavy metal is commonly found as an adulterant in spices?

(a) Mercury **(b) Lead**

(c) Arsenic (d) Cadmium

34. Monellin and thaumatin are natural sweeteners that chemically fall under:

(a) Protein (b) Carbohydrate

(c) Alkaloid (d) Steroids

35. Mycotoxins are:

(a) Fungal metabolites (b) Bacterial metabolites

(c) Plant parasites (d) Enzyme

36. Protein content of foods is estimated by which method?

(a) Kjeldahl method (b) NIR method

(c) Lowry method

37. The purpose of using food additives like emulsifiers in food is:

(a) To improve colour

(b) To prevent separation of ingredients

(c) To improve flavor (d) To increase nutritional value

38. High pressure processing of food in a vessel follows:

(a) Hydro energy rule (b) Isothermal rule

(c) Iso-static rule (d) None of the above

39. The time in minutes required to destroy the organisms in a specified medium at 250°F (121°C) is referred to as:

(a) F-value (b) Z-value

(c) D-value (d) T-value

40. Soft rot in fresh fruits and vegetables is caused due to:

(a) Penicillium **(b) Erwinia**

(c) Saccharomyces (d) Aspergillus

41. In eukaryotes, cell, fatty acid breakdown occurs in:

(a) Mitochondrial matrix (b) Cytosol

(c) Cell membrane (d) Endoplasmic reticulum

42. How many food groups are in the food pyramid?

(a) 3 **(b) 5**

(c) 7 (d) 9

43. Which of the following is termed as "good cholesterol"?

(a) LDL **(b) HDL**

(c) VLDL (d) Triglycerides

44. As per FSSAI, minimum standards for TSS and fruit pulp/juice content in squash are:

(a) 40%, 25% **(b) 45%, 25%**

(c) 48%, 10% (d) 40%, 15%

45. "Neurotoxicity" is caused by which pathogenic microorganism?

(a) *Salmonella* spp. (b) *Shigella* spp.

(c) *Clostridium botulinum* (d) *Escherichia coli*

46. What is the main source of energy for the human body?

(a) Proteins (b) Vitamins

(c) Carbohydrates (d) Minerals

47. The toxic factor present in Lathyrus sativus species is:

(a) Goitrogens (b) Saponin

(c) Cyanogenic glycosides **(d) β-oxalyl amino alanine**

48. Hyperkalaemia is a condition of:

(a) Elevated level of potassium (b) Lower level of potassium

(c) Elevated level of calcium (d) Lower level of calcium

49. Which food additive is commonly used as a flavor enhancer?

(a) Carrageenan **(b) Monosodium glutamate**

(c) Aspartame (d) Sodium nitrate

50. Which food additive is commonly used as a leavening agent in bakery industry?

(a) Monosodium glutamate **(b) Sodium bicarbonate**

(c) Aspartame (d) Citric acid S50.

51. Precursor of niacin is:

(a) Tryptophan (b) Leucine

(c) Isoleucine (d) Tyrosine

52. Celiac disease is caused due to:

(a) Zein (b) Oryzein

(c) Gluten (d) Hordein

53. Which of the following falls in the category of low-acid food?

(a) Tomato (b) Turnip

(c) Carrot **(d) Cauliflower**

54. Curcumin is extracted from:

(a) Turmeric (b) Capsicum

(c) Cucumber (d) Cashew nut

55. Beri-Beri disease is caused by the deficiency of:

(a) Vitamin B12 (b) Vitamin B2

(c) Vitamin B1 (d) Vitamin B3

56. What is the Glycaemic index of carbohydrates?

(a) It shows which another nutrient it is being ingested with

(b) It shows how quickly a carbohydrate increases blood sugar level

(c) It shows how quickly a carbohydrate is digested

(d) None of the mentioned

57. What is the primary role of consumers in preventing food adulteration?

(a) To ignore suspicious food products **(b) To report suspected adulteration**

(c) To buy the cheapest food products (d) To trust food labels blindly

58. Mineral responsible for proper nerve functioning is:

(a) Sodium (b) Potassium

(c) Calcium **(d) Magnesium**

59. Which of the following acid is present in Cola drink?

(a) Malic acid (b) Tartaric acid

(c) Phosphoric acid (d) Acetic acid

60. Agar is extracted from:

(a) Algae (b) Fungi

(c) Bacteria (d) Crops

61. Chemical name of vitamin H is:

(a) Retinol (b) Calciferol

(c) Tocopherol **(d) Biotin**

62. The diet recommended for hypertensive patients is:

(a) BRAT **(b) DASH**

(c) Low protein (d) High fat

63. Richest source of Vitamin C is:

(a) Amla (b) Lemon

(c) Barbados cherry (d) Guava

64. Which method is commonly used to detect chemical adulteration in food?

(a) Sensory evaluation **(b) Gas chromatography**

(c) Microscopic examination (d) Taste testing

65. If vegetables and fruits are washed after cutting, which of the following vitamins are lost?
(a) A and D
(b) C and B
(c) A and B
(d) A and C

66. Which of the following cooking techniques retains more nutrients in vegetables as compared to boiling?
(a) Baking
(b) Steaming
(c) Frying
(d) Microwaving

67. Tocopherol is the name of which vitamin?
(a) B2
(b) D
(c) B6
(d) E

68. Fat percentage in milk cream is:
(a) 25%
(b) 40%
(c) 35%
(d) 60%

69. BMR stands for:
(a) Body Metabolic Rate
(b) Basal Metabolic Rate
(c) Body Mass Ratio
(d) Body Measurement Rate

70. Which technique is commonly used to detect adulteration in honey?
(a) Thin layer chromatography
(b) Polymerase Chain Reaction (PCR)
(c) UV-Vis spectroscopy
(d) Mass spectrometry

71. The red colour of tomatoes is due to the presence of:
(a) Carotene
(b) Lycopene
(c) Anthocyanin
(d) Betalain

72. Which foodborne illness is associated with the consumption of raw or undercooked shellfish?
(a) Botulism
(b) Norovirus
(c) Both A & b
(d) Infection

Q73. Rancid flavor in milk is primarily due to:
(a) Caproic acid
(b) Butyric acid
(c) Palmitic acid
(d) Stearic acid

74. Energy value of 1 gm carbohydrate is:
(a) 4.1 K cals
(b) 5.6 cals
(c) 8.6 K cals
(d) 9.3 K cals

75. Which of the following is an example of a processed food product?
(a) Fresh fruits
(b) Canned soup
(c) Whole wheat bread
(d) Steamed vegetables

76. Spirulina is a rich source of:

(a) Protein
(b) Mineral
(c) Vitamin
(d) All of these

77. Which of the following acid is present in animal fat?

(a) Erucic acid
(b) Palmitic acid
(c) Palmitoleic acid
(d) Linoleic acid

78. Which of the following food groups provides the best source of energy?

(a) Milk and cheese
(b) Meat group
(c) Fats, oils and sweets
(d) Breads

79. Lysine and threonine are absent in:

(a) Rice
(b) Wheat
(c) Barley
(d) Corn

80. The most common adulterant found in vegetable oils is:

(a) Palm oil
(b) Mustard oil
(c) Argemone oil
(d) Mineral oil

81. Quality control as an integrated function may consist of:

(a) Planning
(b) Monitoring
(c) Prevention
(d) All of the above

82. An abnormal immune response to food is called as:

(a) Food allergy
(b) Sepsis
(c) Food fusion
(d) Inflammation

83. Invert sugar in fruit jam should not be more than:

(a) 40%
(b) 50%
(c) 60%
(d) 70%

84. Milk viscosity is due to which constituent of milk?

(a) Albumin
(b) Globulin
(c) Casein
(d) Phospholipids

85. Which nutrient is important for maintaining healthy gut bacteria?

(a) Fiber
(b) Protein
(c) Carbohydrates
(d) Fats

86. Which gas is commonly used for packaging of perishable foods?

(a) Oxygen
(b) Carbon dioxide
(c) Nitrogen
(d) Hydrogen

87. Milk is deficient in:

(a) Vitamin D
(b) Vitamin A
(c) Vitamin B
(d) Vitamin C

88. Which vitamin is known as the "sunshine vitamin"?
(a) Vitamin A (b) Vitamin C
(c) Vitamin D (d) Vitamin K

89. Which vitamin is known for its antioxidant properties?
(a) Vitamin A (b) Vitamin B12
(c) Vitamin E (d) Vitamin K

90. Which enzyme present in saliva is responsible for breakdown and digestion of starches?
(a) Amylase (b) Protease
(c) Glucose oxidase (d) Carboxylase

91. How many times does a normal human heart beat in a minute?
(a) 30-40 **(b) 70-80**
(c) 100-120 (d) 180-200

92. Which sugar is present in fruits?
(a) Fructose (b) Galactose
(c) Glucose **(d) Both a & c**

93. Which of the following is present in ginger?
(a) Eugenol **(b) Oleoresins**
(c) Terpenoid (d) Allicin

94. Which process involves heating milk to a high temperature to kill harmful bacteria?
(a) Homogenization **(b) Pasteurization**
(c) Fermentation (d) Sterilization

95. Brandy is a:
(a) Fermented beverage (b) Fermented and brewed beverage
(c) Brewed beverage **(d) Distilled beverage**

96. Iodine value of a given oil sample is a measure of:
(a) Mean molecular weight of fatty acids
(b) Degree of unsaturation
(c) Free fatty acids (d) All of the above

CHAPTER-11

KERALA FSO 2025

1. The hypertonic solution used in osmotic dehydration of fruits and vegetables consists of

A) NaOH
B) Baking Powder
C) Sugar
D) lactic acid

2. A process where pre-packed food is exposed to radiant energy to kill microbes, pests, prevent sprouting is

A) Cold sterilization
B) Hot sterilization
C) Ultra pasteurization
D) Batch pasteurization

3. Pulsed light technology is mainly used for

A) Condensation
B) Sterilization
C) Cooking
D) Boiling

4. In this advanced thermal processing method, the food material, which serves as an

electrical resistor, is heated by passing electricity through it

A) microwave heating
B) Radiation
C) Ohmic heating
D) Irradiation

5. Maillard Reaction is the result from chemical interactions at high heat between

A) Sugar and minerals
B) Sugar and Sugar
C) Sugars and Amino acids
D) Sugars and vitamins

6. In ________ one end of the can may bulge and on forcing the bulged end back the other end will bulge.

A) Springer
B) Flipper
C) Gun puff
D) Soft swell

7. Which among these microorganisms can easily grow under anaerobic conditions, producing the deadly toxin specially in canned foods ?

A) *Coxiella burnetti*
B) *E. coli*
C) *B. subtilis*
D) *C. botulinum*

8. Which among the following is not an intrinsic factor which affects shelf life of a product ?

A) Initial microbial load
B) Water activity
C) Product formulation
D) Storage condition

9. A nonthermal processing method that uses physical pressure to preserve food, instead

of heat, chemicals or irradiation.

A) HPP
B) HTST
C) ITST
d) UHT

10. Why is it that soft fruits cannot be preserved using freezing ?

A) Hydrogen bonding increases on freezing thus damaging cellular structure

B) Water in fruit tissues reduces its volume on freezing thus damaging the cellular

structure

C) Water in cells gels on freezing due to the presence of pectin

D) Water in fruit tissues expands its volume on freezing thus damaging the cellularstructure

11. Sequence of rice milling process

A) Cleaning-dehusking-separation-polishing-grading

B) Cleaning-grading-polishing-separation-dehusking

C) Cleaning-separation-grading-polishing-dehusking

d) Cleaning-polishing-separation-grading-dehusking

12. Addition of potassium iodide to salt is an example of

A) Nutritive supplement
B) Colourant
C) Flavor addition
D) Anticaking

13. Three stages of freeze drying food in order are

A) freezing, sublimation, secondary drying

B) sublimation, freezing, secondary drying

C) secondary drying, freezing, sublimation

D) secondary drying, sublimation, freezing

14. Which among the following is a still beverage ?

A) Flavoured water
B) Wine
C) Beer
D) Gin

15. Process of breaking down intermolecular bonds of starch molecules in the presence of water and heat is called

A) Retrogradation **B) Gelatinization**

C) vaporization D) dextrinization

16. IR radiation releases energy in electromagnetic wave form in the spectrum from

A) 0.75 μm to 1,000 μm B) 0.10 μm to 0.75 μm

C) 1000 μm to 2000 μm D) 2000 μm to 5000 μm

17. Rosemary is an aromatic herb that has been known from ancient times as a ________of the mint family.

A) Memory herb B) Auspicious herb

C) Spicy herb D) Smiley herb

18. The activity of SO_2 increases

A) With decreasing pH B) With increasing pH

C) With a constant increase in the pH

D) pH has no influence

19. Which among the following is the indicator organism considered for fixing the pasteurization time and temperature ?

A) *Coxiella brunetti* B) *E. coli*

C) *B. subtilis* D) *C. botulinum*

20. In a carbonated drink the degree of solubility of carbon dioxide gas increases

A) At low temperature and high pressure

B) At high temperature and high pressure

C) At low temperature and low pressure

D) None of the above

21. milk pricing system which discourages adulteration with water

i. Payment according to weight

ii. Payment according to use of milk

iii. Payment according to fat content of milk

A) Only i B) Only i and ii

C) Only iii D) Only ii

22. Considering the legal standards the maximum obtainable overrun in butter is

A) 15% **B) 25%**

C) 35% D) 50%

23. Which of the following casein submicelle are hydrophobic ?

i. alpha-s1-casein
ii. beta-casein
iii. alpha-s2-casein
iv. kappa-casein

A) Only i
B) Only i and ii
C) Only i, ii and iii
D) All of the above i, ii, iii and iv

24. Homogenization efficiency can be assessed by

i. Creaming rate
ii. NIZO method
iii. Size distribution method

A) Only i
B) Only i and ii
C) Only i and iii
d) All of the above i, ii and iii

25. Fluffy defect in ice cream is caused due to

i. Excessive overrun
ii. low solids content
iii. Excessive stabilizer content

A) Only i
B) Only i and ii
C) Only i and iii
D) All of the above i, ii and iii

26. Which coagulant gives higher moisture content in channa ?

A) Calcium lactate
B) Citric acid
C) lactic acid
D) Acetic acid

27. In aseptic packaging which of the following can be used for package sterilization ?

i. Superheated steam
ii. Hydrogen peroxide
iii. Peracetic acid
iv. Pulsed light

A) Only i
B) Only i and ii
C) Only i, ii and iii
D) All of the above i, ii, iii and iv

28. The velocity of fat globule is directly proportional to

i. Centrifugal acceleration
ii. viscosity of milk
iii. Radius of fat globule
iv. Separator sludge

A) Only i
B) Only i and ii
C) Only i and iii
D) Only i and iv

29. Which of the following is/are oil-in-water emulsion ?

i. Table cream with 25% fat
ii. Plastic cream with 85% fat
iii. Table butter
iv. margarine

A) Only i
B) Only i and ii
C) Only i and iii
D) Only iii and iv

30. In aseptic packaging the layer that provides rigidity is

A) Paper B) Aluminum foil

C) Polyethylene D) Polypropylene

31. Which method of ghee production produces least amount of ghee residue ?

A) Pre-stratification method B) Direct cream method

C) Creamery butter method D) desi method

32. Factors that can lower the heat stability of milk

i. developed acidity ii. High total solids

iii. Homogenization iv. Addition of chemical stabilizer

A) Only i B) Only i and ii

C) Only i, ii and iii

d) All of the above i, ii, iii and iv

33. lumpy defect in milk powder may be caused due to

i. Insufficient drying ii. Absorption of moisture

iii. drippage from pressure nozzle

A) Only i B) Only i and ii

C) Only i and iii **d) All of the above i, ii and iii**

34. Accelerated ripening in cheese can be done by

i. Increasing ripening temperature ii. Addition of exogeneous enzyme

iii. Addition of whey protein iv. Ultra filtration

A) Only i **B) Only i and ii**

C) Only i, ii and iii D) All of the above i, ii, iii and iv

35. Reagent for detection of added urea in milk

A) Para-phenylenediamine **B) p-dimethylaminobenzaldehyde**

C) Barfoed's reagent D) Diphenylamine

36. Casein can be manufactured from

i. Skim milk ii. Ghee residue

iii. Buttermilk iv. Ultra filtrated whey

A) Only i B) Only i and iv

C) Only i and iii D) All of the above i, ii, iii and iv

37. In UHT heat exchanger the type of deposits formed is/are

i. Type – A ii. Type – B

A) Only i B) Only ii

C) Both i and ii D) None of the above

38. Greasy defect in butter may be caused due to

i. Overworking
ii. Underworking
iii. High meting fats
iv. Overchurning

A) Only i
B) Only ii
C) Only i and iii
D) All of the above

39. Which of the following is a baked traditional Indian dairy product ?

i. Shrikhand wadi
ii. Chhana podo
iii. Chhana murki
iv. Khurchan

A) Only i
B) Only ii
C) Only ii and iii
D) Only i and iv

40. Major Dahi flavor compound is

A) Acetaldehyde
B) Ethyl ester
C) Diacetyl
d) Lactones

41. Which of the following statements is/are correct about the tests used in an abattoir ?

I. Malachite green test is used for detecting imperfect bleeding of carcass.

II. Remington and fowrie's test is used for detecting jaundice in carcasses.

III. Malachite green test is used for detecting both jaundice and imperfect bleeding in Carcasses.

IV. Remington and fowrie's test is used for detecting imperfect bleeding in carcasses.

A) I and III only
B) I and II only
C) II only
D) None of the above

42. Which of the following statements are correct about the abattoir ?

I. The lairage area for cattle abattoirs should have adequate space and facilities to hold at least three days slaughter.

II. The v-race is a path that connects the lairage and slaughtering section of an abattoir.

III. The light intensity at the point of inspection in an abattoir should be a minimum of 540 lux.

IV. The ageing room temperature is normally maintained between 10 – 15°C.

A) I and III only
B) I, III and IV only
C) II and IV only
D) All of the above

43. Which of the following statements is/are correct about the emulsifying properties of eggs ?

I. Egg yolks contain emulsifiers like lecithin that help to stabilise oil-water mixtures.

II. Emulsifying properties are essential in products like mayonnaise and salad dressings.

III. Egg whites are equally effective as yolks in emulsifying mixtures.

IV. The emulsifying action contributes to smooth textures in food products.

A) I only **B) I, II and Iv only**

C) II and III only D) All of the above

44. Which of the following statements is/are correct about the quick freezing of meat ?

I. Quick freezing result in the formation of large ice crystals in the meat.

II. It improves the tenderness of meat by breaking down muscle fibres.

III. The freezing process occurs at temperatures below –30°C in most quick freezing methods.

IV. Quick freezing helps to retain the sensory and nutritional qualities of meat products.

A) I and II only **B) III and IV only**

C) III only d) All of the above

45. Which of the following statements are correct about the benefits of meat ageing ?

I. Ageing improves the overall texture and flavour of meat.

II. It reduces the water-holding capacity of meat, making it less juicy.

III. The ageing in meat is mainly due to the action of the enzyme cathepsins.

IV. Ageing enhances the market value of meat by improving its sensory attributes.

A) I and III only B) I, III and IV only

C) I and IV only D) All of the above

46. Which of the following statements is/are incorrect about the certification of organic meat in India ?

I. The National Programme for Organic Production (NPOP) oversees organic certification.

II. Organic meat production prohibits the use of vaccines and antibiotics.

III. Farmers must undergo a conversion period to transition to organic practices.

IV. Certification allow the use of Genetically Modified Organisms (GMOs) in organic meat production.

A) I and II only **B) II and IV only**

C) II only D) All of the above

47. Which of the following statements is/are correct about curing ingredients in meat processing ?

I. Sodium nitrite is a basic curing agent used in meat products to develop cured meat flavour.

II. Sugar in curing serves as a flavour enhancer and counterbalances the saltiness.

III. Phosphates in curing mixtures improve meat tenderness and water-holding capacity.

IV. Curing agents are primarily used to improve the colour and flavour of the meatproducts and not mainly for preservation.

A) I and II only
B) I, II and III only
C) III only
D) All of the above

48. Which of the following curing ingredients is/are responsible for the characteristic pink colour in cured meat ?

I. Sodium chloride.
II. Sodium nitrite.
III. Ascorbic acid.
IV. Potassium nitrate.

A) II and IV only
B) II only
C) II, III and IV only
D) All of the above

49. Which of the following statements correctly completes the sentences based on the use of irradiation in meat Preservation ?

By irradiation it is very difficult to destroy the ________ and ________ in meat and the off odour that is developed during irradiation is described as ________.

A) Bacteria, virus, metallic odour

B) virus, enzymes, wet dog odour

C) virus, enzymes, rotten egg odour

D) Bacteriophages, bacteria, wet dog odour

50. Which of the following statements correctly completes the sentence about the nutrient composition of eggs ?

Egg is deficient in __________ and __________ mineral.

A) vitamin C and Iron
B) vitamin A and Calcium
C) vitamin d and Zinc
D) vitamin B1 and magnesium

51. In canning or retorting, the time required to destroy a given number of organisms at a specific temperature is known as

A) Z-value
B) d-value
C) TdT-value
D) 12-d

52. In species identification of animal products by PCR-RFLP, the sequence of which mitochondrial gene is commonly employed ?

A) Cyt-b

B) Cyt-b2

C) 12s rRNA

d) None of the above

53. The true indicator of faecal contamination in meat

I. *E. coli*

II. *Salmonella*

III. *Streptococci*

IV. *Campylobacter*

A) I and II only

B) I, II and IV only

C) II and III only

D) I only

54. Which of the following statements about poultry processing is/are correct ?

I. Bleeding time in chicken is approximately 2-3 minutes.

II. In soft scalding, the temperature used is around 50°C for 1.5-2 minutes.

III. Hard scalding is generally followed for water birds and breeders.

IV. Scalding temperature of mature birds is around 65°C (sub-scalding).

A) I only

B) I, II and III only

C) I, II, III and IV

D) II and IV only

55. Which of the following statements about Staphylococcus aureus food poisoning are correct ?

I. *Staphylococcus aureus* causes food poisoning mostly by intoxication.

II. Food poisoning by *Staphylococcus aureus* occurs due to ingestion of endotoxins.

III. *Staphylococcus aureus* produce heat stable toxin.

IV. Inhalation is a common mode of food poisoning by staphylococcus aureus.

A) I and III only

B) I, III and IV only

C) II and III only

D) All of the above

56. Which of the following statements correctly describes the grading of a chicken carcass with the wingette portion of the wing missing ?

I. The missing wingette affects the appearance of the carcass.

II. A chicken carcass with a missing wingette is graded as "A Grade".

III. missing parts such as the wingette typically result in downgrading to "B Grade".

IV. The carcass may still graded for "C Grade" depending on additional defects.

A) I and II only

B) I, III and IV only

C) II and IV only

D) I, II, III and IV

57. Which of the following statements correctly describes the carcass judgment for poultry affected by the following diseases : Avian influenza, fowl pox, avian leukosis and infectious bursal disease ?

I. Avian influenza typically results in hemorrhagic lesions in the trachea, lungs and digestive tract, leading to total condemnation of the carcass.

II. Fowl pox presents with nodular lesions on the skin, comb, wattles and emaciated but the carcass may be acceptable if internal organs are unaffected.

III. Avian leukosis causes tumors in the liver and other organs, leading to total condemnation of the carcass.

IV. Infectious bursal disease often causes damage to the bursa of Fabricius, resulting in weakened immunity and the carcass may be condemned due to secondary infections.

A) I and II only

B) I, III and IV only

C) II and IV only

d) All of the above

58. Which of the following statements about meat and meat products packaging system are correct ?

I. In modified Atmosphere Packaging (MAP), nitrogen is primarily used as a filler gas.

II. Shrink film packaging eliminates pockets for purge accumulation.

III. To prevent irreversible browning in vacuum packaging, the oxygen level must be below 500 ppm.

IV. vacuum packaging offers excellent protection against freezer burn.

A) I and II only

B) II and IV only

C) I, II and IV only

D) All of the above

59. Which of the following statements about gaseous stunning in pigs are correct ?

I. Carbon dioxide stunning results in relaxed carcasses, facilitating easier dehairing and dressing.

II. CO_2 stunning reduces the incidence of PSE (pale, soft, exudative meat) and muscle splashes.

III. Inert gas stunning has a fast induction of unconsciousness but slow recovery, requiring shorter exposure times to be effective.

Iv. CO_2 stunning is associated with lower labour requirements and minimal operator risks due to the absence of clonic convulsions.

A) I only

B) I, II and IV only

C) II and III only

D) All of the above

60. Which of the following practices best ensures the welfare and meat quality of pigs during preslaughter care ?

I. Providing pigs with a molasses-water mix before transport help to prevent glycogen loss.

II. Showering pigs with cold water in lairage help to reduce body temperature and calm them.

III. mixing of pigs of different social group just before transportation help to minimise fighting and stress.

IV. Avoiding rough handling and isolating animals from their social group help to reduce stress.

A) I, II and III only
B) II, III and IV only
C) I and II only
D) All of the above

61. Ribose is a __________ sugar.

A) 5C
B) 4C
C) 3C
D) 6C

62. The enzyme elastase is produced in

A) Intestine
B) Pancreas
C) Stomach
D) liver

63. _________ formation is needed for fat absorption.

A) Chlomicrons
B) Hdl
C) vldl
D) micelles

64. Calbindin formation is induced by

A) Calcium
B) vitamin D
C) Protein
D) Calcium phosphorous complex

65. Selenium competes with ____________ in biochemical pathways.

A) Chromium
B) Sulphur
C) Protein
D) Zinc

66. Curdlan is a type of

A) Pectin
B) Lignin
C) Gum
D) Betaglucan

67. Physical Activity Ratio (PAR) refers to

A) Ratio of physical activity to rest
B) Energy cost of an activity per unit time

C) Ratio of energy for an activity to total energy

D) Ratio of time for a physical activity to total time

68. RDA of iron for adult women is

A) 18 mg
B) 24 mg
C) 29 mg
D) 27 mg

69. The hormone that inhibits calcium absorption

A) PTH
B) vitamin D
C) Calcitonin
D) Thyroxine

70. For dim light vision

A) Cis retinal is converted to trans retinal

B) Trans retinal is converted to Cis retinal

C) Trans retinol is converted to retinaldehyde

D) Cisretinaldehyde is converted to trans retinol

71. HCI and Potassium ferrocyanide are used to detect ____________ in tea.

A) Azo dyes
B) Coal tar dyes
C) Caffeine
D) Chicory

72. The most common polar adsorbent used in Column chromatography

A) Silica gel
B) Calcium carbonate
C) Calcium sulphate
D) Calcium hydroxide

73. lower Retention factor in Tl chromatography indicates

A) lower polarity of solute
B) Higher polarity of solute
C) Higher volatile nature
D) lower volatile nature

74. In reversed phase chromatography, stationary phase is

A) Ionic
B) Neutral
C) Non polar
D) Polar

75. Soap bubble flow meter is used in

A) Gas Chromatography
B) Viscometer
C) Texture Analyser
D) Farinograph

76. Which is the solvent used in IR spectroscopy ?

A) Liquid carbon dioxide
B) Carbon tetra chloride
C) Liquid nitrogen
D) Chlorine water

77. Common reagents used for dissolution of sample in AAS

A) HCl and H_2SO_4

B) HCl and HNO_3

C) H_2SO_4 and HCl

D) H_2PO_4 and HCl

78. Fibre residue after chemical digestion is corrected for ash test with

A) Evaporation

B) Sublimation

C) Cryo freezing

D) Ignition

79. Minimum quantity of sample of spices required for pesticide residue analysis is

A) 0.25 kg

B) 0.50 kg

C) 0.10 kg

D) 0.05 Kg

80. The indicator used for detecting saponification value of fats

A) Methyl orange

B) Phenolphthalein

C) Litmus

D) Methyl red

81. Choose the correct statement on HACCP.

I. Acronym of HACCP is "Hazard Assessment and Critical Control Programme".

II. The Quality management system is framed by safe product design, HACCP andprerequisite GMP programmes.

III. HACCP system can be linear and the principles are applied as the whole.

IV. Critical limits for each CCP are defined by Codex Commission on Food Hygiene,1997.

A) I, II and III are correct; Iv is wrong

B) I and III are wrong; II and Iv are correct

C) I and III are correct; II and Iv are wrong

D) All the statements are correct

82. Identify the animal model method which can be successfully used to test the *Campylobacter jejuni* infection and to assess the virulence of *Aeromonas* spp.

A) Anton test

B) Sereny test

C) RITARD model test

D) Kitten model test

83. A fermented product produced by mixed culture of *Streptococcus thermophilus* and *Lactobacillus bulgaricus* at 1 : 1 ratio is

A) Butter

B) Sour cream

C) Yoghurt

D) Buttermilk

84. Find out the incorrect statement about the intrinsic and extrinsic parameters influencing the microbial growth of food.

A) In general, fungi require higher a_w value for growth than bacteria

B) Presence of natural antimicrobial substances like essential oils in some spices, lactoferrin in milk and hydrocinnamic acid derivatives in some fruits and vegetables have shown varying degrees of antimicrobial activity

C) An environment with high temperature with low relative humidity is preferred for proper storage of food products

D) Yeast can grow at psychrotrophic and mesophilic temperature but generally not at thermophilic condition

85. Choose the correct answer on *Clostridium*.

I. Food poisoning strains of *Cl. perfringens* belongs to type A and produce only traces of alpha toxin.

II. Botulism is caused by the ingestion of highly toxic soluble exotoxin produced by *Cl. botulinum* while growing in foods.

III. Proteolytic strains digest casein and produce H_2S, whereas the non-proteolytic ones ferment mannose.

A) Only II is correct

B) Only I is correct

C) All the three are incorrect

D) All the three are correct

86. Selective medium that can be used to culture and enumerate *Staphylococcus aureus* from food sample is

A) Baird-Parker agar

B) PAlCAm agar

C) PlET agar

d) macConkey agar

87. Below mentioned are the advantages of Single Cell Protein (SCP) as a source of food, except

A) large mass of protein can be produced due to the shorter generation time of microorganisms

B) Readily available raw materials in large quantities can be used for SCP production

C) Production can be performed as continuous culture and hence are independent of climate change

D) The protein content is less

88. Phosphatase test is used to find out the efficacy of

A) Chilling

B) Sterilization

C) Pasteurization

D) Starter activity

89. Identify the mismatched statement on food adulterants. Food

A) Ghee, cheese, butter

B) Black pepper

C) Oil

D) Pulses

Adulterant

– mashed potatoes, vanaspati

– Papaya seeds

– Unhygienic water, chalk powder, urea

– dyes, chemicals and lead chromate

90. Stabilizer used in ice cream is

A) Pectin

B) Potassium sorbate

C) Sodium glutamate

D) GmS

91. Identify the correct statement/statements on enumeration of total number of bacteria from food products

I. In MBRT, The time taken to reduce the dye is directly proportional to the number of organisms present in the sample.

II. The MPN results are generally higher than SPC.

III. The DMC method is relatively simple, rapid and the results are generally higher than SPC.

IV. The MPN method is statistical in nature and requires the usage of large number of glass wares.

A) Only I and II are correct

B) Only I is correct

C) Only II, III and IV are correct

D) Only III is correct

92. Pimaricin is an example of

A) Enzyme

B) Preservative

C) Fungicide

D) Antioxidant

93. Choose the wrongly matched statement.

A) *B. cereus* toxi-infection = Emetic and diarrheic form

B) Cholera toxin = Increase adenylate cyclase activity and the cAmP thus leads to loss of cell nutrients and diarrhea

C) AGMARK = Quality certification mark for agricultural produce

D) Shigella infection in food = diagnosed by Nagler's reaction and stormy clot fermentation

94. The time- temperature combination used for pasteurization is based on the thermal death time of

A) *Brucella abortus*

B) *Mycobacterium tuberculosis*

C) *Coxiella burnetti*

D) *Mycobacterium paratuberculosis*

95. Identify the correct statement/statements on mycotoxins.

A) Toxic substances produced by variety of molds and bacteria

B) They are the secondary metabolites formed during the end of death phase of growth

C) Aflatoxin M1 is most potent and APB1 is hydroxylated products of AFM1 and appears in milk, urine and faeces

D) The toxicity of the potent aflatoxin decreases in the following order

B1 > m1 > G1 > B2 > m2

96. Which is the spoilage indicators of meat ?

A) Cadarerine and putrescine
B) Ornithine and lysine
C) Glucose and glucorronate
D) None of these

97. Below mentioned are the serological tests used to diagnose brucellosis, except

A) Abortus bang ring test
B) Rose Bengal plate test
C) Standard tube agglutination test
D) Polymerase chain reaction

98. The following are enriched media except

A) Blood agar
B) Serum agar
C) Chocolate agar
D) Selenite broth

99. Microscopic Agglutination Test is used for the diagnosis of which disease

A) Brucellosis
B) Leptospirosis
C) Campylobacter infections
D) Pasteurellosis

100. The light source used in fluorescent microscope is

A) Visible light
B) UV light
C) Beam of electrons
D) Infrared rays

CHAPTER-12

Meghalaya FSO - 2025

PART A : GENERAL ENGLISH & GENERAL KNOWLEDGE

1. Directions (Q. Nos. 1–5): Choose the correct sentences.

1.i. This bed is too soft.

ii. This bed is so soft.

iii. This bed is to soft.

(A) i and ii (B) i and iii

(C) ii and iii (D) i, ii and iii

2.i. She is a great actress.

ii. She is a well-known actress.

iii. She is a renowned actress.

(A) i and ii (B) i and iii

(C) ii and iii **(D) i, ii and iii**

3.i. No one is at home.

ii. There is nobody at home.

iii. None are at home.

(A) i and ii (B) i and iii

(C) ii and iii **(D) i, ii and iii**

4.i. He does not like apples.

ii. He dislikes apples.

iii. He isn't liking apples.

(A) i and ii (B) i and iii

(C) ii and iii (D) i, ii and iii

5.i. He is so fat that he cannot jump.

ii. He is fat to jump.

iii. He is too fat to jump.

(A) i and ii
(B) i and iii
(C) ii and iii
(D) i, ii and iii

Directions (Q. Nos. 6–15): Choose the correct meaning for the words or phrases given below.

6. A collection of historical documents or records providing information about a place, institution or group of people

(A) Archive
(B) Museum
(C) Library
(D) Register

7. Alchemy

(A) A form of Physics
(B) A form of Biology
(C) A form of Chemistry
(D) A form of Geography

8. Spoken or done without preparation

(A) Sudden
(B) On the spot
(C) Extempore
(D) Blindly

9. A remedy for all diseases

(A) Antidote
(B) Anecdote
(C) Panacea
(D) Medicine

10. A news article that reports the death of a person

(A) Notice
(B) Advertisement
(C) Bulletin
(D) Obituary

11. A speech delivered for the first time in an Assembly

(A) Debut
(B) Maiden
(C) Inaugural
(D) Initiatory

12. Pseudonym

(A) Real name
(B) Pet name
(C) Namesake
(D) Pen name

13. Incapable of being read

(A) Illiterate
(B) Blind
(C) Illegible
(D) Difficult

14. The life history of a person written by himself

(A) Biography
(B) History
(C) Memoir
(D) Autobiography

15. Several fish swimming together

(A) Bunch (B) Horde

(C) Swarm **(D) Shoal**

Directions (Q. Nos. 16–25):

Choose the correct option to fill in the gaps.

16. He is neither hungry ______ thirsty at the moment.

(A) or **(B) nor**

(C) but (D) and

17. No one of these boys ______ present then.

(A) was (B) were

(C) are (D) is

18. I prefer tea ______ coffee.

(A) or (B) than

(C) to (D) with

19. To ______ is human, to forgive divine.

(A) make mistake (B) fall

(C) err (D) fail

20. ______ the noise, the boy woke up.

(A) Hear **(B) Hearing**

(C) Heard (D) Hears

21. You must reap what you have ______.

(A) sown (B) grown

(C) sow (D) grow

22. To ______ should I give this letter?

(A) who **(B) whom**

(C) what (D) whose

23. ______ being hardworking, he is thoroughly honest.

(A) Although (B) For

(C) Over and above (D) In spite of

24. He walked ______, meditating.

(A) to and fro (B) forward and backward

(C) up and down (D) side to side

25. I will sit ______ my desk to do my work.

(A) on
(B) at
(C) by
(D) in

26. Which is the currency of Indonesia?

(A) Krona
(B) Som
(C) Peso
(D) Rupiah

27. Where is the Headquarters of the World Anti-Doping Agency (WADA) situated?

(A) Rome, Italy
(B) Beijing, China
(C) London, UK
(D) Montreal, Canada

28. Brass gets discoloured in air because of the presence of which of the following gases in air?

(A) Oxygen
(B) Hydrogen sulphide
(C) Carbon dioxide
(D) Nitrogen

29. The concept of differential heating was primarily used to explain which of the following geographical phenomena in India?

(A) Monsoon
(B) Jet streams
(C) Cyclones
(D) Desert storms

30. Potassium permanganate is used for purifying drinking water, because

(A) it is a sterilizing agent
(B) it dissolves the impurities of water
(C) it is a reducing agent
(D) it is an oxidizing agent

31. What is the unit for measuring the amplitude of a sound?

(A) Decibel
(B) Coulomb
(C) Hum
(D) Cycles

32. Who invented the Ballpoint Pen?

(A) Biro Brothers
(B) Waterman Brothers
(C) Wright Brothers
(D) Big Brothers

33. The minimum age to qualify for election to the Lok Sabha is

(A) 35 years
(B) 25 years
(C) 21 years
(D) 18 years

34. The Preamble declares India as a Sovereign State which implies

(A) India is free to conduct her internal affairs

(B) India is free to conduct her external affairs

(C) India is free to conduct her internal as well as external affairs

(D) None of the above

35. Tipu Sultan was the ruler of

(A) Hyderabad (B) Madurai

(C) Mysore (D) Vijayanagar

36. The Reserve Bank of India was nationalized in the year

(A) 1952 (B) 1945

(C) 1949 (D) 1969

37. Alice in Wonderland, the famous TV serial, is based on a book written by

(A) Father Discoste (B) Thomas Hardy

(C) Charles Dickens **(D) Lewis Carroll**

38. The programme, 'Gyan Vani' is broadcasted by

(A) Zee TV **(B) AIR**

(C) Sony TV (D) Doordarshan

39. The name of Pierre Cardin is associated with which of the following fields?

(A) Painting (B) Pop films

(C) Music **(D) Fashion Designing**

40. The Central Rice Research Institute is located at

(A) Cuttack (B) Rajahmundry

(C) Patna (D) Shillong

41. Which country has the highest density of population among the following?

(A) Singapore (B) Bangladesh

(C) India (D) Bahrain

42. Fiscal deficit in the Union Budget means

(A) the difference between current expenditure and current revenue

(B) net increase in Union Government's borrowings from the Reserve Bank of India

(C) the sum of budgetary deficit and net increase in internal and external borrowings

(D) the sum of monetized deficit and budgetary deficit

43. Foreign Direct Investment ceilings in the telecom sector have been raised from 74 percent to

(A) 80 percent (B) 85 percent

(C) 90 percent **(D) 100 percent**

44. Who is the author of the book, *Nineteen Eighty-Four*?

(A) Thomas Hardy (B) Emile Zola

(C) George Orwell (D) Walter Scott

45. Who is the first Indian Female Gymnast ever to compete in the Olympics?

(A) Lovlina Borgohain **(B) Dipa Karmakar**

(C) Karnam Malleswari (D) Nilima Ghose

46. The largest source of power generation in India is

(A) thermal (B) hydro

(C) nuclear (D) non-conventional forms

47. Which is known as the 'City of Seven Islands'?

(A) Port Blair (Andaman & Nicobar) (B) Tokyo (Japan)

(C) Mumbai (Maharashtra) (D) Helsinki (Finland)

48. Moradabad in Uttar Pradesh is known for which industry?

(A) Brass utensils (B) Cotton textile

(C) Sugarcane industry (D) Locomotive industry

49. The disease filariasis is transmitted by

(A) bacteria (B) protozoa

(C) mosquito (D) virus

50. The ratio of width of our National Flag to its length is

(A) 3:5 **(B) 2:3**

(C) 2:4 (D) 3:4

PART—B : FOOD SAFETY STANDARDS & NUTRITION

51. Which of the following is a foodborne pathogen?

(A) *Salmonella* (B) *Lactobacillus*

(C) Both (A) and (B) (D) None of the above

52. HACCP stands for

(A) Hazard Analysis and Compliance Control Points

(B) Hazard Analysis and Critical Control Points

(C) Hazard Assessment and Compliance Control Points

(D) Hazard Assessment and Critical Control Points

53. Vitamin C deficiency causes

(A) rickets (B) pellagra

(C) scurvy (D) night blindness

54. 'Low fat' on a label generally means

(A) no fat at all
(B) less than 3 g of fat per serving
(C) less than 5 g of fat per serving
(D) less than 10 g of fat per serving

55. Sucrose is a

(A) monosaccharide
(B) disaccharide
(C) polysaccharide
(D) None of the above

56. The Codex Alimentarius Commission is a body established by

(A) FAO and WHO
(B) FSSAI
(C) USDA
(D) ISO

57. The Maillard reaction is associated with

(A) caramelization of sugar
(B) formation of fats
(C) browning of food during cooking or processing
(D) proteins breaking down in the stomach

58. Which of the following is a major source of dietary fibre?

(A) Vegetables
(B) Meat
(C) Spices
(D) Milk

59. The common adulterant found in chili powder is

(A) brick dust
(B) sodium bicarbonate
(C) starch
(D) iodine

60. The maximum permissible limit of lead in food items, as per the FSSAI, is

(A) 0.01 ppm.
(B) 0.02 ppm.
(C) 0.1 ppm.
(D) 0.2 ppm.

61. Foodborne pathogen commonly associated with dairy product is

(A) *Listeria monocytogenes*
(B) *Escherichia coli* O157:H7
(C) *Bacillus anthracis*
(D) *Lactobacillus acidophilus*

62. Which of the following foods is rich in folic acid?

(A) Beef
(B) Spinach
(C) Pea
(D) Pork

63. Which of the following is a good source of potassium?

(A) Apple
(B) Banana
(C) Cucumber
(D) Watermelon

64. The chemical formula of lactose is

(A) $C_{12}H_{6}0_{12}$ **(B) $C_{12}H_{22}O_{11}$**

(C) $C_{12}H_{23}0_{34}$ (D) $C_{12}H_{13}0_{14}$

65. The process of turning sugar into alcohol is termed as

(A) glycolysis (B) alcoholysis

(C) hydrolysis **(D) fermentation**

66. FSSAI operates under

(A) the Ministry of Health and Family Welfare

(B) the Ministry of Agriculture and Farmer Welfare

(C) the Ministry of Food Processing Industries

(D) None of the above

67. What is used to adulterate groundnut oil?

(A) Castor oil **(B) Argemone oil**

(C) Mustard oil (D) Olive oil

68. Which of the following is the best source of omega-3 fatty acids?

(A) Flax seed (B) Pumpkin seed

(C) Sunflower seed (D) Cucumber seed

69. Which virus is commonly transmitted through contaminated food or water?

(A) Hepatitis A virus (B) Hepatitis B virus

(C) Hepatitis C virus (D) Hepatitis D virus

70. Fats when fully hydrogenated form

(A) saturated fat (B) unsaturated fat

(C) monounsaturated fat (D) polyunsaturated fat

71. Which milk has the lowest amount of fat?

(A) Whole milk **(B) Skim milk**

(C) Low fat milk (D) Reduced fat milk

72. Chapter III of the Food Safety and Standards Act, 2006 relates to

(A) enforcement of the Act (B) analysis of food

(C) general principles of food safety

(D) None of the above

73. The heavy metal most commonly associated with contamination in seafood is

(A) arsenic **(B) mercury**

(C) copper (D) zinc

74. Which of the following methods of food preservation is known to have the longest shelf life?

(A) Drying (B) Refrigeration

(C) Canning (D) Salting

75. The most common waterborne pathogen is

(A) *Escherichia coli* O157:H7 (B) *Salmonella typhi*

(C) Coliform (D) *Staphylococcus*

76. Which type of water is preferred for food processing to ensure food safety?

(A) Distilled water (B) Soft water

(C) Potable water (D) UV-treated water

77. Dry foods like cereals must be stored in airtight containers to

(A) prevent moisture absorption (B) prevent oxidation

(C) Both (A) and (B) (D) None of the above

78. Microorganisms that grow at refrigeration temperatures are termed as

(A) thermophiles (B) mesophiles

(C) halophiles **(D) psychrotrophs**

79. What is the logo for fortified food products in India?

(A) An '+F' mark inside a triangle (B) An '+F' mark inside a circle

(C) An '+F' mark inside a rectangle **(D) An '+F' mark inside a square**

80. Which certification mark is used in India to label organic food products?

(A) Organic India (B) AGMARK

(C) BIS **(D) Jaivik Bharat**

81. The gas commonly used in Modified Atmosphere Packaging (MAP) is

(A) nitrogen dioxide (B) ethylene oxide

(C) hydrogen dioxide **(D) oxygen**

82. The main purpose of blanching vegetables before freezing is to

(A) decontaminate vegetable (B) soften the vegetable

(C) destroy pests **(D) inactivate enzyme**

83. Proteins are mainly required by the body for

(A) growth and repair of tissues (B) bone strengthening

(C) providing energy (D) muscle formation

84. Fresh oils have a peroxide value below

(A) 5 mEq/kg **(B) 10 mEq/kg**

(C) 15 mEq/kg (D) 20 mEq/kg

85. Aflatoxin is classified as a

(A) bacterial toxin (B) neurotoxin

(C) mycotoxin (D) hemotoxin

86. The Prevention of Food Adulteration Act was enacted in the year

(A) 1944 **(B) 1954**

(C) 1964 (D) 1974

87. Which State topped the State Food Safety Index, 2024 released by the FSSAI?

(A) Tamil Nadu **(B) Kerala**

(C) Gujarat (D) Punjab

88. Which of the following is a fat-soluble vitamin?

(A) Retinol (B) Biotin

(C) Riboflavin (D) Niacin

89. The crispness of potato chips is due to their low

(A) thermal conductivity (B) oil viscosity

(C) moisture content (D) specific gravity

90. DDT is grouped under which class of pesticide?

(A) Carbamates **(B) Organochlorines**

(C) Organophosphates (D) Pyrethroids

91. Agar is most commonly used in food as a

(A) flavouring agent **(B) stabilizing agent**

(C) gelling agent (D) colouring agent

92. Lactose present in milk is a type of

(A) vitamin (B) protein

(C) carbohydrate (D) fat

93. Which microorganism helps ferment milk?

(A) *Streptococcus thermophilus* (B) *Lactobacillus casei*

(C) *Bifidobacterium bifidum* **(D) All of the above**

94. In how many days should an application for FSSAI license renewal be made before its expiry?

(A) 15 days **(B) 30 days**

(C) 60 days (D) 90 days

95. The FSS (Food Products and Food Additives) Regulations, 2011 came into force on

(A) 5th June, 2011
(B) 5th July, 2011
(C) 5th August, 2011
(D) 5th September, 2011

96. Which type of oil blending is prohibited under the FSS (Prohibition and Restriction on Sales) Regulations, 2011?

(A) Sesame oil
(B) Mustard oil
(C) Olive oil
(D) Sunflower oil

97. The permissible limit of Aflatoxin M1 in milk, as per the FSS (Contaminants, Toxins and Residues) Regulations, 2011, is

(A) 0.5 μg/kg
(B) 0.3 μg/kg
(C) 0.1 μg/kg
(D) None of the above

98. As per the FSS (Laboratory and Sample Analysis) Regulations, 2011, the approximate quantity of carbonated water to be supplied is

(A) 500 ml
(B) 1 litre
(C) 2 litres
(D) 3 litres

99. As per the FSS (Food Recall Procedure) Regulations, 2017, who is primarily responsible for initiating a food recall?

(A) Food Safety Officer
(B) Food Business Operator
(C) Food Inspector
(D) State Government

100. As per the FSS (Alcoholic Beverages) Regulations, 2018, the maximum permissible limit of yeast in strong beer is

(A) absent/ml
(B) 10 cfu/ml
(C) 50 cfu/ml
(D) 100 cfu/ml

101. As per the FSS (Fortification of Foods) Regulations, 2018, vegetable oil shall be fortified with

(A) vitamins A and B
(B) vitamins A and C
(C) vitamins A and D
(D) vitamins A and E

102. As per the FSS (Foods for Infant Nutrition) Regulations, 2020, packaging material used for products shall be free from

(A) Bisphenol A
(B) Bisphenol F
(C) Bisphenol S
(D) Bisphenol AF

103. As per the FSS (Packaging) Regulations, 2018, printing inks for use on food packages shall conform to

(A) IS : 14720
(B) IS : 15495
(C) IS : 16815
(D) IS : 17119

104. The consistency and stability of dough can be measured with

(A) Duograph **(B) Farinograph**

(C) Chronograph (D) Monograph

105. Rancidity in sunflower oil is due to

(A) dehydrogenation **(B) peroxidation**

(C) oxidation (D) combustion

106. 1 kilocalorie is equal to

(A) 4184 joule (B) 4284 joule

(C) 4384 joule (D) 4484 joule

107. The Meat Food Products Order, 1973 was promoted under the

(A) Right to Food Act, 1947 (B) Essential Food Act, 1952

(C) Essential Commodities Act, 1955

(D) Consumer Protection Act, 1986

108. According to the FSS Act, the full form of COA is

(A) Certificate of Authority (B) Certificate of Assessment

(C) Certificate of Authenticity **(D) Certificate of Analysis**

109. FoSTaC stands for

(A) Food Safety Training and Certification

(B) Food Security Training and Certification

(C) Food Standards Training and Certification

(D) Food Sustainability and Training Certification

110. MMPO stands for

(A) Meat and Meat Product Order **(B) Milk and Milk Product Order**

(C) Milk and Meat Product Order (D) Meat and Milk Product Order

111. The reaction between amino acid and reducing sugar is known as

(A) sugar inversion (B) enzymatic browning

(C) Maillard reaction (D) neutralization reaction

112. The primary enzyme used in meat tenderization is

(A) amylase (B) lipase

(C) ligase **(D) papain**

113. Which of the following acids is used in non-fruit beverages?

(A) Phosphoric acid (B) Acetic acid

(C) Boric acid (D) None of the above

114. The sweetest natural sugar is

(A) glucose
(B) fructose
(C) sucrose
(D) maltose

115. Sugar-free product means

(A) no sugar per 100 g
(B) less than 0.2 g of sugar per 100 g
(C) less than 0.5 g of sugar per 100 g
(D) less than 1 g of sugar per 100 g

116. The preservation technique using radiation is also known as

(A) gamma sterilization
(B) X-ray sterilization
(C) ion sterilization
(D) cold sterilization

117. Which of the following is *not* a permitted food additive?

(A) Sodium benzoate
(B) Sorbic acid
(C) Tartrazine
(D) Rhodamine

118. In which part of the cereal grain, protein and fat content is maximum?

(A) Germ
(B) Endosperm
(C) Bran
(D) Seed coat

119. Which of the following compounds is commonly used as a preservative in fruit juices?

(A) Hydrogen peroxide
(B) Calcium carbonate
(C) Sodium benzoate
(D) Propylene glycol

120. Soxhlet method is used for the determination of

(A) protein content
(B) fat content
(C) fiber content
(D) oil content

121. The protein of egg white known for its antibiotic activity is

(A) Ovalbumin
(B) Albumin
(C) Lysozyme
(D) Avidin

122. Bread staling is caused by

(A) moisture evaporation
(B) yeast and mold contamination
(C) starch retrogradation
(D) sugar breakdown

123. Carboxymethyl cellulose is used in food products as a/an

(A) preservative agent
(B) antimicrobial agent
(C) colouring agent
(D) thickening agent

124. The primary food constituent that causes astringency is

(A) flavonoid (B) lignan

(C) stilbene **(D) tannin**

125. ISO 9001:2008 has how many clauses?

(A) 6 (B) 7

(C) 8 (D) 9

126. Which Clause of ISO/IEC 17025 deals with sampling and test methods?

(A) Clause 4 : General requirements (B) Clause 5 : Laboratory requirements

(C) Clause 6 : Analysis requirements **(D) Clause 7 : Process requirements**

127. According to FSSAI Manual for meat and meat products, which of the following is *not* a tested parameter?

(A) Determination of total fat (B) Determination of total protein

(C) Determination of agar **(D) Determination of vitamin**

128. According to the FSSAI Manual for fish and fish products, which of the following categories is foreign matter?

(A) Filth (B) Parasite

(C) Shellbit **(D) All of the above**

129. According to the FSSAI Manual for water, the colour of a sample can be measured by visual comparison with

(A) platinum-cobalt standards (B) silver-chlorine standards

(C) chlorine-magnesium standards (D) calcium-magnesium standards

130. According to the FSSAI Manual for honey and other beehive products, honey is ashed at a temperature of

(A) 500 ± 20 °C **(B) 600 ± 20 °C**

(C) 700 ± 20 °C (D) 900 ± 20 °C

131. What type of chemical reaction is saponification?

(A) Hydrolysis (B) Substitution

(C) Addition (D) Combustion

132. Which of the following is *not* a chlorinated pesticide?

(A) Chlordane (B) Chlorpyrifos

(C) Heptachlor **(D) Parathion**

133. Which method is most commonly used to determine protein content in food?

(A) Soxhlet method **(B) Kjeldahl method**

(C) Titration (D) None of the above

134. In the context of food, RDA stands for

(A) Required Dietary Allowance (B) Required Daily Allowance

(C) Recommended Dietary Allowance

(D) Recommended Daily Allowance

135. What does ISO 22000 stand for?

(A) Food Safety Management System

(B) Quality Management System

(C) General Requirements for the Competence of Testing and Calibration Laboratories

(D) Sustainable Procurement

136. What does ISO 17025 stand for?

(A) Food Safety Management System

(B) Quality Management System

(C) General Requirements for the Competence of Testing and Calibration Laboratories

(D) Sustainable Procurement

137. What does ISO 9001 stand for?

(A) Quality Management System (B) Food Safety Management System

(C) Food Laboratory Management System

(D) Audit Management System

138. The Atwater factor for protein is

(A) 1 kcal/g **(B) 4 kcal/g**

(C) 10 kcal/g (D) 25 kcal/g

139. What does BMR refer to in nutrition?

(A) Basic Metabolism Rate

(B) Basal Metabolic Rate

(C) Biological Metabolism Rate (D) Biological Mineral Reserve

140. Ash content in food indicates

(A) total energy content (B) total protein content

(C) total mineral content (D) total fat content

141. The Dumas method is used to analyse

(A) oxygen content **(B) nitrogen content**

(C) carbon dioxide content (D) argon content

142. The main source of dietary energy is

(A) proteins
(B) carbohydrates
(C) fats
(D) vitamins

143. Vitamin B12 is also known as

(A) folate
(B) tocopherol
(C) cobalamin
(D) phylloquinone

144. Which of the following is a water-soluble vitamin?

(A) Thiamin
(B) Riboflavin
(C) Niacin
(D) All of the above

145. Which of the following is a micro-nutrient?

(A) Carbohydrate
(B) Lipid
(C) Vitamin
(D) Protein

146. A food claiming to be 'high fiber' must contain at least

(A) 5 g of fiber per serving
(B) 10 g of fiber per serving
(C) 15 g of fiber per serving
(D) None of the above

147. Trans fats are type of

(A) saturated fatty acid
(B) essential fatty acid
(C) cyclopropane fatty acid
(D) None of the above

148. As per the FSSAI Regulations, which of the following preservatives is allowed in milk?

(A) Sodium benzoate
(B) Formalin
(C) Sorbic acid
(D) None of the above

149. According to the FSSAI Manual for cereal and cereal products, the calculation for determination of mineral matter is

(A) Foreign matter (%) = (Mass of extraneous matter ÷ Mass of sample) × 100

(B) Inorganic matter (%) = (Mass of inorganic residue ÷ Mass of sample) × 100

(C) Mineral matter (%) = (Mass of inorganic matter ÷ Mass of sample) × 100

(D) Mineral matter (%) = (Mass of extraneous matter ÷ Mass of sample) × 100

150. What is the primary microbial concern in canned foods?

(A) *Clostridium botulinum*
(B) *Escherichia coli* O157:H7
(C) *Listeria monocytogenes*
(D) Sulphite reducing clostridia

CHAPTER-13

Madhya Pradesh Food Safety Officer 2025

Section-'A' - General Studies

1. Which of the following Yagya was performed by the Rashtrakuta King Dantidurga at Ujjain?

   A. Tulapurusha **B. Hiranya-Garbhadan**

   C. Saptasagar D. Ratnadhenu

2. With reference to the Divisional Commissioner consider the following statements-

(1) The post of Divisional Commissioner was first created in 1829 during the British rule.

(2) This was created to monitor the work of the District Collectors.

Select the correct answer from the code given below-

   A. Only 1 is correct. B. Only 2 is correct.

   C. Both 1 and 2 are correct. D. Both 1 and 2 are not correct.

3. When was Devi Ahilya Bai Holkar born?

   A. 25 May 1725 A.D. B. 27 May 1725 A.D.

   C. 29 May 1727 A.D. **D. 31 May 1725 A.D.**

4. Who among the following was not the female Nawab of Bhopal?

   A. Qudsia Begum B. Sikandar Jahan Begum

   C. Hazrat Mahal Begum D. Shah Jahan Begum

5. On which tributary of following river is Pandav Falls situated?

   A. Ken B. Narmada

   C. Chambal D. Sindh

6. Why did the "Ratauna Satyagraha" take place in Sagar in 1920-21 A.D.?

   A. Regarding education system B. Against opium cultivation

   C. Against indigo cultivation

   D. Against the establishment of a slaughterhouse

7. Match the Totems and their symbols of the Gond tribe in correct order-

	Totem		Symbol
(a)	Netam	(1)	A wild cat
(b)	Vakara	(2)	Name of a dog
(c)	Teekam	(3)	Mahua tree
(d)	Irapatri	(4)	Teak tree

A. a-2, b-1, c-4, d-3 B. a-1, b-2, c-3, d-4

C. a-3, b-4, c-2, d-1 D. a-4, b-3, c-1, d-2

8. Pithora painting is related to which tribe of Madhya Pradesh?

A. Kol **B. Bhil**

C. Baiga D. Gond

9. When did the publication of "Malwa Akhbar" start from Indore?

A. 3 March 1849 A.D. **B. 6 March 1849 A.D.**

C. 17 March 1849 A.D. D. 31 March 1849 A.D.

10. First Dengue Vaccine phase 3 clinical trial in India is done with which indigenous Dengue Vaccine in August 2024?

A. Dengisure B. Dengvax

C. DengiAll D. D-Vax plus

11. According to the Madhya Pradesh Industrial Promotion Policy 2025, by the year 2030 the state aims to raise its Gross State Domestic Product from Rs. 2.9 lakh crore to approximately what level?

A. Rs. 5.0 Lakh Crore **B. Rs. 6.0 Lakh Crore**

C. Rs. 6.5 Lakh Crore D. Rs. 7.0 Lakh Crore

12. The windmills (Pawan Chakkiya) installed on the Jamgodrani hills are located in which district?

A. Dhar B. Indore

C. Dewas D. Barwani

13. What are 'Atak' and 'Odakh' in the Bhil tribe?

A. Agriculture system B. Occupation

C. Social customs D. Religious activity

14. In which district is the 'Chillar' Dam located?

A. Barwani B. Dewas

C. Shajapur D. Dhar

15. The type of machine learning which allows the model to learn by exploring the environment and receiving rewards or punishments for certain actions, is known as-

A. Supervised Learning B. Unsupervised Learning

C. Refurbished Learning **D. Reinforcement Learning**

16. When was the Mineral Policy declared in Madhya Pradesh?

A. 1990 **B. 1995**

C. 2000 D. 2005

17. What is the main objective of the Mukhyamantri Sugam Parivahan Seva?

A. Promote rural tourism

B. Provide accessible and economic transportation to rural residents

C. Improve urban traffic management

D. Subsidize truck drivers

18. According to the second report of NITI Aayog on the Multidimensional Poverty Index 2023, which of the following districts of Madhya Pradesh has recorded the highest reduction in terms of percentage of the poor between 2015-16 and 2019-2021?

A. Barwani B. Khandwa

C. Alirajpur D. Tikamgarh

19. Which tribe of Madhya Pradesh calls itself "Khutiya Patel"?

A. Sahariya B. Korku

C. Bharia D. Baiga

20. Mandsaur city of Madhya Pradesh is situated on the banks of which river?

A. Ken B. Wainganga

C. Shivna D. Chambal

21. Madhya Pradesh has been awarded by the Government of India in the years 2021-22, 2022-23 and 2023-24 for the best implementation of which of the following ambitious schemes in the country?

A. National Agricultural Development Scheme

B. Kisan Credit Card Scheme

C. Agriculture Infrastructure Fund Scheme

D. State Food Processing Scheme

22. In which year was the Madhya Pradesh State Commission for Scheduled Tribes Act passed?

A. 1994 **B. 1995**

C. 1996 D. 1997

23. Which litterateure from Madhya Pradesh was honoured with Padma Shri in 2025 for their contribution to literature and education?

A. Bheru Singh Chouhan
B. Vinayak Lohani
C. Harchandan Singh Bhatti
D. Jagdish Joshila

24. What is the maximum punishment prescribed under the Scheduled Castes and Scheduled Tribes (Prevention of Atrocities) Act, 1989?

A. 7 years rigorous imprisonment
B. 10 years rigorous imprisonment
C. Life imprisonment
D. Death penalty

25. In Madhya Pradesh 'Bidri' is related to-

A. Painting
B. Food
C. Agriculture festival
D. Marriage

26. Which of the following rivers of Madhya Pradesh is not west flowing?

A. Narmada
B. Betwa
C. Tapti
D. Mahi

27. In which Five Year Plan period did the Special Multipurpose Tribal (SMPT) Development Block renamed as Tribal Development Block?

A. First
B. Second
C. Third
D. Fourth

28. Which woman cricketer of Madhya Pradesh took 6 wickets vs. England in the July 2025 ODI series and earned national recognition?

A. Palak Sharma
B. Kranti Goud
C. Ashwini Chauhan
D. Muskan Kirar

29. According to the Madhya Pradesh budget 2025-26, under the 'Aahar Anudan Yojana' launched to free the Baiga, Bharia and Saharia families belonging to the Special Particularly Vulnerable Tribal Groups from malnutrition, how much money per month is being given into the bank account of the female head of the family?

A. Rs. 1500
B. Rs. 2000
C. Rs. 2500
D. Rs. 3000

30. Where is the birthplace of Shri Mangubhai Patel, the Honourable Governor of Madhya Pradesh?

A. Jamnagar (Gujarat)
B. Navsari (Gujarat)
C. Surat (Gujarat)
D. Vadodara (Gujarat)

31. In which district of Madhya Pradesh is the 'Noorjahan' variety of mango found?

A. Dhar
B. Khargone
C. Alirajpur
D. Barwani

32. The full form of the most commonly used encoding scheme ASCII is-

A. American Simple Code for Information Intelligence

B. American Simple Code for Internet Information

C. American Standard Code for Internet Intelligence

D. American Standard Code for Information Interchange

33. Who is the author of the book "The Agaria"?

A. Amritlal Vegad | B. Jungar

C. Vinay Namdev | **D. Verrier Elwin**

34. In which district of Madhya Pradesh is the Orchha tourist place located?

A. Niwari | B. Tikamgarh

C. Chhatarpur | D. Sagar

35. Which of the following statement is correct?

A. Artificial Intelligence is a sub-domain of Machine Learning.

B. Machine Learning is a sub-domain of Deep Learning.

C. Artificial Intelligence is a sub-domain of Deep Learning.

D. Deep Learning is a sub-domain of Machine Learning.

36. According to the 2011 census, in which part of Madhya Pradesh had the highest population of Scheduled Tribe?

A. Southern Part | **B. Western Part**

C. Eastern Part | D. Northern Part

37. Which subject does not come under Article 243-W of the 12th Schedule of the Constitution of India?

A. Roads and Bridges | B. Vital Statistics

C. Fisheries | D. Fire Services

38. Halali River is a tributary of which river in Madhya Pradesh?

A. Man | B. Son

C. Betwa | D. Parvati

39. In which year the Forest Rights Act was notified?

A. 2006 | B. 2007

C. 2008 | D. 2009

40. 'The Ken-Betwa Link Project' will benefit which of the following states along with Madhya Pradesh?

A. Rajasthan | **B. Uttar Pradesh**

C. Maharashtra | D. Chhattisgarh

41. Who is the author of the book 'Tribal Heritage of Madhya Pradesh'?

A. Buddhadev Chaudhary | **B. H. L. Shukla**

C. Bhupinder Singh | D. H. M. Mathur

42. According to which article of the Constitution, there is a provision to protect the educational and economic interests of the Scheduled Tribes and to protect them from social injustice?

A. Article 25 B. Article 15

C. Article 46 D. Article 16

43. In Madhya Pradesh Budget 2025-26, the amount allocated for the Devi Ahilyabai Skill Development Programme is-

A. ₹ 10 Crore B. ₹ 15 Crore

C. ₹ 25 Crore D. ₹ 50 Crore

44. In which year was the Madhya Pradesh Tribal Museum, Bhopal, established?

A. 2018 B. 2015

C. 2013 D. 2014

45. In which article of the Constitution is the appointment of the State Election Commissioner mentioned?

A. 243 K B. 243 L

C. 243 P D. 324

46. The responsibility for overall control, operation and management of a particular device at the hardware level is delegated to its-

A. Operating system B. System utilities

C. Device drivers D. Disk cleaner

47. Who discovered the archaeological site Kayatha?

A. V. S. Wakankar B. B. B. Lal

C. K. D. Bajpai D. H. D. Sankaliya

48. Internet of Things (IoT) sensors which can detect the presence or absence of objects that approach the sensor through a variety of different technology designs, are known as-

A. Proximity Sensors B. Level Sensors

C. Motion Sensors D. Image Sensors

49. Which fort was given the title of "Pearl of the Forts of Madhya Pradesh"?

A. Asirgarh Fort B. Fort of Burhanpur

C. Fort of Gwalior D. Barwani Fort

50. Where is the headquarters of Railway Service Commission (Railway Recruitment Board) located in Madhya Pradesh?

A. Indore **B. Bhopal**

C. Gwalior D. Jabalpur

Section-'B' - Food Science and Technology

51. Which of the following statements is not true for high pressure processing?

A. Packaged foods are submerged in a liquid and high pressure is applied.

B. The process cannot be operated at ambient temperature.

C. It is applicable for both liquid and solid food products.

D. It is applicable for both pasteurization and sterilization

52. Which of the following preservative is commonly used to delay the spoilage in smoked and salted fish?

A. Acetic acid **B. Sorbic acid**

C. Benzoic acid D. Boric acid

53. ISO was the first international standard for food safety management systems, harmonizing global food safety practices. The 1st and 2nd editions of ISO 22000 came respectively in-

A. 2000 and 2005 B. 2005 and 2008

C. 2005 and 2018 D. 2006 and 2011

54. Green patches in meat are caused by green spores of which of the following microorganisms?

A. *P. expansum* B. *P. putida*

C. *P. syncyanea* D. *P. vulgaris*

55. What do you understand by Food Fortification?

A. Providing tablets containing vitamins and minerals.

B. Proper cooking and storage to avoid loss of nutrients.

C. Replacing processing losses of nutrients in food.

D. Increasing the content of an essential nutrient in food.

56. Fine crystal formation is observed in which freezing method?

A. Quick freezing B. Slow freezing

C. Dehydro freezing D. Normal freezing

57. Which among the following yeast strain is known as distillers yeast ?

Select the most appropriate answer-

A. *S. cerevisiae* var. *ellipsoideus* B. *S. cerevisiae* uvarum

C. *S. cerevisiae* carlsbergensis D. *S. cerevisiae*

58. The yellow colour of cow milk is due to which of the following?

A. Xanthophyll **B. Carotene**

C. Riboflavin D. Flavone

59. The Government of India launched "Stand-Up India" scheme on 5th April, 2016 to facilitate bank loans from Rs. 10 Lakh to 1 Crore per branch to ------- for setting up an enterprise.

A. Only one SC borrower B. Only one ST borrower

C. Only one woman borrower

D. At least one SC or ST borrower and at least one woman borrower

60. ISO 22000 relates to-

A. Pesticide control B. Consumer law

C. Export law **D. Food safety management**

61. Which body approves GM crops in India?

A. BIS **B. GEAC**

C. FSSAI D. ICAR

62. The Government of Madhya Pradesh launched the Mukhyamantri Kisan Kalyan Yojana on 25th October 2023 with the main objective of-

A. Increasing input use efficiency

B. Increasing annual income of farmers

C. Increasing fertility of soil D. Increasing quality of water

63. Slash and burn cultivation is another name of-

A. Shifting Cultivation B. Organic Farming

C. Precision Farming D. Conservation Farming

64. Food safety officer is appointed under which section of FSSA?

A. Section 10 B. Section 20

C. Section 37 D. Section 50

65. The colour of meat is red due to which of the following pigments?

A. Myosin **B. Myoglobin**

C. Collagen D. Albumin

66. Godavari is a breed of buffalo evolved through crossing between-

A. Local breed of coastal Andhra Pradesh with Murrah

B. Nili Ravi with Murrah

C. Surti with Murrah D. None of the above

67. Common millets used by tribal populations in Madhya Pradesh include-

A. Kodo and Kutki B. Wheat and bajra

C. Rice and jowar D. Wheat and rice

68. E. coli potentially contaminates food through-

A. Plants **B. Water**

C. Soil D. Air

69. Deficiency of essential fatty acids in the diet leads to this skin-related disorder/disease-

A. Diabetes mellitus
B. Hypertension
C. Phrynoderma
D. Lactose intolerance

70. Which of the following indices is used for assessment of nutritional status of children under Gomez classification and IAP classification?

A. Weight-for-height
B. Height-for-age
C. Weight-for-age
D. Height-for-weight

71. Food Safety and Standards (Licensing and registration of Food Businesses) Regulations came into force in-

A. 2001
B. 2006
C. 2011
D. 2021

72. The Ministry of Agriculture and Farmers' Welfare, Government of India in association with the NABARD, launched the scheme of Agri-Clinics and Agri-Business Centres (ACABC) in the year-

A. 2002
B. 2004
C. 2006
D. 2008

73. Maximum percentage of which of the following is present in yellow of a raw egg?

A. Lipids
B. Proteins
C. Water
D. Minerals

74. It is by far the most widely used method for determining the number of viable cells in a food product-

A. MPN
B. DEFT
C. DMC
D. SPC

75. Which of the following chemicals is used in blanching water to retain green colour in vegetables before dehydration?

A. Potassium metabisulphite
B. Aluminium chloride
C. Copper sulphate
D. Sodium bicarbonate

76. Which of the following food items is not generally stored in a container coated with zinc oxide enamel?

A. Black pepper
B. Vinegar
C. Cashew nuts
D. Mustard Oil

77. The three primary determinants of food security at national level are-

A. Food Availability, Food Storage, Food Utilization
B. Food Availability, Food Storage, Food Access
C. Food Availability, Food Access, Food Utilization
D. Food Production, Food Access, Food Utilization

78. Richest source of protein in vegetarian food is-

A. Lentils B. Potatoes

C. Soyabeans D. Green Peas

79. In India, which cropping system is having the maximum area under cultivation?

A. Rice-Rice **B. Rice-Wheat**

C. Rice-Gram D. Rice-Lentil

80. The amount of acid in vinegar is expressed as-

A. Grain strength **B. Percent**

C. Parts per million D. Degree Brix

81. The Indian food regulatory framework is governed by which of the following?

A. PFA Act, 1954 **B. FSSA Act, 2006**

C. Essential Commodities Act, 1955 D. BIS Act, 1986

82. As per the FSSAI (Fortification of foods) Regulation tagline under the logo for package of fortified food may be --------.

A. Sampoorna Poshan B. Nirogi Jeevan Poshan Poorna

C. Poshan se Sehat **D. Sampoorna Poshan Swasth Jeevan**

83. Cultivation of two or more than two crops of different heights simultaneously on a piece of land in any certain period is called-

A. Parallel Cropping B. Companion Cropping

C. Multitiered Cropping D. Synergistic Cropping

84. According to WHO, the number of key principles of food hygiene are-

A. Three **B. Five**

C. Seven D. Nine

85. Microorganisms require moisture to grow, which is measured in the form of-

A. Dry basis (percent) B. Wet basis (percent)

C. Water activity D. Absolute value

86. Which of the following statements is incorrect for "Food Safety Management Systems"?

A. It is a reparatory approach for food safety.

B. It assures consistently good quality products.

C. It is a preventive approach for food safety.

D. It enables producers, processors, distributors and exporters to utilise resources efficiently.

87. FSSAI prohibits misbranding under which of the following section?

A. Section 26 B. Section 30

C. Section 52 D. Section 55

88. Jam, jellies and pickles are preserved through which of the following principles?

A. Osmosis B. Freezing

C. Chemical action D. Dehydration

89. Reconstitution test is carried out in which of the following products?

A. Dehydrated cauliflower B. Non dehydrated cauliflower

C. Guava jelly D. Ready to eat food

90. Which of the following is carbohydrate reserve in muscle?

A. Glucose B. Sucrose

C. Glycogen D. Fructose

91. BIS works under which ministry?

A. Agriculture B. Commerce

C. Consumer Affairs, Food & Public Distribution

D. Food Processing

92. Humans cannot synthesize which of the following Polyunsaturated Fatty Acid (PUFA) in their bodies?

A. Linoleic Acid B. Docosahexaenoic Acid

C. Arachidonic Acid D. Eicosapentaenoic Acid

93. The headquarter of 'ISO' is at-

A. New York **B. Geneva**

C. Washington D. Copenhagen

94. Man is unable to digest-

A. Dextrin B. Glucose

C. Cellulose D. Glycogen

95. Which of the following radiation sources is NOT suitable for food products?

A. Caesium-137 B. Cobalt-60

C. Selenium-75 D. X-ray

96. The major disadvantage of liquid nitrogen freezing is-

A. Low boiling point B. Irregular contact with food products

C. High cost D. Toxicity to food constituents

97. Which breed of goat is not native of India?

A. Jamnapari B. Barbari

C. Saanen D. Gaddi

98. The common intermediate of carbohydrate protein and lipid metabolism is-

A. Ammonia B. Pyruvic Acid

C. Acetyl CoA D. Phosphoglyceraldehyde

99. Which of the following statements is not true for microwave processing?

A. Dipole polarization generates heat.

B. Oscillation of ions generates heat.

C. Microwaves are a form of electromagnetic energy.

D. Dry foods are more efficiently heated than wet foods.

100. Brown manuring is beneficial in which of the following crops?

A. Wheat
B. Sorghum
C. Rice
D. Chickpea

101. 'Avidin', a glycoprotein present in raw egg white, can lead to the deficiency of this nutrient if consumed in excess amount-

A. Thiamine Vitamin B_1
B. Pantothenic acid Vitamin B_5
C. Pyridoxine Vitamin B_6
D. Biotin

102. Sahiwal is a breed of which one of the following animals?

A. Buffalo
B. Cow
C. Poultry
D. Pig

103. Sorbic acid and its salts are useful against which of the following?

A. Bacteria but not Yeast
B. Yeast but not Mold
C. Mold but not Yeast
D. Both Yeast and Mold

104. According to ICMR-NIN, RDA 2020, the Recommended Dietary Allowance (RDA) of protein for healthy Indian adult men is-

A. 0.66 g/kg/day
B. 0.83 g/kg/day
C. 0.72 g/kg/day
D. 1.4 g/kg/day

105. The 'Tyrosine' is a non-essential amino acid that becomes conditionally essential amino acid in the absence of its precursor named -----.

A. Methionine
B. Phenylalanine
C. Serine
D. Choline

106. Seed rate of hybrid rice in kg/ha is-

A. 15 kg
B. 20 kg
C. 25 kg
D. 30 kg

107. Glycerol fermentation in wine results in which of the following?

A. Neutral (Pousse)
B. Acidic (Mousy Flavour)
C. Bitterness (Amertume)
D. Sour (Tourne)

108. -------- is the combination of methods used for the inactivation of microorganisms in food preservation.

A. Irradiation
B. Hurdle technology
C. Canning
D. High pressure processing

109. 'Double Fortified Salt (DFS)' is an innovative food product delivering these two nutrients to the population-

A. Iodine and retinol
B. Iodine and folic acid
C. Iodine and calcium
D. Iodine and iron

110. Which species of honeybee is more profitable in plains for apiculture?

A. *Apis cerana*
B. *Apis mellifera*
C. *Apis florea*
D. *Apis dorsata*

111. Seed rate in kg/ha of coriander in Madhya Pradesh is-

A. 10-15 kg
B. 5-10 kg
C. 20-25 kg
D. None of the above

112. In which of the following food product, sulphur dioxide should not be used as preservative?

A. Pineapple jam
B. Pomegranate juice
C. Mango juice
D. Aonla candy

113. RFID technology is used to assist manufacturers and users in tracking packaged food throughout the supply chain. RFID stands for --------.

A. Radio-factor identification
B. Radio-frequency identification
C. Ratio-frequency identification
D. Radar-fraction identification

114. The texture of food is a physical property that can be defined by-

A. How the food tastes
B. Its color and aroma
C. Its nutritional content
D. Its feel in the mouth, including properties like hardness, chewiness and viscosity

115. In order to destroy any Clostridium botulinum spores and extend the shelf life of low-acid foods, which type of packaging may be utilized?

A. Aseptic packaging
B. Controlled atmosphere packaging
C. Active packaging
D. Modified atmosphere packaging

116. Which of the following fermented product is prepared from figs?

A. Boukha
B. Mead
C. Perry
D. Sake

117. What is the ideal internal cooking temperature to ensure poultry meat in safe for consumption?

A. 74°C
B. 55°C
C. 63°C
D. 90°C

118. ISO 22000 has two cycles operating one inside the other, which refers to-

A. P - C - D - A
B. C - P - D - A
C. P - D - C - A
D. P - A - D – C

119.'HACCP' stands for-

A. Hazard Analysis and Critical Control Point

B. Hazards And Critical Control Point

C. Health Analysis and Critical Control Point

D. Health And Critical Control Point

120.FSSAI issues food licenses under which section?

A. Section 15 of FSSA, 2006 B. Section 22 of Codex

C. Section 31 of FSSA, 2006 D. Section 45 of FSSA, 2006

121.Misbranding refers to-

A. Wrong packaging material B. Addition of adulterants

C. Wrong or misleading labelling D. Selling expired product

122.The test to determine efficacy of the pasteurization process of milk is-

A. Alkaline Phosphatase Test B. Polyphenol Oxidase Test

C. Gerber Test D. Catalase Test

123.Papaya seeds are added to adulterate which of the following?

A. Tea B. Mustard

C. Black pepper D. Cardamom

124.Which of the following is one of the key pillars of the 'Eat Right India' movement?

A. Balanced diet B. Proper diet

C. Tasty diet **D. Eat safe**

125.Charcoal rot is a disease of which one of the following crops?

A. Potato B. Tomato

C. Onion D. Brinjal

126.The eggshell is primarily composed of-

A. Lipid **B. Calcium Carbonate**

C. Calcium Phosphate D. Protein

127.Intestinal calcium absorption is mainly controlled by the serum concentration of which substance?

A. Albumin B. Triglycerides

C. Ferritin **D. 1,25 dihydroxy vitamin D**

128.Butter is made mainly from-

A. Whey B. Skim milk

C. Milk solids **D. Cream**

129.Which of the following bacteria is/are used in Yoghurt production?

A. *E. coli* B. *Pseudomonas*

C. *Salmonella* **D. *L. bulgaricus* and *S. thermophilus***

130. CFTRI is a constituent lab of which of the following organizations?

A. CSIR
B. ICAR
C. ICMR
D. FSSAI

131. It is the science of measuring components (cells) and the properties of individual cells in liquid suspension-

A. Flow Cytometry
B. Fibre Optics
C. Ribotyping
D. Polymer chain reaction

132. Green Seeker is a sensing system instrument that estimates crop requirement for-

A. Phosphorus
B. Nitrogen
C. Potassium
D. Zinc

133. The storage temperature for Frozen fish is-

A. -18°C or below
B. -5°C
C. 0°C
D. 5°C

134. Micropropagation is preferred in which fruit plant over conventional propagation owing to faster multiplication and disease-free plants?

A. Banana
B. Grape
C. Apple
D. Pear

135. Which weedicide is generally used for the control of Phalaris minor (Kanki) in wheat?

A. 2, 4-D
B. Metsulfuron
C. Isoproturon
D. None of the above

136. Under 'PM-KISAN Samman Nidhi' how much financial assistance is given to the land holding farmer families per year by Ministry of Agriculture and Farmers' Welfare, New Delhi?

A. Rs. 2000/-
B. Rs. 4000/-
C. Rs. 6000/-
D. Rs. 8000/-

137. Trichothecium is commonly known as-

A. Black Mold
B. Red Mold
C. Green Mold
D. Pink Mold

138. The most effective fumigant employed for the fumigation in grain storage system is --------.

A. Ethylene chloride
B. Hydrogen gas
C. Phosphine
D. Carbon sulphide

139. Scalding of poultry helps in-

A. Killing bacteria
B. Tenderizing
C. Loosening feathers
D. Reducing fat

140. Oozing out of metacryotic liquid is a problem associated with-

A. Dehydrated product
B. Intermediate moisture food
C. Fermented product
D. Frozen product

141. Actinomycetes are the normal microflora of-

A. Raw cereal grains
B. Flour
C. Frozen dough
D. Snacks items

142. Turmeric belongs to the family-

A. Plantae
B. Zingiberaceae
C. Piperaceae
D. None of the above

143. Which of the following nutrients exhibit amphoteric nature?

A. Carbohydrates
B. Lipids
C. Protein
D. Vitamins

144. What are the effects of consuming trans fats on the human body?

A. Serum Retinol increases.
B. Serum LDL decreases.
C. Serum HDL increases.
D. Serum Triglyceride increases.

145. A dietary supplement that provides a concentrated form of bioactive compounds of food to enhance health and prevent diseases is called-

A. Protective food
B. Nutraceuticals
C. Biofortified foods
D. Functional foods

146. Which of the following is the oldest edible coating done on citrus fruits for food safety?

A. Casein
B. Amylose starch
C. Wax
D. Gelatin

147. Which one of the following schemes has now been renamed as "Pradhan Mantri Poshan Shakti Nirman (PM-POSHAN) Yojana"?

A. Mid-day-meal scheme
B. Integrated Child Development Services Scheme
C. Public Distribution System Scheme
D. Antyodaya Anna Yojana

148. Which of the following methods provide qualitative data on diet?

A. 24-hour recall method
B. Food frequency method
C. Weighment method
D. Chemical analysis of duplicate samples method

149. In composite fish culture model, which carp is omnivorous bottom feeder?

A. Katla
B. Common Carp
C. Grass Carp
D. Silver Carp

150. The first principle of 'HACCP' is-

A. Identifying critical control points.
B. Establishing critical limits.
C. Conduct hazards analysis.
D. Constructing the process flow diagram.

Part – 9

Acronyms

ACRONYMS

"It is easier to go down a hill than up, but the view is best from the top"

-Arnold Bennett

- AGMARK - Agricultural Produce Grading and Marking
- AO- Adjudicating Officer
- APEDA - Agricultural and Processed Food Products Export Development Authority
- BIS - Bureau of Indian Standards
- CAC - Central Advisory Committee
- CAG - Comptroller and Auditor General of India
- CEO - Chief Executive Officer
- CFL - Central Food Laboratory
- CFLK - Central Food Laboratory, Kolkata
- CFS - Commissioner Food Safety
- CLA - Central Licensing Authority
- CMSO - Chief Management Services Officer
- CPGRAMS - Centralized Public Grievance Redress and Monitoring System
- CSR - Corporate Social Responsibility
- CTL - Composite Testing laboratory
- DAC - District Advisory Committee
- DARPG - Department of Administrative Reforms and Public Grievances
- DART - Detect Adulteration with Rapid Test
- DLSC - District Level Steering Committee
- DO - Designated Officer
- EDI - Electronic Data Input System
- EFC - Expenditure Finance Committee
- EOI - Expression of Interest
- EOU - Export Oriented Unit
- FA - Food Analyst

- FAO - Food & Agriculture Organization of the United Nations
- FBO - Food Business Operator
- FDA - Food & Drug Administration
- FFRC - Food Fortification Resource Centre
- FICS - Food Import Clearance System
- FLRS - Food Licensing and Registration System
- FoSCoRIS - Food Safety Compliance through Regular Inspections and Sampling
- FoSCoS - Food Safety Compliance System
- FoSTaC - Food Safety Training and Certification
- FPS & FA - Food Product Standards & Food Additives
- FSKAN - Food Safety Knowledge and Assimilation Network
- FSM - Food Safety Mitra
- FSMS - Food Safety Management System
- FSO - Food Safety Officer
- FSS - Food Safety and Standards
- FSS Act - Food Safety and Standard Act, 2006
- FSSAI - Food Safety and Standards Authority of India
- FSSR - Food Safety and Standards Rules/Regulations
- GAP - Good Agricultural Practices
- GFR - General Financial Rules
- GFSP - Global Food Safety Partnership
- GHP - Good Hygiene Practices
- GM - Genetically Modified
- GMP - Good Manufacturing Practices
- HACCP - Hazard Analysis and Critical Control Point
- HFSS - High Fat Salt & Sugar
- HQ - Headquarters
- ICMR - Indian Council of Medical Research
- ICAR – Indian Council of Agricultural Research
- IDEA - Idea Data Analysis Software
- IE Code - Import Export Code
- IEC - Information, Education and Communication
- INfoLNET - Indian Food Laboratory Network
- IT - Information Technology
- ITCFSAN – International Training Centre for Food Safety and Applied Nutrition

- ISO – Indian Organization for Standardization
- JNPT - Jawaharlal Nehru Port Trust
- LSG - Local Self Government
- MDM – Mid Day Meal
- MRL - Maximum Residual Limit
- MT - Metric Tonnes
- NABL - National Accreditation Board for Testing and Calibration Laboratories
- NCC - Non-Conforming Certificate
- NCR - Non-Confirmatory Report
- NetProFan - Network of Professionals of Food & Nutrition
- NFL- National Food Laboratory
- NITI - National Institute for Transforming India
- NLRP - National Level Resource Person
- NOC - No Objection Certificate
- PA - Product Approval
- PA & SC - Product Approval and Screening Committee
- PFA - Prevention of Food Adulteration Act, 1954
- PPSWOR - Probability Proportional to Size Without Replacement Method
- RDA- Recommended Dietary Allowances
- QA - Quality Assurance
- QC - Quality Control
- RBIS - Risk Based Inspection System
- RFP - Request for Proposal
- RO - Regional Office
- RR - Recruitment Regulations
- RUCO - Repurpose Used Cooking Oil
- SAC - State Advisory committee
- SC - Scientific Committee
- SFSC - State Food Safety Commissioner
- SHG - Self Help Group
- SLA - State Licensing Authority
- SLSC - State Level Steering Committee
- SMC - Surat Municipal Corporation
- SOP - Standard Operating Procedures
- SP - Scientific Panel

- SPHL - State Public Health Laboratory
- SRG - Standards Review Groups
- SRO - Sub Regional Office
- SWIFT - Single Window Interface for Facilitating Trade
- TO - Technical Officers
- TOT - Training of Trainers
- TP - Training Partners
- USD - United States Dollar
- UT - Union Territory
- WHO - World Health Organization
- WTO - World Trade Organizationa

References

- Fennma's Food Chemistry, Fourth Edition
- Prescott's Microbiology, Joanne M. Willey, Linda M. Sherwood, Christopher J. Woolverton, Ninth edition
- Handbook of Food Analysis Instruments, Edited by Semih Otles
- Nutrition and Dietetics (With Indian Case studies) Fourth edition, Shubhangini A Joshi. Mc Graw Hill Education (India) Private Limited
- Handbook of Food Analysis Second Edition, Revised and Expanded, Edited by Leo M. L. Nollet
- Fundamental Food Microbiology Third Edition, Bibek Ray. CRC Press
- Food Microbiology Fifth edition, William C Frazier, Dennis C. Westhoff
- Food Science Fifth edition, Norman N. Potter, Joseph H. Hotchkiss
- Food Processing Technology Principles and Practice Second Edition, P. Fellows. Woodhead Publishing Limited
- Food Packaging Principles and Practice, Gordon L. Robertson
- Manual for Food Safety Officers by FSSAI
- Food analysis fourth edition, S. Suzanne Nielsoen
- NCERT Notes - Health and Diseases, Radioactive Isotopes
- IGNOU Notes - Rapid detection techniques for food micro-organisms, nutritional problems, testing and evaluation chemical and microbiological, requirements specific to food testing laboratories - biological parameter

Our Other Fine Titles